CONTROVERSIAL CHEMICALS
a citizen's guide

**Second Edition
Revised and Expanded, 1984**

Editors:
Peeter Kruus and Mary Valeriote

Research Team
First Edition:
Leanne Stuart, Jamie Donaldson, Paul Hope, Ruth Howard

Research Team
Second Edition:
Tina Karel, Mike Kazenel, David Sims

Advisor:
Jim Holmes

CANADA SCIENCE SERIES

Published by
**Multiscience Publications Limited,
1253 McGill College, Montreal, Quebec H3B 2X5
in conjunction with The Chemical Institute of Canada.**

ISBN 0-919868-22-3

INTRODUCTION

The concept of a book on "Controversial Chemicals" arose from a TSE (Technology, Society, Environment) course project at Carleton University in 1975-76. A team of students from biology, engineering, integrated sciences and political science looked at the historical, technological, environmental and economic aspects of Fluorocarbons. Another project team in 1976-77 did a similar study on Asbestos, Fenitrothion, PCBs and Cyclamates.

The Ontario Ministry of the Environment and the Science Council of Canada provided financial support for preparation of the first edition of "Controversial Chemicals", published in 1979 by Multiscience Publications, Montreal. This version contained chapters on 25 chemicals chosen primarily from among those mentioned in news stories. Aspects of Alcohol, Caffeine and Tobacco were included as examples of widely-used, generally-accepted chemicals to provide a basis against which to compare the other chemicals.

A further 3 chapters and 6 audiovisual programs were prepared in 1978 with financial support from the Ontario Ministry of the Environment and the Canadian Chemical Producers' Association. Aid for the revised and extended second edition was provided by Environment Canada. Carleton University has supported this project from the beginning by providing space, materials, word-processing facilities, and most importantly - encouragement.

The list of all the people and organizations to whom we are indebted for aid of various kinds has grown too long to include here. We are however especially grateful to Dr. J. Brydon (Environment Canada), Dr. E. Somers (Health and Welfare) and Dr. F. Cedar (Agriculture Canada) for arranging to have the draft of this edition thoroughly reviewed by specialists in their departments; to Sandra Wright for typing the first draft; and to Annie Kruus for preparation of the final camera-ready copy.

i

We have attempted to collect information regarding the chemicals and to present those aspects deemed interesting to the general reader in an understandable, unbiased manner with no attempt to editorialize. Any misinterpretation of material or other errors are solely our responsibility, and not that of any of those giving us help.

Peeter Kruus, April 1984

CONTENTS

LEAD
Lead is used in gasoline additives, and is therefore an ever-present pollutant in urban areas. There is much speculation about its effect on people.

MERCURY
Disasters due to the use of this metal have occurred throughout the world for centuries. Today some communities in Northern Ontario and Quebec are concerned with mercury in their diets.

NITRITES AND NITRATES
Nitrite is used as a meat preservative. Bacon is a particular problem because cooking accelerates formation of carcinogenic chemicals.

NITROGEN OXIDES (NO_x)
Automobile exhausts contain nitrogen oxides, which can be responsible for the formation of smog in urban areas and can contribute to acid rain.

POLYCHLORINATED BIPHENYLS (PCBs)
The great chemical stability of PCBs has made them useful for several industrial purposes. This stability now poses a problem as the harmful effects of PCBs have been discovered. Although their use is discontinued, PCBs will persist in the environment for years.

PENTACHLOROPHENOL (PCP)
PCP has been used for years as a wood preservative. Doubts have now arisen about its safety.

PHOSPHATES
Phosphates are introduced into lakes and rivers by inadequate treatment of sewage. In excess, they promote the growth of algae, accelerating the natural aging of a lake.

RADON
With increased emphasis on energy conservation people are insulating their homes. This can result in deficient ventilation and subsequently potentially hazardous radon buildup.

ALCOHOL

Alcohol consumption is increasing in most countries. Are the long-term health effects worth the temporary euphoria?

THE CHEMISTRY OF ALCOHOL AND ALCOHOLIC BEVERAGES

The substance frequently called alcohol is actually ethyl alcohol or ethanol. It is one of the group of compounds known collectively as alcohols of which methanol, CH_3OH, is the simplest member.

The starting material for the formation of ethanol is the natural sugar found in grains or fruits. In the process of fermentation the sugar reacts with an enzyme in yeast and is converted to glucose which in turn is acted upon by another enzyme to produce ethanol:

$$\begin{array}{c} \text{sugars} \\ \text{or} \\ \text{starch} \end{array} \xrightarrow{\text{enzyme}} \underset{C_6H_{12}O_6}{\text{glucose}} \xrightarrow{\text{enzymes}} \underset{C_2H_5OH}{\text{ethanol}} + \underset{CO_2}{\text{carbon dioxide}}$$

Beers and wines are the final products of the natural fermentation process of barley and grapes respectively and they contain 3-12% ethanol by volume. Fermentation stops in solutions where the concentration of alcohol is greater than 12% because the growth of yeast is inhibited. Thus beverages with a higher alcohol concentration are made either by distillation or fortification (1): brandy is made by distilling wine; whiskey is made by fermenting barley, rye or corn and subsequently distilling the product; and rum in a similar manner from molasses (1). During the distillation process, a solution of 95% ethanol and 5% water is produced; this distillate also contains some characteristic flavour and colour constituents. After distillation, the solution is diluted to the appropriate ethanol concentration (2).

THE USE OF ALCOHOL

The level of alcohol consumption varies from country to country. The variation is due to demographic characteristics, cultural patterns, attitudes and traditions (3). It appears that alcohol consumption is increasing in most countries. The reasons are complex but longer leisure hours, improved education, urbanization and liberalization of moral attitudes have been suggested as possible factors (3).

In 1980, over 2.5 billion litre of alcohol were sold in Canada. This was equivalent to 133 litre for each person aged 15 or over (4), and marked a 7% increase since 1973. Globally, Canadian per capita consumption ranked 26th on a 1977 list of 65 countries (5).

The Addiction Research Foundation of Ontario, a Crown Corporation of the province, operates specialized research, educational, clinical and service development programs throughout Ontario (6). In the foundation's 1979-1980 statistical report, it presented some results of a Canada-wide survey conducted May 1978 to Mar. 1979. It was found that 80.4% of adults consumed alcohol, of whom 52% were male and 48% were female.

Alcohol has become associated with nearly all leisure activities (3). It is suggested that people drink not only as a social activity, but also to relax, promote sleep, relieve social or physical discomforts or tension, quench thirst, increase appetite, satisfy curiosity, relieve boredom, gain courage, escape personal responsibility or imitate parents or peers (7).

EFFECTS OF ALCOHOL

The effects of ethanol ingestion begin as the alcohol passes into the bloodstream. The results of blood ethanol levels of up to 0.05% by volume are euphoria, a sense of well-being and some impairment of coordination. At 0.15% ethanol, drowsiness and vomiting occur, and at 0.30% ethanol, respiration problems are sufficiently serious to cause death (2), but a person usually becomes unconscious before a lethal dose can be taken (7).

Long-term effects which result from repeated use of alcohol over long periods of time have been linked with increased risk of liver disease (cirrhosis), heart and circulatory problems, certain cancers (of the upper digestive and respiratory systems) and ulcers (7,8). Alcohol has also been linked to congenital defects. In what is called the "fetal alcohol syndrome", one or more of the following symptoms have been displayed by some babies whose mothers drank alcohol during pregnancy: clusters of facial defects, heart murmurs, central nervous system problems and below average weight and height. Abnormalities have been found to occur in varying degrees, from one observation to the next, usually in proportion to the extent of alcohol consumption. However, researchers have not yet determined an absolute safe level of consumption (9). Alcohol has also been implicated (10) in the controversial link between cholesterol and arteriosclerosis (hardening of the arteries). Since cholesterol is quite soluble in alcohol, the latter, consumed with a cholesterol-rich meal, may result in an increase in the cholesterol content of the blood.

On the other hand, there are reports that some alcohol can have beneficial health effects. Wine, having disinfectant properties, has been used to detoxify impure water, and can inactivate viruses in the stomach and intestines (11).

When ethanol is absorbed in the body, the net reaction is the production of carbon dioxide (CO_2), water (H_2O) and energy. The first reaction is the oxidation of the alcohol to acetaldehyde, which is thought to be responsible for the short-term effects of alcohol ingestion (1,12). The second stage is further oxidation to form "acetyl coenzyme A". This chemical is involved in a series of reactions known as the Krebs cycle, in which normal sugars are broken down to carbon dioxide in an energy-producing reaction. A reactant known as a "coenzyme" is required in both steps; it is an imbalance in the different forms of this substance which may lead to liver cirrhosis (2). Other factors, such as individual variation in the mechanism of alcohol elimination, genetic predisposition and nutritional imbalance may modify the above effects (13).

ALCOHOLISM

Opinion concerning the nature of alcohol addiction is divided. Some believe that alcoholics are persons predisposed, by virtue of their physical or mental characteristics, to the illness regardless of the environment or the availability of alcohol. Some think that it is a psychological illness accompanied by a dependence on alcohol. Some think that the addiction has a physiological basis which is aggravated by availability of alcohol. If it is physiological, the chemistry of the illness may eventually be understood with the result that methods of treatment or prevention will improve (8).

Estimates of the numbers of alcoholics are achieved in various ways: from death statistics, arrest information, hospital admissions, alcohol sales records, cirrhosis data and specific research studies. All sources of information lend support to the fact that alcohol consumption and deaths from cirrhosis of the liver are increasing (8). Interest in understanding treatments of alcoholism has likewise increased, particularly in the last decade. Treatments include group or individual psychotherapy (for hospital inpatients or outpatients); drug treatment using disulfiram, citrated calcium carbimide, tranquilizers or antidepressants; development of dedication to the principles of Alcoholics Anonymous, which is a self-help organization founded in 1935 and described as "probably the single most effective method of treatment" (14). It has been suggested (8) that none of the above methods, or development of programs of preventive education, or development of rehabilitation facilities, can be effective without controls. The latter, which are the responsibility of federal and provincial governments, include control of number, type and hours of operation of outlets, of the legal drinking age, and of advertising and cost (8).

A strong argument in favour of control of alcohol is that it is futile to prohibit other drugs as long as alcohol remains freely available. Opponents of prohibition or strict control likewise have a powerful argument because history has shown that prohibition does not work; instead it can be accompanied by additional adverse effects (15).

DRINKING AND DRIVING REGULATIONS

One area where control is currently under discussion is that of drinking and driving. It is an offence under the Criminal Code of Canada to drive with a blood alcohol level of 0.08% (80 milligrams of alcohol per 100 millilitres of blood) or more. It is also illegal for a driver to refuse to take a breathalyzer test (7). The Ontario government is considering amendments to the Highway Traffic Act which would empower the police to suspend a driver's licence for 24 hours if a roadside analysis shows a blood alcohol level of 0.05% or more (16). For a 70 kilogram person, this level corresponds roughly to 2 to 3 bottles of regular beer consumed within the previous hour (17). At the end of 1983, the federal government announced proposed changes to the Criminal Code to increase times, licence suspensions and prison terms for drivers impaired by alcohol. Impaired driving causing death would have a maximum penalty of life imprisonment (18). About 2500 people in Canada die each year due to drunken driving.

REFERENCES

1. Jones, M. M., Netterville, J. T., Johnston, D. O. and Wood, J.L., "Chemistry, Man and Society", Second edition, W. B. Saunders Company, Toronto,1976.
2. Pyle, J. L., "Chemistry and the Technological Backlash", Prentice-Hall, Inc., New Jersey, 1974.
3. Sulkunen, P., "Drinking Patterns and the Level of Alcohol Consumption: An International Overview", in Research Advances in Alcohol and Drug Problems, Vol. 3, edited by Gibbins, R. J.,Israel, Y., Kalant, H., Popham, R. E., Schmidt, W. and Smart, R.G., John Wiley and Sons, New York, 1976.
4. Statistics Canada, "The Control and Sale of Alcoholic Beverages in Canada", annual issues (Ottawa: Statistics Canada Catalogue No. 63-202).
5. "Statistical Supplement to the Annual Report 1979-1980", Addiction Research Foundation of Ontario, Toronto, 1981.
6. "Annual Report 1980-1981", Addiction Research Foundation of Ontario, 1981.
7. "Facts About Alcohol", Addiction Research Foundation of Ontario, Toronto, 1975.
8. Archibald, H. D, "Toward Saturation--in Search of Control. Alcohol Use in Ontario in The Mid-70s", Addiction Research Foundation of Ontario, Toronto, 1975.
9. Kazenel, M., "Alcohol and The Unborn: A Disastrous Mix", Future Health, 3(3), 1981. "Alcohol Can Damage Unfertilized Eggs", New Scientist, Mar. 24, 1983.
10. "Alcohol, Cholesterol and Arteriosclerosis", Chemical and Engineering News, May 1, 1978
11. "Drinkers Rejoice: A Little Wine May Kill Your Virus", Science, 196, 1074, 1977.
12. Labianca, D. A., "Acetaldehyde Syndrome and Alcoholism", Chemistry 47(9), 21, 1974.
13. Lelbach, W. K., "Organic Pathology Related to Volume and Pattern of Alcohol Use", in Research Advances in Alcohol and Drug Problems, Volume 1, 1974 (see Reference 3).
14. Baekeland, F., Lundwall, L. and Kissen, B., "Methods for The Treatment of Chronic Alcoholism: A Critical Appraisal", in Research Advances in Alcohol and Drug Problems, Volume 2, 1975 (see Reference 3).
15. Brecher, E. M. and the Editors of Consumer Reports, "Licit and Illicit Drugs", Little, Brown and Company, Boston, 1972.
16. "Information Review" of the Addiction Research Foundation, Toronto, Dec. 1979.
17. Memorandum of the Addiction Research Foundation, "Re: Drinking and Driving", Dec. 11, 1981.
18. Sallot, J., "Ottawa Proposes Tougher Penalties for Drunk Drivers", The Globe and Mail, Toronto, Dec. 20, 1983.

RECOMMENDED READING

The Addiction Research Foundation publications (e.g., (16) and (17)) summarize the detrimental effects of alcohol in an easy-to-read style. References (1) and (2) try to present scientific information concerning the metabolism of and addiction to, alcohol. The volumes (published annually since 1974) of "Research Advances in Alcohol and Drug Problems" (e.g., reference (3)) contain many detailed papers, with extensive bibliographies on the many aspects which contribute to an understanding of the problems related to alcohol.

ARSENIC

Arsenic poisoning occurs mainly in industrial and agricultural workers. However, atmospheric emissions may affect water, snow, soil, vegetation and eventually people.

OCCURRENCE, SOURCES AND USES OF ARSENIC AND ITS COMPOUNDS

Arsenic occurs widely in minerals, ores, coal and soil. In the earth's crust the average concentration is 2 ppm (part per million). It can be deposited into water systems by the dissolution of minerals and ores, as well as through the industrial effluents associated with coal and mineral mining and refining, and related chemical industries. It can also be washed into water systems as a result of the use of insecticides and fungicides containing arsenic. The contribution of arsenic to the environment through human activities is thought to be much higher, overall, than through natural phenomena (1).

The major use of arsenic is as a pesticide in agriculture in the form of calcium arsenate, arsenic acid, lead arsenate and sodium arsenite. In recent years, other chemicals have been used as substitutes for the more widely used arsenates. For example, DDT was a popular alternative before its ban (see DDT); organic phosphate compounds are now also used (see Fenitrothion). Sodium arsenite was widely used to defoliate potato plants prior to harvesting but this was phased out in 1971. Arsenic compounds are also used in wood preserving, hide tanning and in the manufacture of paint pigments (2).

Metallic arsenic is used mainly in the making of alloys because of its hardening properties. The addition of up to 3% of arsenic hardens lead and minimizes the softening of lead-base bearing alloys used in internal combustion engines. Minor amounts (less than 0.1%) of arsenic may be added to copper to improve corrosion and erosion resistance and to lead-base battery plates to increase hardness. The addition of arsenic (0.5% to 2%) is known to improve the sphericity of lead shot.

During the last few years there has been a demand for very pure arsenic metal for use in the electronics industry. The arsenic in the form of gallium or indium arsenide is used to form semi-conductors which are used to make transistors, solar cells, lasers and infra-red devices (2). It is also used as a dopant to confer semi-conductive properties to germanium and silicon. Such high purity arsenic is produced in Canada by Cominco Ltd. in Trail, B.C. using the residues from their lead smelter.

Arsenic trioxide, As_2O_3 is an unavoidable byproduct of the roasting of ores and smelting of lead and copper. A roasting step is needed in many metallurgical processes to remove the sulphur from concentrates. The desired metals are then usually separated from the waste by smelting, i.e., bringing the material to a high temperature and separating the molten metal from the slag.

The arsenic released in such operations can be a hazard for smelter workers, because arsenic compounds are now accepted as proven human carcinogens (3). Cancer rates 5 to 10 times higher than expected were reported in a study of smelter workers in Rouyn, Que. exposed to arsenic, cadmium and lead (4). It can also be a hazard to the general public. The arsenic trioxide produced during the roasting of gold ore concentrate in the Giant Yellowknife Mines in the Northwest Terriories was said by Environment Canada in 1976 to be carefully collected in baghouses (filters) and disposed of in special underground works (2). Since then, there have been doubts as to how safe this procedure is. The present situation in Yellowknife is discussed further, later in this chapter.

In addition to arsenic trioxide, small amounts of arsenic may be found in some foods (resulting from the use of agricultural sprays). Some drugs, such as arsphenamine (which has been used to treat syphilis), contain arsenic.

THE BIOLOGICAL EFFECTS OF EXPOSURE TO ARSENIC OR ITS COMPOUNDS

Arsenic has acquired the reputation of being the classical homicidal poison. The white powder, arsenic trioxide, was a poison known to the Assyrians and the ancient Egyptians. It became well known during the Italian Renaissance; Flaubert vividly described a case of acute arsenic poisoning in his novel "Madame Bovary" and it has been

suggested (with much subsequent controversy) that it was used
in several attempts to kill Napoleon Bonaparte when in exile
(5,6). It has, however, been so well studied by forensic
scientists that it is no longer popular with poisoners (5).

Poisoning with any appreciable amount of arsenic develops
very quickly. Gastric and intestinal problems and vomiting are
accompanied by intense pain and thirst. Death caused by
complete cardiovascular collapse may follow within a few
hours. In acute cases the patient may die before showing the
usual nervous symptoms of arsenic poisoning. A dose of about
100 mg (milligram) is lethal (5).

Today, arsenic poisoning occurs mainly in industry and
agriculture among workers who handle materials which contain
arsenic as an impurity. In these cases of arsenic poisoning,
one of the symptoms is a painful paralysis of the lower limbs
which resembles the polyneuritis (nerve inflammation) of the
chronic alcoholic. Other symptoms include a scabby ulceration
of the skin and a cafe au lait discolouration of the palms of
the hands and soles of the feet (5).

Arsenic and other heavy metals owe their toxicity
primarily to their ability to react with and inhibit certain
enzyme systems such as those involved in the production of
cellular energy. The mechanism of arsenic poisoning was
determined by British scientists during World War I (7). The
researchers were trying to develop a compound to counteract
Lewisite, a poisonous gas containing arsenic used in the
war. It was found that arsenic reacted with protein
sulphhydryl groups (-SH) in enzymes, so a chemical compound
was sought which contained highly reactive sulphhydryl groups
which would compete for the arsenic with the sulphhydryl
groups in the poisoned molecule, i.e., the inactivated enzyme,
and thus render the poison ineffective. The name British Anti-
Lewisite (BAL) was coined for the successful compound. Since
it bonds the arsenic at several sites, the sulphhydryl groups
in the vital enzymes are freed to resume thier normal
functions. BAL is a standard item in hospital poison emergency
centres and can be used routinely to treat cases of heavy
metal poisoning (7).

Several epidemiological studies, which determine the
frequencies and distributions of diseases, have shown a

correlation between cancer and exposure to arsenic (6,8). The U.S. Occupational Safety and Health Administration (OSHA) set stricter standards for exposure to arsenic in 1978 (3). OSHA is a government agency responsible for establishing and enforcing standards for exposure of workers to harmful materials. In 1982, OSHA announced that excess deaths (relative to the general population) due to lung cancer of workers with some exposure to arsenic had decreased dramatically (9). Under the new exposure standard (0.010 mg/m^3 (milligram per cubic metre)), the number of excess deaths is only about 2% of the number expected under the old standard ($0.500mg/m^3$). Even stricter standards were proposed in 1983 (10).

THE ARSENIC CONTROVERSY IN THE NORTHWEST TERRITORIES

In 1975, Health and Welfare Canada conducted a study to determine the extent of the arsenic contamination of the 12,000 residents who live in the shadow of Giant Yellowknife Mine, a gold mining company. This study was criticized by some as being invalid, so that another study was conducted by the National Indian Brotherhood and the United Steelworkers of America (11).

These studies were subsequently used by a task force on arsenic (commissioned by Health and Welfare Canada and made the responsibility of the Canadian Public Health Association) to assess the extent of arsenic uptake in Yellowknife. In its report (12), the Task Force recommendations included regular monitoring of air samples at Giant Yellowknife Mine and Cominco Con Mine, regular medical examination of employees (including electromyography, hair and urine analyses), strict enforcement of clean working conditions, prevention (by removing the need) of the use of snow as drinking water, monitoring of drinking water for arsenic, further assessment of arsenic levels in fish and routine surveillance of arsenic emission, waste disposal and storage procedures. The report states that "outside of the mine mill workers, no immediate health effects can be found which are due to the present environmental levels of arsenic in Yellowknife". The Task Force does, however, suggest that consideration be given to a review of the lung cancer and skin cancer histories of past and present employees of mines in the area.

CONTROL OF ARSENIC IN THE ENVIRONMENT

As previously noted, arsenic is one of the substances separated out in the production of gold. The separation process can lead to the entry of arsenic into the environment in three main ways: atmospheric emissions, effluent and solid wastes.

Emission of arsenic into the atmosphere has been considerably reduced in the Yellowknife area over the last 20 years. For example, electrostatic precipitators and bag-house filters are used and are subsequently buried. By the process of decantation from several ponds, liquid effluent is eventually passed into a previously designated body of water. However sometimes seepage occurs from the ponds and contaminated effluent may enter sources of drinking water and may affect soil and vegetation in the area. For example, in the spring of 1976, it was reported (14) that incidences of arsenic contamination were found in wells in the area of a former gold mine near Halifax in Nova Scotia. A survey of a 30 mile area surrounding the mine showed that contamination was quite widespread. The water supply of one school was cut off when it was found that the arsenic content was 15 times greater than the level considered safe by the province.

There has been an interesting development by Cominco Ltd. in connection with removal of arsenic from stack scrubbing wastes at its gold mine in Yellowknife. By treatment of the arseniferous sludge, arsenic trioxide crystals (used in pesticides, desiccants and wood preservatives) are produced. Thus a useful product is extracted from the potentially hazardous wastes (15).

Allowable exposure levels for arsenic vary considerably. In the U.S., the OSHA standard for arsenic in air is 0.010 mg/m^3 (3). In Canada, the federally recommended Threshold Level Value (TLV) is 0.200 mg/m^3. Two provinces have set lower levels; B.C., 0.050 and Alberta, 0.050 with a 0.150 peak. Ontario follows the 0.200 guideline and Quebec allows 0.500 mg/m^3 (13). The Canadian Drinking Water Standard for arsenic sets the maximum permissible aresenic level at 0.050 mg per litre. Maximum allowable arsenic limits in food (set by the Health Protection Branch, Health and Welfare Canada) are

2 ppm for fruits and one ppm for fresh vegetables (12).

The carcinogenicity of arsenic seems now to be generally accepted. More studies are required to clarify the effects of long-term, low-dose exposure of arsenic on man, animals and fish. Such research is difficult because of the lack of a good animal model; the rat has a unique arsenic metabolism which is unlike that of man or other mammals. The restrictions on the emission levels of arsenic and disposal of arsenic wastes, medical surveillance of workers, and stringent controls on working conditions are thought to have significantly reduced the incidence of arsenic-induced cancer.

REFERENCES

1. Demayo, A., Taylor, M. C. and Reeder, S. W., "Guidelines for Surface Water Quality: Arsenic", Inland Waters Directorate, Environment Canada, Ottawa, 1979.
2. National Inventory of Sources and Emissions of Arsenic (1972), Environment Canada, International Report APCD 75-5, Air Pollution Control Directorate, 1976.
3. "OSHA Issues New Tough Standard for Arsenic", Chemical and Engineering News, May 3, 1978.
4. "Committee to Probe High Cancer Rates at Noranda Smelter", The Citizen, Ottawa, Jan. 18, 1983.
5. Bodin, F. and Cheinesse, C. F., "Poisons", trans. Harold Oldroyd, McGraw Hill Book Co., New York, 1976.
6. "Arsenic", Medical and Biologic Effects of Environmental Pollutants, National Academy of Sciences, Washington, D.C., 1977.
7. Jones, M. M., Netterville, J. T., Johnson, D. O. and Wood, J. L., "Chemistry, Man and Society", Second edition, W. B. Saunders Co., Toronto, 1976.
8. "Effects of Arsenic in the Canadian Environment", National Research Council of Canada, Ottawa, No. 15391, 1978.
9. Chemical Engineering, p. 20, May 3, 1982.
10. "Copper Smelters Face Tougher Arsenic Emission Standards", Chemical Engineering, Aug. 8, 1983.
11. Tataryn, L., "Notes from the Territories: Arsenic Poisoning", Alternatives, 1, 12, 1978.
12. Final Report of Canadian Public Health Association Task Force on Arsenic, Yellowknife, N.W.T., Dec. 1977.
13. Canadian Occupational Health and Safety Law, Corpus Information Services Ltd., Don Mills, Ontario.
14. "Nova Scotia Wells Spot Checked for Contamination Levels", The Citizen, Ottawa, June 10, 1976.
15. "A First-of-its-Kind Facility Producing Arsenic Trioxide from Goldmine Wastes", Chemical and Engineering News, Nov. 1, 1982.

RECOMMENDED READING

Reference (6) is a detailed and interesting account of arsenic and research concerning, in particular, arsenic as a carcinogen. Reference (12) is a recent report on the Yellowknife situation, while (8) gives a thorough scientific review.

ASBESTOS

Asbestos can be a health hazard. It is a major Canadian export and stricter regulations for exposure will have severe economic effects, especially in Quebec.

HISTORY AND USES OF ASBESTOS

Asbestos - the word is derived from the Greek "asbesta" which means unquenchable or inextinguishable. The substance was so named by the Greeks because they found that asbestos wicks in their temple lamps were never consumed by the surrounding flames. It was used to strengthen clay pottery 4500 years ago and was known in ancient Egyptian, Greek and Roman civilizations but was scarcely used there because of cost and the mystery surrounding its origin. The Roman historian, Pliny the Elder, ascribed a vegetable origin to it and wrote, "this substance grows in the deserts of India, here scorched by the burning rays of the sun. Amid multitudes of deadly serpents it becomes habituated to resist the action of fire" (1). It appears that the Greeks knew the secret however; they obtained their asbestos from deposits in Euboae, a large island off the east coast of Greece, and from Cyprus. Today there is little left of these deposits. The Romans mined the Italian Alps and a region near the Urals.

The fibre from these sources was difficult to spin because it was short, so a vegetable fibre was added to facilitate spinning; cloth so produced is preserved in the Vatican Library. The wealthy could afford to wrap their dead in asbestos shrouds for the cremation ceremony and Pliny referred to asbestos cloth as "the funeral dress for kings". The use of asbestos meant that the ashes from the cremation could easily be separated from the fuel and placed in urns for worship. Throughout the Middle Ages asbestos earned a certain superstitious awe because of its special qualities. Charlemagne mystified dinner guests by throwing a soiled asbestos table cloth into a fire. When removed the cloth was clean and unblemished.

From the 13th to the 17th century there were few references to asbestos. The modern industry dates from about 1870. Canada shares the distinction with the U.S.S.R. and Italy of being the first countries in which asbestos was mined and milled. Between 1862 and 1877, deposits in the Eastern Townships of Quebec were being mined on a commercial basis. In British Columbia, the Cassiar deposits started producing asbestos in 1954. Baie Verte, Newfoundland, joined the industry in 1963. Mines are also in operation elsewhere in Quebec, in Ontario and in the Yukon Territory. Canada is now the second largest producer of asbestos (2); the U.S.S.R. is first and the Republic of South Africa is third (3). Canada produces only white asbestos (chrysotile); blue asbestos (crocidolite), and brown asbestos (amosite) are produced chiefly in South Africa (4).

Canada's asbestos production in 1977 amounted to 1.5 million tonne (1 tonne=1000kg) and was valued at $564 million (3). Eighty-nine percent of Canadian production is from the province of Quebec, the largest single source being the open-pit mine of Johns-Manville Co. in Asbestos, Quebec. The 70 mile long rock in the Eastern Townships between Asbestos and East Broughton, Quebec, is the world's largest known deposit of asbestos (5).

Approximately 96% of Canadian asbestos is exported. The major markets are the U.S., Japan, Britain, West Germany and France, but exports go to about 70 countries. Production used in Canadian manufacturing accounts for about 4% of total shipments. Asbestos is used to make construction materials such as asbestos cement (used, for example, in water conduit pipes); floor covering; friction products (in brake linings) and gaskets; asbestos paper and felts; insulation and textiles. There are many other minor but important uses (3).

The large number of practical uses for asbestos is due to its extraordinary properties. Asbestos is a general term applied to a variety of silicate minerals which share unique physical and chemical properties. The 2 groups of asbestos substances (serpentine and amphibole) result from differences in the host rock in which asbestos occurs. Chrysotile (white asbestos) is a serpentine asbestos, and crocidolite (blue asbestos) and amosite are the most common of the amphiboles. In general, amphibole asbestos contains a larger percentage of silica, less magnesium and more iron, aluminum, sodium and calcium than serpentines (6). The chemical compositions from different sources may vary.

All the asbestos minerals are fibrous, inorganic poly-
mers. Individual fibrils have an outer diameter of 0.02-0.04
micron (10,000 micron equals 1 cm) but fibres (the term
usually used in connection with asbestos), are a collection of
fibrils and occur as fragments ranging from 1 to 100 micron in
length. These properties give chrysotile a fibrous nature with
flexible, silky, tough fibres which are easy to spin. In
addition to this property, chrysotile resists heat, but not
acid.

Crocidolite has a chain-like crystal structure giving
fibres which are larger in diameter than chrysotile, straight
and solid. It resists acid and is thus used to make acid-
resistant cement pipe and electrolysis separators (7,8); it is
not, however, a good thermal insulator. Amosite is acid-
resistant and a good heat insulator, it is used for bulk
insulation and is moulded into pipe insulation.

ASBESTOS AS A HEALTH HAZARD

Exposure to asbestos fibres can occur in several ways.
Occupational exposure of workers can occur during the mining,
milling and processing of asbestos, and while using products
containing asbestos, e.g. asbestos in insulation. Consumer
exposure is possible through the many products which contain
asbestos. The public can also ingest asbestos from food, water
and other beverages (9,10).

The hazards to health resulting from occupational exposure to high airborne concentrations of asbestos have been
recognized since the beginning of the 20th century. Attempts
to control the progressive respiratory disease known as
asbestosis led the United Kingdom to issue the first asbestos
regulations 45 years ago. There are now controversies in
countries producing and using asbestos which have raised questions, not only about the adequacy of regulations covering its
industrial use, but about the possibility that asbestos poses
a threat to the public at large.

Asbestos pneumoconiosis has come to be known as asbestosis. It is a severe scarring of the lungs caused by continual-
ly inhaling asbestos fibres over the course of approximately
20 years. The symptoms begin with shortness of breath, which

develops into near paralysis that makes breathing and body movement increasingly difficult.

If the disease progresses, the individual can die from other respiratory diseases, or eventually suffocate. Usually, however, asbestosis leads to heart strain and ultimately cardiac failure (2). The incidence of the disease is dependent upon a number of factors, including the concentration of dust in the air; the size, type and processing history of the fibres; the duration of exposure; and individual susceptibility.

Asbestos does not only cause asbestosis; it is now accepted that it can cause cancer (11). Judging from expected and observed death rates among asbestos workers (11) this may be a more serious effect than asbestosis. Several countries have noted an increasing incidence of asbestos-induced lung cancer and mesothelioma, a malignant, inoperable cancer which affects the pleura and peritoneum (lining of the chest and abdomen respectively).

Mesothelioma is rare in the general population, but asbestos factory workers and shipyard workers have had significantly higher incidences of mesothelioma (3). It is so rare that even the occurrence of 2 or 3 cases in a group of workers becomes statistically significant. Recently published maps of cancer mortality in England (12) show that almost all deaths resulting from mesothelioma occurred in areas close to industrial sites where large amounts of asbestos have been made or used in the past 40 years.

The incidence of mesothelioma varies with the degree of exposure. It has also been suggested that mesothelioma may be contracted through the ingestion of asbestos fibres. Fibres deposited in the lungs are able to penetrate the respiratory membranes and be transported to other sites in the body through the circulatory and lymphatic systems (3). Pleural thickening and calcification may result from prolonged exposure to asbestos but are not necessarily associated with symptoms of ill-health.

Male asbestos workers have at least twice the chance of developing lung cancer as their counterparts in the normal population. Female workers have a tenfold greater risk. The risk of lung cancer appears to be higher in smokers; it has been shown that an asbestos worker who smokes cigarettes has 8 times the lung cancer risk of other smokers, and 92 times the risk of non-smokers not exposed to asbestos. Asbestos has also been implicated in causing cancer of the lip, tongue, salivary gland, mouth, small intestine, diaphragm, testes, ovaries, chematopoietic system, and stomach (3). Some estimate that 40% of the occupationally exposed population in the U.S. will die from asbestos related causes (13). In the past, there were few regulations governing occupational exposure to asbestos, and many workers had substantial exposure.

It is known that crocidolite is the most hazardous form of asbestos, but it is not known whether asbestos fibres per se are carcinogenic, or whether they are carriers of carcinogenic chemicals or trace metals. Recently, it has been found to contain the carcinogen benzopyrene (3) (see Tobacco). The fact remains, though, that asbestos exposure is in some way directly related to cancer. The dimensions of the fibres seem to be important in determining carcinogenicity.

The general public is not usually in danger of massive inhalation of asbestos fibres. However the general population is exposed to higher than background levels due to asbestos fibres released from building materials used in airports, post offices and schools. Due to the role of the media in alerting the public of such hazards, measures are being taken to remove or stabilize the asbestos in public buildings (14). The danger seems to lie in the area of pleural and peritoneal mesothelioma (15). The initial symptoms exhibited by people with these tumours are chest pains and abdominal discomfort, together with a deteriorating general condition, and may not appear until at least 20 years have elapsed since first exposure to asbestos (3).

The properties of asbestos make it highly suitable in filtration and thus it is used in the chemical, food and beverage industries. However, Health and Welfare Canada reports that, based on available survey data, most manufacturers now use cellulose or diatomaceous earth rather than asbestos fibres. Asbestos filters may add fibrous contamination of their own to the filtrate. As a result, asbestos fibres may be found in beers, wines and liquors, soft drinks, sugar and lard. Such filters are also widely used in the pharmaceutical industry because they prevent bacterial growth and allow rapid filtration. Common antibiotics such as streptomycin, tetracycline and most penicillins have been found to contain chrysotile asbestos (16). In addition, asbestos is found in varying amounts in many city water supplies (17) and in both rural and urban drinking water in Ontario (18). This is due to a combination of natural processes of weathering and erosion and industrial sources. For example, Health and Welfare Canada suggests that typically, background levels in rivers and lakes are considered to be one million fibres per litre, although values may range from less than one to 10 million fibres per litre.

There has been public concern over asbestos levels in beverages, particularly wine. A paper by 2 medical researchers sparked general concern and investigation into the hazards of asbestos fibres in drinking water and beverages. Cunningham and Pontefract (19) reported that "millions of fibres" were present in a single litre of soft drinks, tap water and liquor ingested by the general public. In 1973 they showed that the asbestos fibres found in these liquids could penetrate the mucosa of the stomach and the intestine and have been found in some gastric cancerous tissue in rats (19). This information is supported by research in Germany (20) and in the U.S. (21). A survey in the summer of 1977 showed asbestos levels in domestic and imported wines ranging from 250,000 fibres per litre to 1.9 million fibres per litre (20). Following the release of this survey the President of the Wine and Spirits Association of Canada was reported as saying "Swallow for swallow, wine has fewer asbestos fibres than beer, ginger ale, sherry or even ordinary run-of-the-mill tap water" (22).

Much research has been done on inhaled fibres and subsequently standards have been promulgated by various regulatory agencies (7,11). However, the problems of inhaled and ingested fibres are so different that any extrapolation of data on the effects of inhaled fibres to the problems of ingested fibres is complicated, and there has been a lack of research in the area of human tolerances to determine a maximum allowable quantity of ingested asbestos fibre. The absence of a threshold limit value led "Canadian Consumer" to recommend "outright prohibition of the use of asbestos filters in the preparation of any material which will find its way

into the human body" (20). Molecular cellulose filters can be
used to remove very fine matter (23).

CONTROL OF ASBESTOS

Asbestos poses a serious threat to human health. Yet,
without destroying the industry it seems impossible to
eliminate the risk of asbestos-related diseases affecting
workers and the general population. To control the hazard,
occupational and environmental asbestos standards are set,
usually expressed as the number of fibres/cm^3 (fibres per
cubic centimetre) of air. There are also regulations which
stipulate requirements for the operation of specific control
equipment.

Standards may be set federally and/or provincially. The
resulting division of responsibility can lead to differences
in standard setting and enforcement in different provinces. A
common paradox of regulation was created when Environment
Canada announced in 1975 a standard of 2 fibres /cm^3 in the
air surrounding asbestos mining and milling operations;this is
in conflict with the existing standards in some provinces
(e.g. 5 fibres/cm^3 in Quebec).

Federally, under the Hazardous Products Act, advertising,
selling or importing toys or clothing products containing
asbestos is prohibited unless the product is designed as
protection from fire or heat or is made such that the asbestos
fibres will not become separated from the product under conditions of reasonable use. As yet, there are no labelling
requirements for products that do contain asbestos. Also prohibited are substances containing any type of asbestos which
are for use in modelling or sculpture or by children (24). As
recently as 1960, children in schools were using modelling
material which probably contained at least 15% of blue asbestos fibres (2). This type, crocidolite, has the reputation of
being the most hazardous variety of the mineral (25) and is
now banned in Saskatchewan (26) and controlled in other
provinces. There is also a ban on the use of asbestos in dry
wall joint cements and compounds for patching.

Crocidolite was initially the only mineral associated
with mesothelioma. However, in recent years amosite and
chrysotile have been implicated (11) and this means that

asbestos fibres in the ambient air have become an important
public concern. The Ontario Ministry of the Environment has
set an ambient air standard of 0.04 fibres/cm^3 but measurement
of low concentrations of asbestos fibres is difficult (7).
Sampling techniques may lead to inaccurate results and the
cost is high. Sampling the air in one location once a week,
using light microscopy would cost thousands of dollars annually, and there are not enough skilled technicians for the task.

The problem of asbestos exposure has been examined from a
global point of view (27) by the International Labour
Organization. Sweden has banned asbestos completely (27),
Britain has made its workplace standards more restrictive,
from 2 fibres/cm^3 in 1971 to 1.0 in 1979 to 0.5 in 1984 (0.2
fibres/cm^3 for crocidolite)(28). The European Common market
has however had difficulty in legislating more restrictive
common rules on asbestos (29).

Ontario had an occupational standard of 5 fibres (greater
than 5 micron in length) of asbestos/cm^3 until 1972, but this
level was subsequently lowered to 2 fibres/cm^3. The 5 fibre
limit had been thought to be a safe one, but the toxicities of
the various types of asbestos are not well understood, and
thus a safety factor was included. Alberta and Saskatchewan
have set standards at 2 fibres/cm^3. Saskatchewan has banned
blue asbestos (crocidolite). British Columbia and Nova Scotia
also have a 2 fibre limit (3).

It should be realized that the 2 fibre limit is a "time
weighted average" over an 8 hour period. Thus, it is deemed
acceptable for a worker to spend 8 hours a day, 5 days a week,
breathing air which carries a discernible 2 fibres/cm^3. Some
excursion beyond that limit is permitted during the 8 hour
period, but the excursion is limited to 10 fibres/cm^3 for 15
minutes.

Failure to meet the standards has led to the closure of
mills in Ontario. The United Asbestos Incorporated Mill at
Matchewan, Ontario, near Kirkland Lake, started production in
late 1975 and was initially called "one of the better
operations" in Ontario by the Natural Resources Minister. It
was temporarily closed in 1976, after results of dust level
tests worsened progressively (7). The week before production
was stopped, the average asbestos levels were 12 to 14

fibres/cm^3. The plant employed 180 people.

Because mines and mills in Quebec are generally older and have more serious problems than those in other parts of the country, much controversy arises because several firms, even after spending large amounts of money, are doubtful that they will be able to meet the standards. In 1975 Judge Beaudry was appointed head of a commission to look into the asbestos situation in Quebec and by 1976 he had criticized the provincial government for its lax standards and inspections. This aspect of the interim report of the commission was supported by the federal-provincial working group (25) which was also critical of Quebec and total regulatory procedures (30). The final report of the Quebec enquiry was published in 1977; it stressed the necessity for reducing asbestos levels to acceptably low values (2). In 1979, l'Institut de Recherche et de Developpement de l'Amiante was created in order to measure the amount of fibre emission into the environment, to research methods of its elimination, as well as to develop new asbestos-based products (5).

In order to mine and mill asbestos, it seems that a certain level of dust must be accepted. Thus, in the setting of standards, governments have the difficult task of weighing health risks against economic considerations (30). Even with the standards quoted in this report, there is still a risk to asbestos workers. In fact, the declared purpose of the 2 fibres/cm^3 standard is the protection of workers against a 1% risk of asbestosis. In Britain, the Trade Union Council (TUC) says that this ceiling does not provide effective protection against even this risk and that it is totally inadequate as protection against cancer risks (28). The TUC and the U.S. National Institute for Occupational Safety and Health (NIOSH) wanted asbestos banned because it is impossible to specify a safe exposure level for a carcinogen (13).

THE FUTURE

In view of the hazardous nature of asbestos perhaps there should be more emphasis on the development of safe substitutes than on safety standards. Since 1920 there has been research in progress to fabricate asbestos substitutes, but nothing has been found that can do exactly what asbestos can do.

An alkali-resistant glass fibre, "Cenifil", was developed in the United Kingdom. This substance could be substituted for asbestos in order to reinforce cement. However the glass fibre does not have the same strength in cement reinforcement, and its melting point is too low for friction products. Polyvinyl chloride has been used instead of asbestos in the manufacture of water pipes but the monomer from which this material is made (see Vinyl Chloride) has been shown to produce health risks too. Fibreglass has been tried as a substitute for asbestos in textiles, but it lacks that combination of strength, fire resistance, wear resistance and flexibility. Other materials which presently serve as substitutes for asbestos are: polypropylene and glass in the reinforcement of cement; silicon nitride and glass in friction materials; mineral wool in insulation board; vermiculite in fire protection and friction materials; ceramic paper in dental castings; and alumina and zirconia in high temperature insulation and filtration (3). There is much controversy in the scientific community about substitutes however, as few data are available on their safety. Some believe that substitutes have fewer health risks while others believe that their risks are worse than those of asbestos.

The economic forecast for asbestos producers depends on environmental control and product use regulations adopted in the U.S. and the European Economic Community (24). Also, Canada is not developing new deposits and thus, as demand increases, Canada's share of world production will decrease notwithstanding Canada's consistent level of production. For example, Canada's share of world production dropped from 66% in 1947 to 29% in 1977 (3).

The asbestos mining and milling industries employ about 8,000 people (31). Related secondary industries bring the total number of people who use asbestos in their work to roughly 100,000 (2). Thus, proposals for more stringent controls may be received with little enthusiasm by those they are intended to protect. Public and worker awareness programs and product labelling are necessary to alert people to the dangers of asbestos and to reduce unnecessary exposure to it (3).

In the U.S., people with past occupational exposure to asbestos have sued their former employers for damages caused to their health. It is reported that about 52,000 lawsuits with $2 billion in damages may be filed against Manville Corp. (32). The burden of litigation costs is blamed for the bankruptcy of the company.

Yet another problem which is arising is the disposal of asbestos waste. It was reported (33) that demonstrators prevented the dumping of asbestos waste removed from an airport building because of fear of asbestos contamination from the dumping site. In Britain, the sale of redundant electrical power stations was complicated (34) because of the problem of asbestos in these stations. Demolition of such buildings can lead to higher asbestos levels in the neighbouring community.

Generally, it is believed that present technology can reduce the fibre count in the air around emission sources to the levels required by governments. It is doubtful that the industry could survive if it was required that no dust be emitted. Detection techniques are now so sensitive that a proven "zero emission" is essentially impossible. It is also doubtful that satisfactory substitutes can be found for all the mineral's uses.

REFERENCES

1. Badollet, M. S., "Asbestos: A Remarkable Mineral Fibre", Johns-Manville Corporation, 1975.
2. Charlebois, C., "An Overview of the Canadian Asbestos Problem", Chemistry in Canada, Mar., 1978.
3. Shugar, S., "Effects of Asbestos in the Environment", National Research Council of Canada, 1979.
4. "Asbestos", Mineral Bulletin MR 155, Mineral Policy Series, Energy Mines and Resources Canada, 1976.
5. Vagt, G. O., "Asbestos", Canadian Minerals Yearbook Bulletin, Energy, Mines, and Resources Canada, 1980.
6. "Asbestos", Occupational Health Branch Data Sheet No. 18, Ontario Ministry of Labour, Dec. 1976.
7. Assad, J. R. and Rajhans, G. S., "The Technical Aspects of Asbestos", A report to the Science Council of Canada, 1976.
8. "Caution: Asbestos Dust...", Channing L. Bete Co. Inc., Greenfield, Mass., in cooperation with the National Institute for Occupational Safety and Health, Cincinnati, Ohio, 1973.
9. Carter, L. J., "Asbestos: Trouble in the Air from Maryland Rock Quarry", Science, 197, 237, 1977.
10. "A Study of the Problem of Asbestos in Water", American Water Works Association Research Foundation, American Water Works Association Journal, Sept. 1974, Part 2.
11. Ahmed, A. K., MacLeod, D. F. and Carmody, J., "Control for Asbestos", Environment, 14 (10), 16, 1972.
12. "New Maps Reveal Death Trail of Asbestos", New Scientist, Aug. 25, Sept. 8, 1983.

13. McGinty, L., "A Ban on Asbestos?", New Scientist, July 14, 1977.

14. Doern, G. B., "The Politics of Risk: The Identification of Toxic and Other Hazardous Substances in Canada", Royal Commission on Matters of Health and Safety Arising from the Use of Asbestos in Canada, Jan. 1982.

15. Selikoff, I. J., Nicholson, W. J. and Langer, A. M., "Asbestos Air Pollution", Arch. Environmental Health, 25, 1, 1972.

16. Nicholson, W. J. et al, "Asbestos Contamination of Parenteral Drugs", Am. Med. Ass., p. 171, July 14, 1972.

17. "Asbestos in Water", Science News, 109 (20), 311, 1976.

18. "Environmental Protection and Control, Asbestos Studies", Brown, W. F. M., Editor, Chemistry in Canada, 29 (7), 11, 1977.

19. Cunningham, J. M. and Pontefract, R. D., "Asbestos Fibres in Beverages and Drinking Water", Nature, 232, 332, 1971 and "Penetration of Asbestos Through the Digestive Tract of Rats", Nature, 243, 352, 1973.

20. "Test: Asbestos in Wine", Canadian Consumer, 7 (3), 44, 1977.

21. "Asbestos: A Threat by Air or by Water", Science News, 113 (1), 5, 1978.

22. Henry, S., "Who Leads the Asbestos Race? Wine? Beer? Water? Snow?", The Citizen, Ottawa, Aug. 24, 1977.

23. "Progress in Asbestos-Free Filters", New Scientist, Oct. 13, 1977.

24. Franson, R. T., Lucas, A. R., Giroux, L. and Kenniff, P., "Canadian Law and the Control of Exposure to Hazards", Science Council of Canada, Background Study No. 39, Oct. 1977.

25. Schreiber, G., Smith, J. H., Euinton, L. and Bergeron, P., "Report of the Asbestosis Working Group", Subcommittee on Environmental Health, Health and Welfare Canada, 1976.

26. Williams, R. and Bates, D., Canadian Public Administration, 19, 603, 1976.

27. "Global Focus on Asbestos", Financial Post, Mar. 5, 1983.

28. "Britain Leads World in Asbestos Controls", New Scientist, Sept. 1, 1983.

29. "Asbestos Ban is Dropped by Brussels", New Scientist, Jan. 27, 1983.

30. Doern, G. B., "Regulatory Processes and Jurisdictional Issues in the Regulation of Hazardous Products in Canada", Science Council of Canada, Background Study No. 41, Oct., 1977.

31. Ostiguy, G., "Health Hazards of Asbestos Exposure, Preliminary Report", Report to the Science Council of Canada, 1976.

32. "Asbestos-Related Lawsuits are Blamed for the Bankruptcy of Manville Corp." Chemical and Engineering News, Sept., 1982.

33. Lowe, M., "Demonstrators Block Dump to Keep Asbestos Waste Out", The Globe and Mail, Toronto, Sept. 24, 1983.

34. "Asbestos Scare Causes Rethink on Power Station Sales", New Scientist, July 28, 1983.

RECOMMENDED READING

There is a considerable amount of literature concerning asbestos and the above list is by no means exhaustive. Good general summaries are reference (3), and in particular reference (2). Numerous readable articles and reports are available on more specific aspects: references (1), (7) for uses of asbestos, reference (3) for economic aspects, references (6), (15), (31) for health aspects, reference (17) for a discussion of the costs and benefits of lower asbestos levels. Reference (14) offers a case study of identification of asbestos in schools. The proceedings of the World Symposium on Asbestos held in Montreal in May 1982 are now also available.

BENZENE

Benzene as an occupational hazard has become a focus of attention; there is controversy regarding the levels of exposure which will protect the health of workers.

Benzene, chemical formula C_6H_6, was first isolated by Faraday in 1825, but its unique properties were known many years before its structure was understood. In 1865, the German chemist August Kekule suggested that the "six carbon atoms of benzene form a ring in which one hydrogen atom is joined to each carbon atom, which is joined to adjacent carbon atoms by one single and one double bond" (1).

Moreover, he realized that the double bonds "move around" the benzene ring so as to spend part of their time between alternate pairs of carbon atoms. Today, benzene would be described as a substance in which the electrons forming the bonds are delocalized, that is, a structure in which each carbon forms one and a half bonds to each of its neighbouring carbon atoms, rather than one single and one double bond. It is therefore represented as the second structure shown below. A multitude of chemical reactions and products involve compounds with this structure.

Compounds which contain the benzene ring structure are traditionally called "aromatic" compounds by chemists. The term "aromatic" originally arose because of the odour of benzene and related compounds, but this aspect is of little importance in practice.

Benzene is a colourless, flammable liquid at room temperature with a boiling point of 80 deg. C. It evaporates more readily than water and appreciable concentrations can be established in the air. At 20 deg. C it has a vapour pressure of 0.075 atmosphere, which means that air saturated with benzene contains approximately 75,000 ppm (part per million) of benzene.

Until 1941, the chemical was extracted mainly from coal tar, although petroleum was known to contain small quantities. In 1941, the commercial production of benzene from petroleum was started and expanded during World War II (as was the production of other petrochemicals). Eventually, the demand for benzene for use in the plastics and other chemical industries was so great that petroleum became the principal source (2). In 1976, more than 5 million tonne of benzene were manufactured in the U.S.; 94% from petroleum and the remaining 6% from coal (3). The production of benzene has now become the second largest (after ethylene) of all organic chemicals in terms of amount and value. Commercial benzene is produced in 3 grades which contain varying levels of toluene, xylene, phenol and traces of related chemicals (4).

The major use of benzene is as a starting material for other chemical compounds. Styrene, for making polystyrenic plastics and rubber (tires, in particular); cyclohexane for making fabricated nylon products such as carpet; nitrobenzene, pesticides and many other compounds are all manufactured from benzene. Approximately 8% of production is used for such other purposes such as gasoline additives to improve starting and antiknock characteristics by promoting more even burning. Canadian gasolines contain from one to 2% benzene, an amount unlikely to increase as there are suitable alternatives to boost octane ratings (5).

Benzene is a natural product and it is not as environmentally dangerous as many man-made chemicals derived from it (see PCBs, DDT). Its lack of chemical reactivity indicates that it is a relatively stable compound as suggested by consideration of its previously described structure. However, because of its physical properties (slight solubility in water, relatively high vapour pressure), it may be quite mobile in the environment and have a high bioaccumulation (6). It can be degraded by some bacteria and in mammalian systems (e.g. rabbits) it is metabolized primarily to phenol and other hydroxy-benzenes which, after further conversion, are expelled from the body (7).

A considerable amount of benzene is released into the environment annually (an estimated 2 million tonne in 1971) but only relatively low concentrations are normally observed. For example, ambient concentrations in Toronto ranged from 2-98 ppb (part per billion) in 1973, substantially lower than the standards quoted below (4). It is estimated that 80-85% of benzene emitted to the environment is from vehicular exhaust gases (5). These levels are not the principal reason for concern with respect to benzene. It has been studied as a potential hazard to those exposed to high concentrations of it and it is known to be poisonous (7), having both an acute and a chronic toxicity. Acute poisoning causes a depression of the central nervous system, which may lead to narcosis, paralysis, asphyxia and death. Exposure to benzene fumes (in air) of levels 19,000-20,000 ppm is fatal within minutes; 7,500 ppm can cause death in about an hour (2) and concentrations about 100 ppm may result in fatigue, weakness and confusion (7). The effects of drinking benzene are similar.

Chronic poisoning (as a result of exposure for several years) may be due to inhaled benzene or through skin absorption. Several studies have been reported (4,7) which indicate that blood formation in the bone marrow is affected. This may be exhibited by a lowering of the number of white blood cells in the bloodstream. The concentration of benzene in vapours to which subjects in the above studies were exposed varied from 12 to 352 ppm; exposure to less than 12 ppm for 26 years did not appear to produce any significant effects. Considerations of this toxicity led to exposure limits in industrial plants in the U.S. being set at 10 ppm averaged over 8 hours, with a maximum level of 25 ppm (3).

In early 1977, there were several reports (8,9) that linked long-term benzene exposure with leukemia, a blood cancer. In leukemia, the bone marrow which produces the blood is damaged; the number of white cells becomes permanently increased and there is a swelling of the spleen and lymph nodes. Although the disease can be controlled to some extent, some types of leukemia are incurable (10). West Germany and Sweden have officially recognized benzene as a carcinogen. Canada included it on a list of confirmed occupational carcinogens in 1980 (18).

American opinion is still divided. The Second Annual Report on Carcinogens (11) states that benzene causes Zymbal gland carcinomas and an enhancement of mammary carcinomas and leukemias in rats. The Zymbal gland is a specialized sebaceous gland located near the ear in rodents. No similar gland exists in humans (12). Patty's Industrial Hygiene and Toxicology (4) states that benzene is not a carcinogen, but is a suspected teratogen.

While leukemia-like effects among shoe workers exposed to benzene were 13 per 100,000 instead of 6 for the general population, a study of 38,000 petroleum and petrochemical workers found no increase in leukemia cases. The benzene-leukemia link is attributed to inaccuracies in translation and differences in the use of medical terminology in European countries (4). Results of yet another epidemiological study have become available recently (22). It concludes that there is a higher, but not statistically significant, rate of lymphatic cancer deaths in an exposed group as compared to a control group of over 3000 workers.

In April 1977, after the correlation between exposure and disease had been suggested, the U.S. Occupational Safety and Health Administration (OSHA) established emergency levels of worker exposure, setting a maximum level of 1 ppm over 8 hours and of 5 ppm for a 15 minute period (3). This regulation was imposed on workers in plants and (marking a change from previous regulations (13)) in industrial and private academic laboratories.

A federal court suspended the temporary emergency standard (14, 15). The Manufacturing Chemists Association (MCA) opposed the introduction of a new permanent standard of 1 ppm, claiming that the study suggesting the leukemia-benzene relation was defective and that the existing 10 ppm limit already makes the risk of exposure to benzene equal to the average risk in all manufacturing industries (14). OSHA introduced its 1 ppm permanent standard in February 1978, only to have it challenged in court by the American Petroleum Institute. In October 1978, the 1 ppm standard was struck down. The court cited the lack of evidence that a 10 ppm level was hazardous and the failure of OSHA to provide an estimate of expected benefits from reducing the exposure limit in light of the $500 million cost to industry (16).

The Justice Department took the case to the Supreme Court for review in January 1979 (17). The Supreme Court announced in July 1980 that it upheld the previous decision (11). Since then, there have been requests by unions for OSHA to reduce the permissible level of exposure to benzene, but that agency has not made new attempts to reduce the level (21). OSHA is however pursuing its search for more information regarding benzene.

Ontario follows the American Conference of Government Industrial Hygenists' threshold limit values (TLV). A TLV may have 3 components, depending on the nature of the substance: time-weighted average (TWA), the average concentration over an 8-hour period; the short-term exposure level (STEL), a peak level which can occur up to 4 times for 15 minutes with one hour between exposures; a ceiling level, which is a maximum permissible concentration. The TWA for benzene is 10 ppm with a STEL of 25 ppm. As benzene can be dangerous in very high concentrations, it also has an "immediate danger to life and health" (IDLH) level. The American Industrial Hygiene Association warns that 20,000 ppm will be fatal in 5 to 10 minutes.

Setting exposure limits for a chemical like benzene is complicated. Industry officials argue that more stringent standards are unnecessary and prohibitively expensive when a cost-benefit analysis is considered. Labour officials press for even lower exposure limits on the grounds that there is no known safe exposure limit for carcinogens (19). The issue of quantitative risk assessment has been debated for some time and continues to be a controversial issue (20).

REFERENCES

1. Breslow, R., "The Nature of Aromatic Molecules", in Readings from Scientific American, General Chemistry, W. H. Freeman and Company, San Francisco, Aug. 1972.
2. "Kirk-Othmer Encyclopedia of Chemical Technology", Vol. III, second edition, John Wiley and Sons, New York, 1964.
3. "OSHA Pushes Stiffer Benzene Exposure Rules", Chemical and Engineering News, Aug. 1, 1977.
4. "Patty's Industrial Hygiene and Toxicology", Vol. 2B, 3rd edition, John Wiley & Sons, New York, 1981.

5. "Benzene", Environmental Health Directorate, Health and Welfare Canada, No. 79-EHD-40, 1979.

6. Howard, P. J. and Durkin, P. R., "Sources of Contamination, Ambient Levels and Fate of Benzene in the Environment", Office of Toxic Substances, Environmental Protection Agency, 560/5 75-005, Dec. 1974.

7. "Vapor-Phase Organic Pollutants; Volatile Hydrocarbons and Oxidation Products", Committee on Medical and Biologic Effects of Environmental Pollutants, National Academy of Sciences, Washington, D.C., 1976.

8. Emmerson, D. W., Editor, "Government Scan: Death from Benzene", Chemistry in Canada, Oct. 1977.

9. "Another Link Between Benzene, Cancer", Chemical and Engineering News, July 18, 1977.

10. Thomson, W. A. R., "Black's Medical Dictionary", 27th edition, A and C Black Ltd., 1967.

11. "Second Annual Report on Carcinogens", U.S. Dept. of Health and Human Services, Dec. 1981.

12. "The Laboratory Rat", Vol. I: Biology and Diseases, Baker, H. J., Lindsey, J. R. and Weisbroth, S. H., Editors, Academic Press, 1980.

13. "OSHA Benzene Rules Affect Research Labs", Chemical and Engineering News, June 13, 1977.

14. "MCA Opposes Stiffer Exposure Rule on Benzene", Chemecology, Manufacturing Chemists Association, Washington, D.C., Sept., 1977.

15. "Benzene Worker Exposure Limits Delayed", Chemical and Engineering News, Mar. 20, 1978.

16. "Court Overturns OSHA Benzene Standard", Chemical and Engineering News, Oct. 16, 1978.

17. "Supreme Court Asked to Review Benzene Rule", Chemical and Engineering News, Jan. 8, 1979.

18. Wandelmaier, F. W., "Report on Confirmed Occupational Carcinogens", Health and Welfare Canada, Apr. 10, 1980.

19. "Industry Doctoring of Benzene Charged", Chemical and Engineering News, Aug. 23, 1982.

20. Sun, M., "Risk Estimate Vanishes from Benzene Report", Science, 217, 914, 1982.

21. "OSHA Won't Tighten Curbs on Benzene", Chemical Engineering, Aug. 8, 1983.

22. "Benzene Study Details Cancer Risks", Chemical and Engineering News, Jan. 2, 1984.

CADMIUM

Advances in technology lead to higher levels of cadmium in food and water. Severe cases of cadmium poisoning have occurred in industrialized countries.

The word cadmium is derived from "Kadmeia", the ancient name for calamine (zinc carbonate), as the element cadmium was discovered in 1817 as an impurity in this mineral. Cadmium often occurs together with zinc in the sulphide ores commonly mined for extraction of zinc. On the average, cadmium is, however, present in only 1 part in 250 of zinc (1).

An estimated 1000 tonne of cadmium metal are produced each year in Canada, usually from residues of zinc manufacture. Nearly an equal amount of cadmium is present as an impurity in the zinc concentrate produced. A large proportion of such cadmium is exported in the form of concentrates and commodities containing cadmium (2).

Canada exports cadmium selenide, a compound used in photoconductors, semi-conductors and ceramics. We are, however, a net importer of manufactured products containing cadmium such as pigments, batteries and plastic stabilizers (2). The major use of cadmium in Canada is for plating steel, especially steel used in marine environments (1,3).

Some cadmium enters the environment due to natural weathering phenomena, but anthropogenic sources now predominate in industrial countries. The main sources are emissions from zinc, lead and copper smelters and industries using cadmium. Lesser sources are agricultural use of sludge, fertilizers and pesticides, and combustion of fossil fuels (4). People are also exposed to cadmium through smoking (2,5).

Cadmium and solutions of cadmium compounds are toxic, so that workers in the numerous occupations involving production or use of cadmium can expose themselves to dangerous levels of cadmium-containing fumes. Since 1962, Japan has recorded over 230 cases of degenerative bone disease attributable to cadmium poisoning from mine tailings (6). The Japanese name for the disease is "itai-itai" (ouch-ouch) disease because of severe pain in the joints. The U.S., Britain and Sweden also recognize that chronic exposure to cadmium can result in lung and kidney disease (1,6). Cadmium is implicated in cardio-vascular disorders (7,8) and cadmium compounds are suspected carcinogens of connective tissue, lungs and liver (8). An epidemiological study in England showed, however, that there was no excess in cancer death rates among inhabitants of a village where garden soil cadmium levels are nearly 200 times the average (9).

Exposure to cadmium can occur through ingestion of food and water, use of tobacco, air pollution and occupational exposure. The intake from food gives the largest contribution for the vast majority of people. Vegetables normally contain 0.05 ppm (part per million) of cadmium (1), but some very high values have been recorded in vegetables grown near a zinc smelter in Trail, British Columbia (6). Meat has a cadmium content typically around 0.02 ppm, but beef kidney averages 0.06 ppm (1). Some types of seafood also have very high cadmium content: salt cod (2.5 ppm) and lobster paste (3.4 ppm) (1). The above values are on a fresh weight basis, and there is some controversy surrounding their accuracy.

The average Canadian is estimated to ingest between 0.050 to 0.098 mg (milligram) of cadmium per day per person (1). This may slightly exceed the recommended tolerable intake of about 0.060 suggested by the World Health Organization (1). There are some older reports which estimate the average Canadian intake to be much higher, e.g., 0.200 mg per day per person (7), but the older higher values may be due to dis-tortions caused by the procedure used for analysis (5). The intake in Denmark is estimated to average 0.032 mg per day per person, but it is forecast to nearly double in the next cen-tury due to increased concentration of cadmium in soil from atmospheric deposition and fertilization (3).

Approximately 95% of cadmium ingested by humans is eliminated, but some builds up in the body, particularly in the cortex of the kidney (1,3). There seem to be no direct symptoms of cadmium build-up until irreversible damage has occurred. There is a correlation between cadmium exposure and kidney disease (proteinuria) (1,3). The threshold value for kidney damage is assumed to be 200 ppm cadmium in kidney cortex, but malfunctions may occur at lower levels. In Denmark, the average concentration in 50-year-old people is 40

ppm, varying greatly depending on eating and smoking habits;
the concentration in non-smokers is only about half that in
smokers (3).

The build-up of cadmium in the kidney cortex is believed
to increase with an increase in the daily intake of cadmium.
Hence, the concern in Denmark; if the daily intake is likely
to double in the next century, then the fraction of people
with cadmium above the threshold level will increase considerably. It has thus been recommended that in Denmark, cadmium
levels be controlled by: reducing the use of cadmium in
products; establishing a recycling system for nickel-cadmium
batteries; and improving cadmium removal from incinerators and
power plant flue gases (3).

Sweden has gone even further. It has prohibited the use
of cadmium in pigments, as stabilizers and for electroplating.
Importation of products such as the above containing cadmium
was also prohibited. The date at which this was to come into
effect was July 1, 1980. However, the regulation was delayed
until July 1, 1982 because of the difficulty for manufacturers
and importers to eliminate products containing cadmium (17).

In a recent draft version of a Canadian government report
which examines entry of cadmium into the environment, it is
concluded that the evidence available would not support a
recommendation for restrictions under the Environment Contaminants Act (10). There has, however, been a recent report of
harmful effects of cadmium in an industrial plant where solder
containing cadmium was used (18). the Ontario Ministry of
Labour was reported to be considering stricter workplace
controls for the metal (18).

The "half-life" of elements such as cadmium is essentially infinite. Thus, the problems involving cadmium pollution
are even more long-term than those involving persistent organic pollutants such as DDT and PCBs. An increasing amount of
cadmium is set into the biogeochemical cycle when it is released from stable forms through metallurgical processes and
the burning of fossil fuels. The cadmium used in the products
of modern industry concentrates itself to a large extent close
to population sources. Thus, the cadmium (and other heavy
metal) content of sewage sludge from municipalities can make
application of such sludge to agricultural land hazardous

(11). Municipal incinerators are also a major source of air-borne cadmium which can be deposited on agricultural land (3). If a consistent increase of cadmium in our diet is to be prevented, then long term decisions must be made regarding the use of cadmium-containing sewage sludge.

Cadmium is not the only metal which is being mobilized into the environment. Lead, mercury and arsenic are three others discussed in this book. Concern has also been expressed about chromium (12,13), nickel (14,15) and vanadium (16). Such metals are released to the environment naturally by the weathering of rocks and volcanic activity. Atmospheric emissions, which distribute the elements into the environment, are predominantly anthropogenic, mostly resulting from the burning of coal and oil.

Chromium is an essential element for life, but it may also be a carcinogen. There have been no reports yet of adverse human effects due to chromium at its normal background level. It is, however, an industrial hazard; epidemiological evidence suggests an increased lung cancer rate among workers producing chromates.

Nickel is somewhat like chromium in that epidemiological studies suggest exposure to airborne nickel increases the incidence of cancer in workers. Nickel is believed to be an essential element for mammals, but elevated exposure can cause toxic effects. Although natural sources of nickel to the biogeochemical cycle are thought to be much greater than anthropogenic, atmospheric emissions are primarily due to the combustion of coal and oil.

Vanadium is yet another example of a metal mobilized into the biogeochemical cycle. Its concentration in air can be considerable if fuel oil with high concentrations is being burned. As with cadmium, chromium and nickel, the level of vanadium in food and drinking water seems to be at an acceptable level. However, as in the case of the other metals, we can expect these levels to increase as industrial activity proceeds. We must be vigilant to ensure that higher levels do not lead to health problems.

REFERENCES

1. "Effects of Cadmium in the Canadian Environment", National Research Council of Canada, Ottawa, No. 16743, 1979.
2. Lymburner, D. B., "The Production, Use and Distribution of Cadmium in Canada", Environmental Contaminants Inventory Study No. 2, Cat. No. En36-508/39, Environment Canada, 1974.
3. "Cadmium Pollution", Ministry of the Environment, Denmark, (in Danish with English summary), Oct. 1980.
4. Reeder, S. W., Demayo, A. and Taylor, M. C., "Guidelines for Surface Water Quality: Cadmium", Inland Waters Directorate, Environment Canada, 1979.
5. Friberg, L., Piscator, M., Nordverg, G. F. and Kjellstrom, T.,"Cadmium in the Environment", 2nd edition, CRC Press, Cleveland, Ohio, 1974.
6. Bryan, R., "Much is Taken, Much Remains", Duxbury Press, North Scituate, Mass., 1973.
7. Hall, Ross Hume, "Food for Naught: The Decline in Nutrition", Vintage Books, Random House, New York, 1976.
8. Hazardous Substances Programme, Hazardous Substances List and Handbook, Report No. ARB-TDA-33-76 (Revised), Ontario Ministry of the Environment, 1976.
9. New Scientist, p. 647, June 3, 1982.
10. In press, Environmental Protection Service, Contaminants Control Branch, 1982.
11. Naylor, L.M. and Loehr, R. C., "Increase in Dietary Cadmium as a Result of Application of Sewage Sludge to Agricultural Land", Environmental Science and Technology, 15, 881, 1981.
12. "Effects of Chromium in the Canadian Environment", National Research Council of Canada, Ottawa, No. 15017, 1976.
13. Taylor, M. C., Reeder, S. W. and Demayo, A., "Guidelines for Surface Water Quality: Chromium", Inland Waters Directorate, Environment Canada, 1979.
14. "Effects of Nickel in the Canadian Environment", National Research Council of Canada, Ottawa, No. 18568, 1981.
15. Taylor, M. C., Demayo, A. and Reeder, S. W., "Guidelines for Surface Water Quality: Nickel", Inland Waters Directorate, Environment Canada, 1979.
16. "Effects of Vanadium in the Canadian Environment", National Research Council of Canada, Ottawa, No. 18132, 1980.
17. "The Swedish Ban on Cadmium", Products Control Division, National Swedish Environment Protection Board, 1981.
18. Mullington, D., "Cadmium Solder Removed from Plant", The Citizen, Ottawa, Aug. 10, 1983. Robin, L., "War Against Cadmium Province-Wide", ibid, Aug. 12, 1983. Benzing, K., "Shadow Cast over Gananoque Workers", ibid, June 28, 1983.

RECOMMENDED READING

Reference (1) is a comprehensive study of the technical and economic significance of cadmium in Canada; reference (7) is a most interesting text to read and while some readers may find it "alarmist", that in itself is no reason to ignore the seriousness of the cadmium problem. Reference (5) is a thorough review of the problems of analysis, occurrence, routes of exposure, metabolism and health effects.

CAFFEINE

Most of us ingest caffeine--from coffee, tea, soft drinks, chocolate. A combination of fact and fiction has resulted in confusion concerning the effects on our health of this stimulant drug.

A waitress drank 15-18 cups of coffee each day for at least 6 months. During this time she lost 20 pounds and complained of a low grade irregular fever, insomnia, irritability, and cramps in the stomach and extremities. She noticed the fever began 30 minutes after she had drunk her first coffee and subsided during the evening some hours after she had stopped drinking coffee. When she entered the hospital, where she only drank one cup of coffee per day, the fever ceased, her appetite improved and the insomnia lessened. The patient was suffering from a syndrome commonly called caffeinism (1).

HISTORY

Caffeine is a natural stimulant drug which has been known for many centuries. The drug effect of coffee beans was discovered in Arabia by shepherds who noted that goats eating coffee beans pranced around all night long (2), and the word caffeine has its origin in the Arabic word qahwah (pronounced kahveh in Turkish) which once meant wine. It is reported that an abbot wishing to pray all night made a drink from the bean to keep himself awake (2). Caffeine is also present in tea, which was discovered in China, the kola nut in West Africa, and the cocoa bean in the West Indies. Europeans started using caffeine in the 15th century after explorers brought caffeine-containing products back to Europe from their various journeys (4).

From historical accounts it appears that caffeine-containing drinks were not easily accepted in countries that had not previously known them. In Arabia and Egypt the sale of coffee was prohibited , and wherever stacks of coffee were found, they were burned. In Europe, there were also repression efforts. In 1674, in "The Women's Petition Against Coffee", coffee was referred to as "base, black, thick, nasty, bitter, stinking, nauseous puddle water" (5). Medical opposition to coffee and tea persists in the 20th century. The textbook "A System of Medicine" (1909) used in American and British medical schools reported:

"We have seen several well-marked cases of coffee excess...The sufferer is tremulous and loses his self-command; he is subject to fits of agitation and depression; he loses colour and has a haggard appearance. The appetite falls off and symptoms of gastric catarrh may be manifested...The heart also suffers: it palpitates or it intermits. As with other such agents a renewed dose of the poison gives temporary relief, but at the cost of future misery" (1).

In spite of the adverse publicity and attempts at prohibition, coffee and tea became, and still are, very popular drinks (see also Tobacco and Alcohol).

CONSUMPTION

Coffee is the most popular Canadian beverage and it is drunk by 64% of the adult population. On average, 2.9 cups per day of coffee are drunk by persons in the 35 to 39 years age group. This exceeds the rate for any other age group (6), the lowest rates being amongst teenagers and persons over 75 years (1). Tea and coffee consumption data in Ontario are as follows: 8% abstain from both; 28% drink the caffeine equivalent of 5 or more cups of coffee each day (1); 1.5% of Ontario's adult population, or about 60,000 persons, drink 15 or more cups of coffee per day (6). Canada's consumption of coffee and tea is compared with that in other countries in the following Table (5).

Per Capita Consumption of Green Coffee Bean and Tea Leaf in Certain Countries During 1972.

Country	Green bean consumption (kg)	Ratio to Canadian consumption	Tea leaf consumption (kg)	Ratio to Canadian consumption
Sweden	13.5*	3.3	0.2	0.3
USA	6.3	1.5	0.3	0.4
France	5.1	1.2	0.1	0.1
Canada	4.1	1.0	0.9	1.0
United Kingdom	2.2	0.54	3.8	4.0
Czechoslovakia	1.1	0.27	0.1	
Japan	0.5	0.1	1.0	0.1
Iraq	0.1	0.0(2)	2.1	2.2

* Data for 1974-76 give 10.7 kg. (7).

Caffeine is not only consumed as tea or coffee. It is found in chocolate bars, hot cocoa and soft drinks, in particular colas, and is the main or subsidiary ingredient of a number of prescription and non-prescription drugs. The following Table compares the caffeine content of various substances (3). Cocoa and its products, including chocolate bars, contain widely differing amounts of caffeine.

Caffeine-Containing Product	Caffeine Content mg (milligram)
Coffee	30-180 mg/cup
Tea	10-100 mg/cup
Colas	20-45 mg/can
Wake-up pills	100-150 mg/pill
Some headache pills	30-65 mg/pill

There are virtually no restrictions on the use of caffeine. The only existing law states that cola drinks in Canada must not contain more than 200 ppm (part per million), or approximately 57 mg caffeine in an ordinary can of cola (3).

CHEMISTRY AND PHYSIOLOGICAL EFFECTS AND TOXICITY

Caffeine is a white, bitter, odourless, slightly soluble, powdery solid, resembling cornstarch in appearance. Its chemical name is 1,3,7-trimethylxanthine.

Caffeine consumption can produce a variety of physiological effects. It is a powerful stimulant to the central nervous system and is known to increase attentiveness. Caffeine will improve performance of physical tasks, particularly those involving speed. Intellectual performance is not affected (8). Caffeine can raise blood sugar level and its action on the cardiovascular system can be detected as changes in heart rate, heart rhythm, blood vessel diameter, coronary circulation and blood pressure (4,9). Within the gastrointestinal system, caffeine significantly affects gastric secretion resulting in an increase in both volume and acidity. The renal system is also affected, resulting in increased urine production. Caffeine can also relax smooth muscles, especially of the bronchi, so increasing air supply to the lungs. It can strengthen the contractions of skeletal muscles and increase the basal metabolic rate an average of 10% among regular coffee drinkers (9). Caffeine has a half-life in the body of about 3 hours with the peak level occurring about one hour after ingestion. Regular consumption does not reduce its stimulant effects (8).

Dosage is an important consideration in the study of caffeine pharmacology. The Addiction Research Foundation of Ontario reports that there is little evidence that harm is caused by regular consumption of moderate amounts of caffeine. About 250 mg/day is regarded as moderate for an adult of normal weight, especially if consumption is spread over a number of hours and does not occur in the evening (3). It appears however, that a regular consumption of 350 mg/day, about 4 cups of coffee, can produce physical dependence. The dependence can exist without much danger to health, but unpleasant withdrawal symptoms can occur 12-16 hours after caffeine intake has ceased. The symptoms, which usually include irritability, inability to work effectively, nervousness, restlessness, lethargy and headache (6), can be relieved by another dose of caffeine.

Although doses of less than 600 mg/day of caffeine are not normally harmful, there may be 3 exceptions (3). First, such doses may have more effect on younger and lighter people. For example, it has been estimated that a 30 kg (kilogram) 10 year old child who consumes 4 bottles of Coke and 3 chocolate bars a day could be ingesting more caffeine per kg than a 75 kg adult whose daily intake is 7 cups of coffee (1).

Second, to be safe, pregnant women should restrict or eliminate caffeine consumption. The U.S. Food and Drug Agency (FDA) confirmed earlier studies that linked caffeine to skeletal deformities in the fetuses of pregnant rats (10). However, some flaws were discovered so that the FDA study is being repeated (11). A Harvard University study of 12,000 pregnant women and their coffee-drinking habits found no evidence of teratogenicity. This study has been criticized as it looked only at coffee, not overall caffeine consumption and ignored habits such as smoking (12). Until the metabolism of caffeine in humans is understood, definitive answers are unlikely.

Third, caffeine may be harmful in low dosages where other drugs are used. It has been shown to interact with many drugs

including alcohol, opiates, barbiturates, aspirin and anti-
anxiety drugs. Depending on dose levels, caffeine can interact
synergistically or antagonistically with the same drug. "In
vitro" studies have shown caffeine (100 mg/kg) to antagonize
insulin-stimulated glucose metabolism, raising the possibility
that caffeine ingestion may interfere with blood-glucose regulation by insulin in diabetes (5).

Excessive amounts of caffeine (e.g., more than 600
mg/day) can lead to development of the symptoms of caffeinism,
such as those described at the beginning of this chapter.
Reports of caffeinism are infrequent but the condition may be
prevalent. Toxicity is generally an extension of caffeine's
usual actions in the nervous, gastrointestinal, respiratory
and cardiovascular systems and large doses are acutely toxic.
In an animal, a fatal dose of caffeine produces convulsions
with subsequent death from respiratory failure (5). The lowest
fatal doses recorded in humans were 3.2 g (gram) administered
intravenously to a 35-year-old woman, and 5.3 g self-
administered orally by a 5-year-old girl (5). Most authors on
caffeine suggest that 10 g or 70-100 cups of coffee, would be
the human fatal dose (1).

PATHOLOGIC EFFECTS

At a consumption level of 600 mg/day, or approximately
8 cups of coffee, caffeine has been linked to several human
health problems such as heart diseases, gastrointestinal
ulceration, bladder cancer and reproductive disorders (3).
Most of these associations are controversial but a brief
review of some of the evidence is relevant.

In 1972, a report from the Boston Collaborative Drug
Surveillance Program, which includes 2 hospitals in London,
Ontario, indicated that patients with acute myocardial infarction, or heart attack, were found to drink more coffee
than matched controls (6). Since then there have been a few
studies supporting this linkage (5) but most physicians empha-
size the fact that myocardial infarction is a complex health
problem and there could be other risk factors, such as elevated cholesterol, hypertension, smoking, obesity and physical
inactivity. The results of 5 recent large studies have not
resolved the issue of coffee and heart disease (16).

A number of investigators have sought to establish a relationship between caffeine and the production of peptic ulcers. There is no firm evidence to substantiate this relationship in humans. However, some researchers have brought about ulcer formation in animals by administering caffeine to them (5). It is known that a marked stimulation of gastric secretion occurs when caffeine is given to human subjects with the result that some doctors have been advising patients who already have active peptic ulcers to restrict their intake of caffeine-containing beverages. A review of the role of drugs with regard to gastroduodenal ulcers concluded that "although caffeine has not been shown to produce peptic ulcers in man, the prolonged daily consumption of 10 to 15 cups of coffee may exert a contributing influence" (5).

Whether caffeine consumption and cancer are at all related is quite controversial. Caffeine has been shown in the laboratory to be teratogenic and mutagenic (13). In 1971, an examination of the coffee drinking histories of 468 patients who had cancer of the lower urinary tract revealed a high correlation between the two (5). A recent Harvard University study linked coffee drinking to a statistically higher occurrence of cancer of the pancreas, the 4th leading type of fatal cancer. The risk compared to non users was double for 2 cups per day and triple for 5 or more. This supports the association that British researchers found between a nation's pancreatic cancer rate and its import of coffee (11).

There have however also been researchers who have found no association at at all between cancer and caffeine (13). It is interesting to note that some researchers have suggested that caffeine actually inhibits cancer. Caffeine in concentrations similar to those found in beverages have been found to protect mouse skin against cancers induced by ultraviolet light (5) and at higher concentrations it is reported that it may inhibit the carcinogenic action of cigarette smoke condensate (14).

An appropriate summary of the situation states that "although there has yet to be experimental demonstration that caffeine is carcinogenic -- indeed, caffeine has been shown to inhibit tumour formation under some circumstances -- there seems to be little doubt that caffeine is active with respect to genetic material at concentrations similar to those occurring in caffeine-beverage drinkers. Thus, a laboratory demonstration of caffeine-induced carcinoma would not be surprising" (5). It has however been suggested that the self-imposed guilt felt by some on ingesting caffeine in moderate amounts is more harmful than the caffeine itself (15).

BEHAVIOURAL EFFECTS

It is generally accepted that caffeine can enhance performance of humans and elevate mood by partially restoring a degraded or impaired performance such as may occur after sleep loss or physical fatigue. This effect is the reason caffeine containing beverages have been so popular.

Although it is a common belief that a cup of coffee will help to sober up an intoxicated person, there is little scientific support for this. Dr. Gilbert of the ARF (Addiction Research Foundation) writes that coffee ingested after becoming intoxicated on alcohol would produce "not the familiar sleepy and therefore manageable drunk, but a dangerous being called the wide-awake drunk" (1). There is evidence, however, that in rats caffeine taken before alcohol may reduce blood alcohol levels by relaxing the muscles in the stomach and thus slowing the passage of the alcohol into the small intestine where most of the alcohol is normally absorbed (1).

Caffeine is often used as a therapeutic agent. It is used as a mild respiratory stimulant especially in cases of morphine-induced depression. Some headache and migraine pills contain caffeine, the rationale being that the drug has a beneficial vasoconstrictor effect on cerebral blood vessels. However, headache is a conspicuous symptom of caffeine withdrawal, and as such, is relieved by caffeine (1). In Russia and France, caffeine is being used on a trial basis to treat neurotic depressions and geriatric syndromes (6). Caffeine is also used to calm hyperactive children, although there is criticism of this practice. One doctor has reported that 16 out of 17 hyperactive children have been treated successfully with caffeine. Other stimulant drugs, such as amphetamine, have been used for this purpose, but these have annoying side effects (5).

Caffeine is one of the most widely used stimulants (see also Tobacco and Alcohol) and it has become a controversial chemical mainly because of its prevalence. Sufficient evidence exists to suggest that there is considerable health risk for an average adult who consumes more than 600 mg of caffeine per day and there are many ways in which this amount can be consumed daily: more than 8 cups of coffee, or about 22 cups of tea or about 15 cans of cola or about 9 of certain headache pills or some equivalent combination (5). The variables, such as weight and age of the consumer and type and source of beverage, create numerous problems in establishing relationships between beverage consumption and health effects. Further research should be concerned with caffeine consumption instead of caffeine-containing beverage consumption.

For those concerned about intake of caffeine (a voluntarily ingested drug) the Addiction Research Foundation of Ontario makes some positive suggestions (3): drink tea instead of coffee and brew it for a shorter time; use instant rather than coffee made by percolator and drip methods; consider natural substitutes for caffeine such as juices or some herbal teas and the flavouring carob, which can replace cocoa.

REFERENCES

1. Gilbert, R. M., "Caffeine Beverages and their Effects", Addictions, 21(1), 68, 1974, Addiction Research Foundation of Ontario, Toronto.
2. Jacobson, M. F., "Eater's Digest. The Consumer's Factbook of Food Additives", Doubleday and Co. Inc., Toronto, 1972.
3. "Caffeine", Addiction Research Foundation, Information Review, 1977.
4. Brecker, E. M. and Editors of Consumer Reports, "Licit and Illicit Drugs", Little Brown and Co., Boston, 1972.
5. Gilbert, R. M., "Caffeine as a Drug of Abuse" in "Research Advances in Alcohol and Drug Problems", Vol. 3, Editors: Gibbins, R. J., Israel, Y., Kalant, H., Popham, R., Schmidt, W. and Smart, R. G., J. Wiley and Sons, New York, 1976.
6. Furlong, F. W., "Possible Psychiatric Significance of Excessive Coffee Consumption", Canadian Psychiatric Association Journal, 20(8), 577, 1975.
7. Sundquist, A., The National Food Administration, Food Research Department, Uppsala, Sweden, Personal Communication, Nov. 24, 1977.
8. Graham, D. M., "Caffeine--Its Identity, Dietary Sources, Intakes and Biologic Effects", Nutrition Reviews, 38(4), 1978.
9. Greden, J. F., "Anxiety of Caffeinism: A Diagnostic Dilemma", Am. J. Psychiatry, 131(10), 1089, 1974.
10. Lecos, C., "Caution Light on Caffeine", FDA Consumer, Oct. 1980.
11. "FDA Agrees to Take a Second Look at Possible Caffeine-Cancer Link", Drug Merchandising, May, 1981.
12. "Caffeine in Pregnancy: A Risk or a False Alarm?", Consumer Reports, May, 1982.
13. "Caffeine, Coffee and Cancer", British Medical Journal, May 1, 1976.

14. Rothwell, K., "Dose-Related Inhibition of Chemical Carcinogenesis in Mouse Skin by Caffeine", Nature, 252, 69, 1974.
15. "Caffeine: Guilt More Harmful?, The Citizen, Ottawa, July 19, 1983.
16. "Five Studies Fail to Resolve Coffee and Cholesterol Ties", ibid, Nov. 17, 1983.

RECOMMENDED READING

Reference (5) has an extensive bibliography and gives a thorough review of studies and problems related to caffeine. References (1), (4) and (8) also give good general accounts of caffeine. A book "Caffeine and Chromosomes" by Bengt A. Kihlman, Elsevier Scientific Publishing Co., Amsterdam, in 1977 gives further insights to the caffeine question.

CAPTAN

Captan is Canada's most important agricultural fungicide. Its safety was questioned when an American testing laboratory was found to be falsifying results.

In 1976, a U.S. Food and Drug Agency official became suspicious of chemical safety study results submitted by Industrial Bio-Test Laboratories (IBT) of North Brook, Illinois. By 1977, it became apparent that the firm was fabricating results to cover-up shoddy testing practices (1). The implications were far-reaching.

"IBT's clients included 31 of the largest pharmaceutical and pesticide producers in the world -- companies with household names like American Cyanamid, Ciba-Geigy, Chevron, Dow, DuPont, 3M, Sandoz, Shell and Uniroyal. The safety of a startling array of products, including over-the-counter drugs and food additives as well as fully one-third of the active ingredients in all the pesticides used in the country (the U.S.), was suddenly thrown open to doubt" (1).

Among the pesticides in doubt was captan, a widely-used fungicide.

Captan is a broad-spectrum fungicide used to protect fruit, vegetables, seeds and foliage against fungal pathogens (2). The name captan is derived from the mercaptans, a series of organic sulphur compounds which are similar in structure to alcohols (3). Researchers in the late 1940s used perchloromethyl mercaptan to synthesize a series of new compounds. The chemical we now call captan exhibited "exceptional fungicidal activity" (4) and was registered for use in Canada in 1951 (2).

Captan is relatively insoluble; the standard agricultural formulations are in the forms of dusts or dispersable powders. As for toxicity and persistence, captan has qualities found in other synthetic insecticides. Like the organochlorides (see DDT), captan has a low toxicity to warm-blooded animals. In the case of rats, the acute oral LD_{50} (the dose that is lethal to 50% of the test animal population) is 9000 mg/kg (milligram per kilogram) body weight. By comparison, the LD_{50} for DDT is

113 mg/kg (5). Like the organophosphates (see Fenitrothion) and carbamates, captan breaks down rapidly. Because it readily hydrolyzes, captan does not persist in aquatic systems or moist soils; thus, it does not bioaccumulate. Although a broad-spectrum fungicide, there is no evidence that birds, small animals, beneficial insects or spiders are affected to any large degree (2).

Only 5 plants in the world manufacture captan, North America being supplied by the Chevron-Stauffer plant in Ohio (2). Approximately 300 tonne of captan are imported by Canadian formulators who then market 82 registered products; 37 are for domestic use, 45 for commercial and agricultural purposes. Home and garden use accounts for 5% of the total, non-agricultural for 3%, seed treatment for 10% with fruit, vegetables and trees using the remainder. Non-agricultural use consists of small amounts added to paints, adhesives and wallpaper paste as a preservative (2). Agricultural uses are: seed treatment, particularly of corn, to allow for earlier planting; protection of seedlings from mould in reforestation; application to vegetable crops, peaches, apples and strawberries. About half the captan used in Canada is to prevent apple scab, which blemishes the apples, making them less marketable to a public which demands perfect produce.

As a result of the "IBT affair" of 1977, Health and Welfare Canada (HWC) began the laborious task of re-evaluating a list of pesticides that was to reach 113 compounds (6). However, it was not until 1980 that this information was released to the provinces and the public, after a concerted effort by politicians, journalists and public interest groups (7). During this re-evaluation of the IBT pesticides, HWC reviewed 2 studies that fed the same high dose of captan to mice. Both studies, one done by the National Cancer Institute in the U.S. and the other done privately for Chevron-Stauffer, found that captan caused tumours of the intestinal tract.

One positive test using one species is sufficient to indicate carcinogenicity. In light of the new evidence on captan, HWC issued a series of recommendations to Agriculture Canada in Mar. 1981. The recommendations were that: captan be removed from domestic use; commercial application be such that no residues remain on food at a retail level; and the provinces be asked to regulate and educate captan applicators (2).

The implementation of such recommendations could have serious economic consequences. Canada imports on the order of $1.5 billion worth of fruits and vegetables each year (three-quarters of our fruit and one-third of our vegetables). As some of these imports could be carrying captan residues, there could be serious trade disruptions and adverse consequences for Canadian consumers (16).

Normally, pesticide registration in Canada is controlled by Agriculture Canada under the Pest Control Products Act. The registration process begins with a data submission by the manufacturer to the Pesticides Division. From there, sets of data are sent to advisors in the national departments of Agriculture, Environment, Fisheries and Oceans, and Health and Welfare. These departments are concerned with : agronomic aspects; persistence and movement in soil; methods for analysis; effects on wildlife and aquatic organisms; environmental fate and disposal; tolerances in food and hazards to spray operators and bystanders. An evaluation officer will send copies of data to the advisors he or she deems appropriate. It is the evaluation officer in Agriculture Canada who makes the decision to register or not register a product, based on the original submission and the advisors' comments. Once accepted, a product remains registered for 5 years and can be renewed for 5-year periods as long as current standards are met. Re-evaluation is undertaken if new data indicates that the present use pattern should be altered or that the product constitutes a health or environmental hazard (8).

There was no immediate reaction from Agriculture Canada concerning HWC's recommendation to alter the use pattern and residue tolerances for captan. Agriculture Minister Eugene Whelan announced on May 20, 1981 that an independent committee would be formed to examine IBT pesticides (9) and on Sept. 30, the Minister announced that the Consultative Committee on Industrial Bio-Test Pesticides would begin an examination of captan (2). This included 3 days of public hearings held in Toronto during Mar. 1982. Representatives from industry, government, farm workers' unions, public health and environmental groups were asked to appear. The report was completed on Apr. 28, 1982.

The Committee made the following recommendations: captan be retained for domestic use in the absence of equally safe

and effective alternatives; labels be amended to clearly state
the potential hazard and advise that the minimum pre-harvest
interval (i.e., the last spray before harvesting) should be 7
days; residue tolerances be reduced for a 2-year period;
pre-harvest intervals be increased; an increased monitoring
program which would be publicized be initiated; a publicity
campaign to impress upon consumers the need to wash fruit and
vegetables be launched; the feasibility of posting signs at
retail level giving details of the produce's treatment be
studied, and more resources be committed to the research and
development of new pesticides. The education of applicators
should refer to all pesticides, and not captan alone. Further,
the federal government should assist provinces in upgrading
pesticide legislation and regulations. Finally, a system
should be developed to post all sprayed areas (2).

The Minister's reactions to the Committee's report were
issued on May 31, too late to affect the use of captan for the
1982 growing season. Mr. Whelan allowed captan to remain for
home use but suspended registration on formulations containing
more than 10% captan. Thirteen products were affected.
Cautionary labelling on existing products would be expanded.
The Minister also promised to implement the recommendations
concerning tolerance reduction and education of applicators
(10).

As indicated earlier, the question of safety arose because 2 studies found intestinal tumours in mice fed large
amounts of captan. However, similar tests with rats found no
tumours (2). There is no evidence to relate captan to human
cancer at this time (2). Captan has seen 30 years of safe use
in Canada, in spite of the fact that applicators frequently
ignore label instructions and do not use protective equipment
regularly (2). Incidences of apple growers not using recommended protective equipment can be found (11,12).

The issue of captan safety saw 2 distinct sides being
taken, a common occurrence in many environmental health
issues. On one side, industry and agriculture stressed the
economic benefits; on the other, environmentalists and public
interest groups questioned health risks. The loss of Canadian
fruit crops would be an estimated 25% (equivalent to about
$120 million annually (16)) if captan were banned entirely
(2). Yet the argument about safety is also valid. It is widely

accepted that well-established animal carcinogenicity is an indicator of potential human carcinogenicity. This is the basis for American regulatory action (13).

The "IBT affair" was a shock to the scientific community. Scientific methods and ethics had been abused by private laboratories to provide manufacturers with positive results. Industrial Bio-Test Laboratories conducted over 22,000 chemical safety tests. Examining 900 studies, the U.S. EPA concluded that 80-90% were invalid (1).

As of July 1983, the EPA estimates that 34 pesticides could face suspension because of the invalid testing (17). In Canada, the safety of 43 chemicals is considered suspect, and 4 have been taken off the market by Agriculture Canada (18). The status (as of June 1983) of the 43 chemicals are summarized in reference 18.

A 3-year audit of 82 private laboratories by the EPA found serious deficiencies in the work of 25 firms (7). Such events seriously erode public confidence in science and scientists. Criminal charges were brought against 4 scientists associated with IBT in the 1970s, and the trial began Apr. 13, 1983 in Chicago after considerable delay (19).

Present practice for chemical safety tests has been to have industry contract with private laboratories. Two alternatives have been suggested. The first is a double blind system in which the manufacturer would apply to the government, who would in turn contract with a private lab, with neither the manufacturer nor the lab knowing by or for whom the study is being done (1,9). The second possibility is to have all studies conducted by government laboratories (14,15). The IBT affair suggests our dependence on American studies for the pesticide registration process. However, since such studies are expensive it is unlikely that manufacturers would be willing to duplicate these tests for the relatively small Canadian market.

As it stands, 13 of 37 domestic formulations of captan have been removed from the market. Further animal studies are under way. The Consultative Committee's recommendations will be re-evaluated in 1985. It is possible that captan use will be futher restricted.

REFERENCES

1. "The Illusion of Safety", Mother Nature, June/July, 1982.
2. "Captan: A Report by the Consultative Committee on Industrial Bio-Test Pesticides", Ottawa, Apr. 28, 1982.
3. "Kirk-Othmer Encyclopedia of Chemical Technology". Second edition, John Wiley and Sons, New York, 1964.
4. Kitleson, A. R., "A New Class of Organic Fungicides", Science, 115, Jan. 25, 1952.
5. "Guide to the Chemicals Used in Crop Protection", 7th edition, Agriculture Canada, 1982.
6. "Current Status of IBT Pesticides", Press Release, Health and Welfare Canada 1982-47, May 6, 1982.
7. Rosenbaum, L., "Implication of the 'IBT Affair'", Canadian Environmental Law Association Newsletter, 7(3), June 1982.
8. Cedar, F. J., "The Registration and Regulations of Pesticides in Canada", Text of speech, Dec. 11, 1981.
9. "Consultive Committee on IBT Pesticides, Background Information", Press Release, Agriculture Canada, Ottawa, May 31, 1982. (see 10)
10. "Captan Recommendations", Press Release, Agriculture Canada, G-27, Ottawa, May 31, 1982.
11. "Pesticide Committee Faces Tough Task Sifting Testimony", The Globe and Mail, Toronto, Mar. 13, 1982.
12. "The Spread of Silent Springs", Maclean's, May 18, 1981.
13. Baker, H. J., Lindsey, J. R. and Weisbroth, S. H., Editors, "The Laboratory Rat", Vol. II, Research Applications, Academic Press, 1980.
14. "Law and the Conserver Society", (Conserver Society Notes), Alternatives, 10(4), 1982.
15. "Safety Last: Tests that Fail the Tests", Maclean's, Aug. 25, 1980.
16. Dunnett, E., "An Economic Assessment of the Benefits of Captan Use in Canada", Canadian Farm Economics, 18, 31, 1983.
17. "Audit of IBT Tests: 34 Pesticides Could Face Suspension", Chemical and Engineering News, July 18, 1983.
18. Cox, K., "Safety of Chemicals Queried 10 Years after Bogus Tests", The Globe and Mail, Toronto, June 30, 1983.
19. Marshall, E., "The Murky World of Toxicity Testing", Science, 220, 1130, 1983.

RECOMMENDED READING

Reference (2) covers all aspects of the issue thoroughly. It is available from Agriculture Canada, Pesticides Division, Ottawa, K1A 0C5. A summary of the status of the 43 chemicals considered suspect in Canada is given in a thorough article in The Globe and Mail (18).

CARBON DIOXIDE

Carbon dioxide is a trace component of the atmosphere. It is predicted that man's activities are upsetting nature's balance, threatening global climate change.

Carbon dioxide cannot be considered a pollutant in the same sense as a chemical like sulphur dioxide. The controversy over carbon dioxide concerns the effects on global climate that may result from an increasing atmospheric concentration of the gas. Making up 0.03% of the atmosphere, carbon dioxide exerts a profound influence on the radiation balance of the earth; it is a primary cause of the "greenhouse effect", which warms the earth's atmosphere and surface to a hospitable mean temperature of 15 deg. C (1).

Monitoring of carbon dioxide levels began at Mauna Loa in Hawaii in 1957. The initial level was 310 ppm (part per million by volume). By 1980, the level was 335 ppm, an 8% increase in 23 years (2). This figure has been observed by other stations, 3 of which are in Canada: Alert, Northwest Territories; Sable Island, Nova Scotia; and ocean weathership PAPA in the North Pacific (3). The carbon dioxide concentration in 2025 is expected to be twice as high as before the Industrial Revolution (1). This is the result of man's burning of fossil fuels, particularly in the last 4 decades, and the clearing of forests.

VARIATIONS IN NORMAL LEVELS OF CARBON DIOXIDE

The radiation balance is the result of a complex series of interconnected factors which affect the incoming solar radiation. The sun emits radiation energy primarily in the ultraviolet and visible (short wavelength) region of the electromagnetic spectrum. In the upper atmosphere, ozone screens out the harmful ultraviolet rays (see Fluorcarbons). Passing through the troposphere, some of the light is reflected by clouds, aerosols, airborne dust and droplets. On the surface, snow, ice, vegetation and bodies of water reflect some additional light. The sunlight that is absorbed by the ground is converted to heat.

The warm ground emits energy in the infrared (long wavelength) region of the electromagnetic spectrum. Carbon dioxide and water vapour, although relatively transparent to ultraviolet and visible light, absorb infrared radiation. A portion of the energy being emitted to space is thus absorbed by carbon dioxide and water vapour, which in turn re-radiate this energy, some towards the Earth's surface and some towards space. Other gases in the atmosphere can also contribute: nitrous oxide from fertilizers, synthetic halocarbons such as Freons (3), and methane (marsh gas) (4) also absorb infrared radiation.

The normal level of carbon dioxide in the atmosphere has been determined by the balance between what is given off by respiring plants and animals and what is taken up by photosynthetic organisms and dissolved in the oceans. This "carbon cycle", one of several biogeochemical cycles (see also Fluorides), is shown schematically in the following figure.

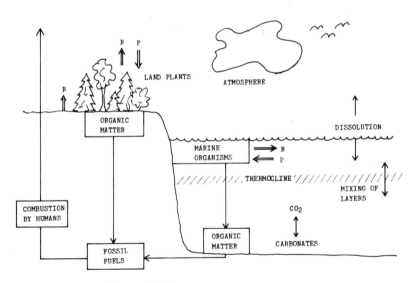

R ⟹ Respiration (Release of CO_2)
P ⟹ Photosynthesis (Uptake of CO_2)

THE CARBON CYCLE

Monitoring has shown that carbon dioxide levels in the Northern Hemisphere undergo yearly cycles. The concentration peaks in late winter and reaches a minimum in the fall (5). This corresponds to the production of carbon dioxide by respiration and fuel-burning in the winter and the surge of photosynthesis during the summer.

Man's use of fossil fuels augments the quantity of carbon dioxide that must be cycled through the biosphere. It is estimated that 50% of the carbon dioxide produced by combustion of fossil fuels remains in the atmosphere. The fate of the remaining 50% is presumed to be divided between the oceans and photosynthetic aquatic and land plants (6). However, man introduces additional carbon dioxide into the atmosphere by clearing forests, particularly in tropical regions. Forests hold 10 to 20 times more carbon than the equivalent area of agricultural land (4). Deforestation also lays bare a great deal of organic matter, such as humus and litter. This matter is decomposed by organisms which release carbon dioxide. While the large forests of the world are being encroached upon more and more, reforestation and regrowth of abandoned farmland in the Northern Hemisphere compensates to some degree (4).

Another source of carbon dioxide could be the oceans themselves. Apparently, the Southern Pacific Ocean undergoes an episodic 3 to 4 deg. C rise in temperature. This is a natural phenomenon of unknown cause. The warmed ocean could change the carbon dioxide balance as less of the gas can dissolve at warmer temperatures (7). Variations in salinity also affect the ocean's capacity to absorb carbon dioxide (8). The role of the oceans in the carbon cycle is not well understood; oceanographers disagree on how much carbon dioxide the oceans can hold and how much is exchanged between the surface layers and depths.

EFFECTS OF CHANGES IN CARBON DIOXIDE LEVEL

There appears to be no contention that the combustion of fossil fuels is contributing to the higher atmospheric concentration of carbon dioxide. The question many scientists are asking is: "What effect will this increased level have on the global climate?". Computer modelling has proved to be the most useful tool in dealing with this question. The most widely accepted model was developed by Manabe, Wetherall and Stouffer of Princeton University. The Global Circulation Model (GCM) is 3 dimensional, devised to explore the geographic distribution of climate change caused by a doubling and quadrupling of atmospheric carbon dioxide. A doubling resulted in the following increases, in deg. C: 2 deg. in tropical latitudes, 3 deg. at 35 deg. N (Los Angeles, Tokyo), 4 deg. at 50 deg. N (Toronto, Paris) and 7 deg. in the high Arctic (4). These are average increases; there would be seasonal variations. Carbon dioxide would not be the sole cause; higher temperatures would mean more water evaporation because warmer air holds more water vapour (4).

The GCM predicts that precipitation will increase at high northern latitudes, but decrease significantly between 35 and 45 deg. North (4). The latter is of concern as it could seriously harm North American agriculture, despite the fact that a higher carbon dioxide level increases the yield of some crops (4).

There are concerns about a global temperature rise bringing about a decrease in the arctic and antarctic ice coverage, causing a rise in sea levels (9). Arctic climate may be affected by humans not only by way of carbon dioxide, but also a haze containing industrially used chemicals (9). There has however as yet not been any definitive longterm decrease in the extent of antarctic sea ice (10).

It is not expected that atmospheric carbon dioxide will double until after the next century (3,8). Should this occur, there will be many changes in the Canadian climate; some beneficial, some neutral and some detrimental. The Prairie grain belt would be pushed northward but might be accompanied by an expansion of the dry belt into what is now the main wheat-growing area. The higher carbon dioxide concentration is expected to increase yields of some crops, alfalfa and wheat being examples (4). Southern Ontario and Quebec could expect to benefit from a longer growing season. Forestry is expected to benefit, with the exception of mid-latitude regions where precipitation may decline. Northern Canada would warm significantly. Continuous permafrost would retreat northward, and discontinuous permafrost start a gradual, irreversible melting. Projects such as pipelines would have to adjust. Navigation would benefit from easier ice conditions. Heating requirements would decrease, but air conditioning costs would increase (3).

Both global population and per capita energy consumption are likely to increase. More coal and synthetic fuels would be used, producing more carbon dioxide than the equivalent amount of oil or gas (3). Inevitably, the carbon dioxide concentration will increase. Yet, for now, the various predictions of climate change remain speculation. Studies of the planet Venus, its atmosphere mostly carbon dioxide, confirm the greenhouse effect (4). Until the temperature increase surpasses the natural variation, or "noise level" of plus or minus 0.5 deg. C (18), there is no "signal" to tell us that real climatic change is occurring (3).

When that signal appears, the social, political and economic questions will be numerous. Can we adapt? Can international co-operation be achieved to combat a global problem? What will be the effect on the developed nations, with their high energy consumption? What of the developing nations, who will need energy to help feed themselves and raise their standard of living?

REFERENCES

1. Idso, S. B., "CO$_2$--An alternative View", New Scientist, Nov. 12, 1981.
2. Gribbin, J., "The Politics of CO$_2$", New Scientist, Apr. 8, 1981.
3. Hare, F. K., "Future Climate and the Canadian Economy", Extended text of Keynote Address, Seminar on Climate Change, Canadian Council of Resource and Environment Ministers, Regina, Mar. 17, 1981.
4. Revelle, R., "Carbon Dioxide and World Climate", Scientific American, 247(2), 35, 1982.
5. Woodwell, G. M., "The Carbon Dioxide Question", Scientific American, 238(1), 1978.
6. Kerr, R.A., Carbon Dioxide and Climate: Carbon Budget Still Unbalanced", Science, 197, 1352, 1977.
7. "Warming Ocean Adds to Rising CO$_2$", Chemical and Engineering News, Oct. 10, 1977.
8. Smith, I., "Carbon Dioxide and the 'Greenhouse Effect'--an Unresolved Problem", A report for International Energy Agency Coal Research, London, England, Apr., 1978.
9. Immen, W., "Haze May Alter Arctic Climate, Scientists Say", The Globe and Mail, Toronto, Apr. 22, 1983.
10. Zwally, H. J., Parkinson, C. L. and Comiso, J. C., "Variability of Antarctic Sea Ice and Changes in Carbon Dioxide", Science, 220, 1005, 1983.
11. Keating, M., "Greenhouse Effect: What Happens in Canada?", The Globe and Mail, Toronto, Oct. 22, 1983.

RECOMMENDED READING

Reference (4) is an interesting, well-written summary of the situation. Reference (1) gives an alternative opinion. Reference (3) gives a detailed description of the implications for Canada. The consequences of increased atmospheric CO_2 for Canada as predicted by 2 recent U.S. studies is summarized in reference (11).

CHLORINE

Chlorination of water has been a great step forward in public health; but there may be some problems.

The most familiar use of chlorine is as a disinfectant -- in swimming pools and in most municipal water treatment plants. Another familiar use is as a bleaching agent, both in households and in industry. It is also used in industry for preparation of numerous compounds, several of which are discussed in this book (DBCP, DDT, Fluorocarbons, PCBs, PCP, 2,4-D and Vinyl Chloride). In 1981, nearly 1.3 million tonne of chlorine were produced and used in Canada (1). By far the the most common use of chlorine is as a bleach in the pulp and paper industry.

Chlorine is produced by electrolysis of brine, a solution of sodium chloride, the same material as common table salt. Many of the problems of mercury pollution (see Mercury) arose because of leaking of mercury from the electrolytic cells used in chlorine production. The "mercury cells" are now being phased out and being replaced by "diaphragm cells". Since such plants must be large to be economical, there are only about 20 plants in Canada. Thus there is considerable transport of chlorine in Canada.

THE MISSISSAUGA DERAILMENT

Chlorine is a gas at normal temperature and pressure. In order to liquify it, it must be either cooled to -34.1 deg. C, its boiling point at atmospheric pressure, or be held under a pressure of about 10 atmosphere. It is commonly transported by rail in tank-cars under pressure. It was the derailment and subsequent rupture of a tank-car containing chlorine that caused evacuation of over 200,000 people in Mississauga, Ontario, in 1979 (2,3).

The evacuation was ordered because of the risk of widespread exposure of the population to chlorine gas. Chlorine in the normal gaseous form Cl_2 has a higher density than air. Thus, on escaping from a ruptured tank-car, it will tend to stay close to the ground on spreading out. It is a severe irritant even at levels as low as 0.5 ppm (part per million)

(4); this is why it was one of the gases used in chemical warfare in the First World War.

The dangers arising from the chlorine released from the train derailment were more limited than originally feared. Fires from combustible chemicals in nearby ruptured cars created an upward draft of air which sucked up a portion of the gas and dispersed it widely in minute concentrations. The release of chlorine was also spread over some time. Heat is needed to vapourize a liquid, whether it be at its normal boiling point or below it (e.g., our bodies give off heat and cool when sweat vapourizes). Thus, the rate at which chlorine escaped from the ruptured tank-car was limited by the rate of transmission of heat to the chlorine, and did not occur all at once.

The Grange Commission (3) considered many of the risks involved in the transport of dangerous goods. International and interprovincial transport of such materials is under federal jurisdiction, but in the case of road transport, the federal government delegated this regulatory task to provincial transport boards (5). All railways in Canada are governed by the federal Railway Act, except for intraprovincial railways in Ontario and British Columbia. The regulations for rail transport of hazardous materials are extensive and detailed (5,6).

CHLORINATION OF WATER

The use of chlorine in disinfecting water supplies advanced public health considerably by effectively eliminating outbreaks of cholera and other communicable diseases. In the past decade, however, some concern has been raised about the use of chlorine for water treatment (7) because of the possible danger of formation of potentially carcinogenic chemicals in chlorination (20).

Attempts have been made to find the causes of various diseases, particularly cancer, by preparing atlases showing geographic regions of frequencies of various diseases. Such "geocancerology" indicated high cancer rates in parishes in Louisiana drawing water from the Mississippi River. Almost at the same time, an analysis of water supplies in the region indicated the presence of many chlorinated organic chemicals

(8). Some of these, such as chloroform ($CHCl_3$) are proven carcinogens in rodents and suspected carcinogens in humans (9,10). Improved methods of analysis have resulted in the detection in drinking water in the U.S. of a new class of potentially hazardous compounds, the dihaloacetonitriles (DHAN s). Studies are underway to determine the biological effects of these chemicals (19).

Organic compounds can enter drinking water sources in different ways. Water may become contaminated by waste effluents and natural degradation products, as well as through run off from agricultural land. At the same time as the New Orleans survey, it was reported (9) that halomethanes such as chloroform were not present in the raw water source but were introduced during the chlorination process used to purify the water.

In response to these results, the Environment Protection Agency (EPA) initiated a survey of 80 water utilities and the Province of Ontario analyzed drinking water for halomethanes at 48 water treatment plants (9). Subsequently, a national survey of 70 municipalities was carried out for the Health Protection Branch of Health and Welfare Canada (12) in an attempt to correlate levels of halomethanes with water source and treatment procedures. The concentrations of chloroform varied with the analytical procedure used, time of year (13), water source, total organic carbon content of raw water and treatment; the approximate range was 0-0.121 mg/litre or ppb (milligram per litre or part per billion)(12). The report on this survey concluded that "on the basis of our present knowledge, it cannot be concluded that the consumption of water, containing the levels of halo-methanes found in this present survey, represents a health hazard" (12).

The chlorination process, first introduced in England in 1904, is the most common of the disinfectant processes. Chlorine is relatively inexpensive and easy to handle; it can be applied under controlled conditions and is measurable in the water supply at all points in a distribution system (11). The chemistry of the production of chloroform and other halomethane compounds in water is the result of a complex reaction between chlorine and substances usually described as "precursors" (7). It is reported (14) that the main source of precursors is humic material (not man-made pollution) and some reactions in which chlorine-containing compounds are produced may be photochemical processes (15). It has been proposed that coagulation, flocculation and sedimentation, followed by filtration through activated carbon (instead of sand) would provide an effective method for precursor removal. Alternatives to chlorine treatment are under investigation (7). These include treatment with ozone, which is being increasingly used, chlorine dioxide (ClO_2) and recently, bromine chloride (BrCl), but potentially harmful effects of these processes are, as yet, not fully investigated.

Since there is some doubt whether or not chloroform can cause cancer at present levels in drinking water, it was suggested in 1976, at a conference of the American Water Works Association, that the maximum allowable level should be 70 ppb, on average. More recently, early in 1978, the EPA released proposals which within 2 years would require municipal water systems to maintain a limit of 100 ppb for chloroform and related halomethanes (16). The EPA is an American government agency established in 1970 to control all aspects of air and water pollution and the manufacture and transportation of toxic materials.

A new study by the President's Council on Environmental Quality has strengthened the evidence linking chlorinated water and cancer and has resulted in a new federal regulation requiring that concentrations of trihalogenated methanes remain below 100 ppb (17).

CHLOROFORM AND CARBON TETRACHLORIDE

Chloroform ($CHCl_3$) and carbon tetrachloride (CCl_4) are two of the common halomethanes ("halogen" means chlorine, fluorine, bromine and iodine, and "methane" means one carbon, see "Fluorocarbons"). They have been used for over a century for various purposes: chloroform as an anaesthetic, a toothpaste additive, and in the pharmaceutical industry in, for example, cough syrup (18). Prior to 1934 carbon tetrachloride was used as a dry-cleaning agent and in fire extinguishers, and for degreasing metals.

Many uses of these halomethanes have been discontinued because of their adverse health effects (18). Often they are collectively described as carcinogens but only chloroform is a weak carcinogen to rodents. Use of carbon tetrachloride was discontinued because it was shown to cause liver damage. A substitute, the halocarbon trichloroethylene, (C_2Cl_3H) was eventually also shown to cause liver damage. Thus since the 1960s Dow Chemical, manufacturer of these chemicals, has instead encouraged the use of 1,1,1-trichloroethane ($C_2H_3Cl_3$) for which there is negative evidence of carcinogenicity from animal bioassays (10). This provides refreshing evidence of voluntary self regulation by industry.

Workers and the general public have had exposures to these halocarbons for decades. In nearly all cases, there is no direct evidence that they are human carcinogens. An exception is vinyl chloride (C_2H_3Cl), which is considered a confirmed human carcinogen (see Vinyl Chloride). However, past exposures to chloroform, carbon tetrachloride, etc. may nevertheless have been harmful (10).

Large scale use in the past of these chemicals has contributed to long-term pollution of groundwater. Soil microorganisms do not break down many chlorinated hydrocarbons (see DDT, PCBs). When these chemicals reach the aquifers, they are stable for a long time in the cool dark regions. Thus past contamination of groundwater could be reponsible for high levels of halocarbons in drinking water for many years to come (10).

REFERENCES

1. "Facts and Figures for the Chemical Industry", p. 74, Chemical and Engineering News, June 14, 1982.
2. Gerard, W., "Mississauga Nightmare", Maclean's, p. 23, Nov. 26, 1979.
3. Grange, S. G. M., "Report of the Mississauga Railway Accident Inquiry", Dec. 1980.
4. U.S. Department of Labour, Occupational Safety and Health Administration Recommendations, Sept. 1978.
5. Silverstone, M. J., "Transportation of Dangerous Goods by Road and Rail: Jurisdiction and Liability", Library of Parliament, Apr. 1982.
6. Canadian Transport Commission 1979-8-Rail, Dec. 5, 1979, (The 10th Amendment of General Order No. 1974-1-Rail, July 31, 1974, known as the "Red Book").
7. "The Chlorination Quandary", Environmental Science and Technology, 12(1), 15, 1978.
8. Ember, L., "The Chlorination Quandary", ibid, 9, 1116, 1975.
9. "Organics in Ontario Drinking Waters. Part II, A Survey of Selected Water Treatment Plants", Ontario Ministry of the Environment, OTC 7703, Project Number AAN-7504, Apr. 1977.

10. Pye, V. I. and Patrick, R., "Ground Water Contamination in the United States", Science 221, 713, 1983.
Burmaster, D. E. and Harris, R. H., "Groundwater Contamination: an Emerging Threat", Technology Review, 50, July, 1982.

11. Pfafflin and Ziegler, "Encyclopedia of Environmental Science and Engineering", Vol. II, Gordon and Breach Science Publishers Inc., New York, 1976.

12. "National Survey for Halomethanes in Drinking Water", Environmental Health Directorate, Health Protection Branch, Health and Welfare Canada, 77-EMD-9.

13. Smillie, R. D., "Chloroform Levels in Ontario Drinking Water", Water Pollution Control, Dec. 1977.

14. "Chloroform Precursors Found in Natural Waters", Chemical and Engineering News, June 6, 1977.

15. Oliver, B. G. and Carey, J. H., "Photochemical Production of Chlorinated Organics in Aqueous Solutions Containing Chlorine", Environmental Science and Technology, 11(9), 893, 1977.

16. "Trihalomethane Limits in Water Proposed", Chemical and Engineering News. Jan. 30, 1978.

17. Maugh, T. H., "New Study Links Chlorination and Cancer", Science, 211, 694, 1981.

18. "U.S. Bans Chloroform in the Chemist's Shop", New Scientist, Apr. 15, 1976.

19. "Another Potential Problem in Drinking Water", Science, 212, 431, 1981.

20. Keating, M., "Effective Water Treatment: the Vital Puzzle", The Globe and Mail, Toronto, June 9, 1983. See also June 4, 6, 7, 8, 1983.

RECOMMENDED READING

The 2 government reports, references (9) and (12) give good technical discussions of the methods for determination of chloroform and factors which affect the results. References (9) and (7) are interesting accounts of the chloroform in drinking water problem. A series of major articles in The Globe and Mail (20) discusses the problem of water supplies from Lake Ontario. A "Position Document" on chloroform dated Sept., 1982 is available from the Environmental Protection Agency in Washington D.C.; it provides an update of the knowledge and U.S. regulations pertaining to chloroform.

DBCP AND EDB

Following reports of sterility among male workers handling this soil fumigant, production and sale of DBCP has virtually ceased. Another chemical used as a fumigant, EDB, has recently become controversial.

DBCP, 1,2-dibromo-3-chloropropane, is another halogenated hydrocarbon involved in controversy (see Chlorine). Since the 1950s, DBCP had been used as a soil fumigant to kill nematodes, microscopic worms, which destroy the roots of crops such as carrots, peanuts, tomatoes, cabbage and soybeans (1).

Concern about the safety of DBCP was initiated in July 1977, when it was found that some workers in 3 different U.S. companies became sterile after being exposed to low doses of DBCP. At an Occidental Chemical plant in California, where the first problems were discovered, 10 out of 23 workers were found to be completely sterile (2) and subsequent tests by the National Institute for Occupational Safety and Health showed that 28 of 79 exposed workers had low sperm counts (3). Dow Chemical at Magnolia, Arkansas, found that half of its workers (about 37) were affected and Shell Chemical in Mobile, Alabama, found that a small number of workers were affected (4). When these results were released it was not known whether the sterility was reversible, but it has since been reported (5) that tests made by Dow Chemical suggest that recovery is taking place in some of the workers, particularly those exposed to the chemical for only a short time. As a result of the initial findings, the Occidental plant was closed and Dow and Shell stopped production in Sept. 1977, and began recalling the pesticide from retailers and users (5,6).

The publicity put pressure for action on various agencies. The Environmental Protection Agency (EPA) ordered a halt on the use and sale of DBCP, Oct. 28, 1977 (6). The Occupational Safety and Health Administration imposed an emergency temporary standard, Sept. 9, 1977 (7), limiting worker exposure to 10 ppb (part per billion) during an 8-hour work day and 50 ppb for any 15 minute period. Earlier, 1000 ppb was believed to be a safe exposure limit. The Food and Drug Administration is working on an analytical method for determination of DBCP in foods (7) for a food monitoring program to determine the amounts of the pesticide residue on agricultural crops (8). It was recognized that other pesticides, such as ethylene dibromide (EDB), which is also used in the manufacture of gasoline, should be examined and that investigations should be extended to include farmers, homeowners and other users as well as plant workers (9).

A disturbing aspect of this issue is that the reports indicate that manufacturers of the DBCP knew as early as 1961 that the chemical could be a health hazard (2,9). Toxicology studies sponsored by Dow and Shell companies showed testicular damage and reduced sperm production in guinea pigs, rats, rabbits and monkeys exposed to 12,000 ppb DBCP for 10 to 13 weeks. Higher concentrations caused kidney damage and acute depression of the central nervous system in rats (2). More recently (1973) the National Cancer Institute reported that DBCP is carcinogenic in rats and mice (1,3).

It was reported in 1977 (10) that DBCP was no longer marketed in Canada. Dow Chemical of Canada said that the product, called Fumizone, was dropped in 1976 because of poor sales. In March, 1981, the EPA cancelled all uses of DBCP in U.S. except for pineapple fields in Hawaii. This use was cancelled in 1983 when detectable levels of the chemical were found in groundwater (11). Even though the production and use of DBCP has been terminated, the DBCP controversy can continue for some time because of possible persistent groundwater contamination and law suits (12).

Soil fumigants are used primarily in vinyards and citrus orchards, and are not very important for agriculture in northern regions where soil freezes (13). Another chemical which has been used as a soil fumigant is EDB. Its chemical structure is not very different from that of DBCP:

EDB   DBCP

The primary use of EDB is not as a soil fumigant, but as a gasoline additive to scavenge for lead in leaded gasoline. In addition it was used as a fumigant for stored grain, citrus fruit and vegetables and as a spot fumigant in milling equipment (14, 15).

There seems to be no controversy with regard to the use of EDB in gasoline. EDB was discovered to be present in the ppb range in the drinking water in over 100 wells in areas where it was used as a soil fumigant (Florida, California, Georgia, Hawaii). Its use as a soil fumigant and insecticide was therefore effectively cancelled in 1983 by the EPA (14). A controversy has been developing regarding its use as a fumigant for stored food products because of detection of residues (13, 14, 15). Besides being carcinogenic to both rats and mice, and thus a suspected human carcinogen, EDB has been associated with other health problems involving organs, the central nervous system, the eyes and the respiratory tract (14).

In Canada, EDB has been registered for use as a fumigant and as a spot fumigant in milling equipment. It can be present in foods due to these uses, but also due to residues in imported foods. Indications are that cooking of foods destroys essentially all of any EDB residues. Although EDB has been found in foods in Canada, the levels are within Canadian limits. These are however not as strict as those in other areas, e.g. Florida (15). Agriculture Canada announced a ban of agricultural uses of EDB other than as a spot fumigant in milling equipment (16). No suitable alternatives are currently available for such uses.

REFERENCES

1. "Pesticide Causes Sterility in Workers", New Scientist, Sept. 1, 1977.
2. "Federal Action Urged Against Soil Fumigant", Chemical and Engineering News, Aug. 29, 1977.
3. "DBCP: Government Moves on Problem Pesticide", Chemecology, Manufacturing Chemists Association, Washington, Oct. 1977.
4. "More Tests Link DBCP to Worker Sterility", Chemical and Engineering News, Sept. 5, 1977.
5. "Sperm Count Rise in DBCP-Exposed Workers", ibid, Dec. 19, 1977.
6. "EPA Put the Lid on DBCP", ibid, Nov. 7, 1977.
7. "Emergency Exposure Limits Set for DBCP", ibid, Sept. 19, 1977.

8. "OSHA, EPA, FDA Announced Emergency Temporary Standards for DBCP...", in "Currents", Environmental Science and Technology, 11 (12), 1043, Nov. 1977.
9. "A Sterility Score Sends OSHA Scurrying" Business Week, Sept. 12, 1977.
10. "Pesticide Under Study Isn't Sold in Canada", The Globe and Mail, Toronto, Aug. 24, 1977.
11. "Last Use of One Pesticide Cancelled......and Further Limits on Another Considered", Chemical and Engineering News, Jan. 16, 1984.
12. "Pesticide Suit Hits Dow: Six Workers Awarded $5 Million, ibid, Apr. 25, 1983.
13. Butters, B., "Canada May Gain by US Fear of Grain Pesticide", The Citizen, Ottawa, Jan. 30, 1984.
14. "Ethylene Dibromide: Worker Exposure, Use Restricted", Chemical and Engineering News, Oct. 10, 1983.
15. Immen, W., "Banned Chemical Still Presents Risk, Researchers Find", The Globe and Mail, Toronto, Jan. 26, 1984.
16. "Action on Fumigant Products" Agriculture Canada, Press Release I-4, Jan. 23, 1984.

RECOMMENDED READING

Good summaries of the EDB controversy which have recently become available are: Sun, T., "EDB Contamination Kindles Federal Action", Science, 223, 464, Feb. 3, 1984; Hanson, D.J., "Agricultural Uses of Ethylene Dibromide Halted", Chemical and Engineering News, Mar. 5, 1984.

DDT

DDT had fantastic initial success as an insecticide, saving millions of lives by controlling pests which cause malaria, yellow fever and typhus. It has now proved to be a persistent widespread poison in the environment.

HISTORY

DDT's (see below) spectacular success in controlling disease-carrying insects during World War II earned it the reputation of being the "atomic bomb of insecticides" (1). The first of a new generation of pesticides, the organochlorides, it was readily accepted by the public. DDT was first synthesized in 1874 by Othmar Zeidler, a doctoral chemistry student in Germany (2). In 1939, Paul Mueller, a Swiss chemist, discovered the insecticidal properties of DDT while searching for new mothproofing chemicals. As a result of this work, Mueller was awarded a Nobel Prize in 1948 (2,3).

DDT, dichlorodiphenyltrichloroethane or
1,1,1-trichloro-2,2-bis(p-chlorophenyl)ethane

As a result of wartime production, several American plants were producing the chemical at low cost and it was soon widely used for agriculture, public health protection and household insect control (1).

DDT is a convulsive poison which attacks the central nervous system of the insect, producing hyperexcitability, convulsions, paralysis and death (4). It acts by contact or ingestion (5). It kills insects in very small concentrations while it has low toxicity to vertebrates. Because of this, problems arising from its use were not initially foreseen. Pure DDT is only very slightly soluble in water (1-2 ppb (part per billion)) but it is quite soluble in fatty substances, indicating its lipophilic nature, the ability to accumulate in fatty tissues (6). DDT is a highly stable compound which breaks down very slowly in the environment. Due to its synthetic chemical structure it is not subject to normal bacterial degradation. This is the cause of DDT's persistence, a valuable part of its insecticidal powers.

In the 1950s and 1960s DDT was at the height of its popularity and used extensively. Gradually its use decreased for 3 reasons. First, it became apparent that some insects were developing resistance to the pesticide. Second, DDT's broad spectrum, non-selective action was affecting many beneficial insects as well as birds and fish. Third, there was growing public concern about the safety of DDT and other pesticides as a result of Rachel Carson's book, "Silent Spring" (8).

DISADVANTAGES OF DDT USE

Resistance develops when a small number of slightly resistant insects survive an insecticide application. These insects will in turn produce a high proportion of resistant offspring. In this way, the quality of resistance is selected as being necessary for survival. Since insects have relatively short lifespans, a resistant population can develop in several years. Resistance tends to be specific to one group of pesticides. However, there have been a number of incidences where insects resistant to organochlorides proved to be resistant to organophosphates and carbamates as well. This is called cross resistance (7). Another form of resistance is a behavioral one. One example is a Central American mosquito that has learned to avoid insecticide-sprayed indoor walls, instead resting outside (7).

The problem of resistance was first detected about 1947 when Italian researchers reported that the housefly was becoming immune to DDT. Because of its vast expanse, numerous untreated areas and low tempertatures, Canada has been more fortunate than many countries with respect to the immunity problem. DDT resistance was reported in the Ottawa Valley in 1956, New Brunswick in 1960, and British Columbia in 1961 (4).

There was evidence that DDT and other persistent pesticides were causing damage to certain birds, fish, and other
non-target species (2,3). This was thought to be due to the
accumulation in waterways of up to 25% of all DDT used.
Although concentrations are low (a few ppb in fresh water and
ppt in ocean water), because of the large dilution factor,
many plants and animals can concentrate DDT in body tissues,
particularly in fats and oils (2). This procedure, during
which levels up to 10,000 times the background concentration
can occur, is known as biological magnification or bioaccumulation (6). This process has been cited as the cause of
mortality and impaired reproduction in Canadian fish such as
salmon in New Brunswick (8) and birds such as the Sun Life
peregrine falcons in Montreal (4). Typical food chain concentrations and paths of transport are shown in the figure.

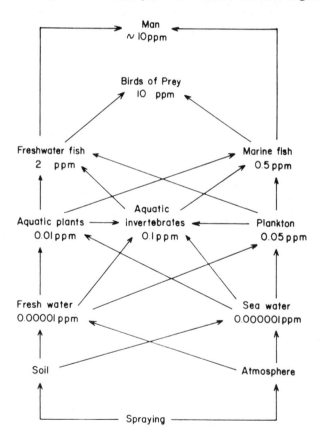

It has been suggested that the environmental effects attributed to DDT may have actually been caused by polychlorinated biphenyls (See PCBs) (9,10). Trace analysis was not highly refined in the mid-1960s; DDT and PCBs would have given nearly-identical readings (10,11). Still, recovery was noted in several bird species within several years of the 1972 American ban of DDT (11). Further research has suggested that DDT and PCBs may have a synergistic effect (12).

Since humans are at the top of the food chain, they too should accumulate DDT in their tissues. Samplings have found that this is the case; residues in humans varied from an average of 5 ppm in Canada to 27 ppm in India as of 1973 (4). As with any pesticide a potential health risk exists for humans, either as a result of exposure or ingestion. Apple growers in Quebec who were exposed to high concentrations of DDT suffered an unusually high incidence of neurological problems and leukopenia, an abnormal decrease in the number of white corpuscles in the blood (4). Two World Health Organization (WHO) studies, one in Brazil, the other in India, compared men with 5 to 13 years occupational exposure as sprayers to control groups. The first examinations noted slight neurological changes which were not observed during subsequent examinations. The blood level of DDT in the exposed group was about 10 times that of the control group (13). Since it has been found that the body burden of DDT decreases if intake is reduced or eliminated (11), DDT should not pose a problem for most North Americans. However, DDT residues may be present on some imported produce.

There are other disadvantages to DDT use. It is one of the most stable and persistent of the organochlorine group, which includes aldrin, dieldrin and chlordane. It is essentially insoluble in water and very resistant to destruction by light, oxidation (4) or hydrolysis (15) (See also PCB and 2,4-D). In the early 1970s, it was estimated that DDT requires 25 years to significantly degrade in the natural environment (4). DDT has global mobility; residues are found in places such as Antarctica where spraying has never occurred. Two explanations are drift loss from aerial spraying (4) and volatilization of that sprayed in tropical climates (16).

RESTRICTIONS ON USE OF DDT

Rachel Carson's "Silent Spring" first appeared as a series of 3 articles in the "New Yorker", starting June 16, 1962. Carson questioned the hazards, the failures and inefficiencies of chemicals such as DDT. The reaction of the chemical industry was to stress the benefits of pesticide use. As a consequence of public pressure resulting largely from the book, the U.S. Federal Council of Science and Technology set up a committee to examine pesticide use and regulation. It confirmed many of Carson's criticisms. Out of the recommendations of this committee the Environmental Protecton Agency (EPA) was formed. Regulatory reform followed in the U.S. and Canada. "Silent Spring" changed our perceptions of nature, laying the foundations for the environmental movement of the late 1960s (8,12,14).

In Nov. 1969, the Canadian government began to restrict the use of DDT on food crops. In the years following, the allowed uses of DDT were increasingly restricted. By the end of 1978 it was essentially banned in Canada. DDT remains registered for bat and mouse control in certain circumstances, but since it is classified as a restricted pesticide a special permit is required to apply it (17). In 1983, a wet spring resulted in an anomalously large number of mosquitoes in southern Manitoba. An outbreak of equine encephalitis, a crippling disease carried by mosquitoes, was feared and a mosquito eradication campaign was carried out. The pesticide used was however not DDT but malathion (23).

Even though there has been a virtual stop in DDT use in North America, the issue of effluent treatment and plant decommissioning remains. This was recently brought to light with the report of DDT contamination in Triana, Alabama. Here, at the former location of a DDT plant, widespread contamination was found. A group of Triana residents has launched a suit against Olin Corporation on the grounds that this contamination is responsible for a high incidence of disease and illness (18).

In the world as a whole, however, DDT production has increased to meet the demands of developing nations. DDT can result in substantial increases in crop yields in tropical regions. However, yields will quickly fall off to pre-DDT levels as soil contamination kills off beneficial soil organisms (16). DDT is used in many tropical countries to control disease-carrying pests. It has been used against yellow fever (3); African trypanosomiasis, a form of sleeping sickness (19); typhus (3); kala-azar, a malaria-like fever (7); and malaria (19). The WHO of the United Nations estimates that between 1950 and 1975, DDT freed one billion people from the risk of malaria and saved five million lives (3).

Malaria is a blood parasite transmitted by the female mosquito of the Anopheles genus. The disease is characterized by acute attacks of chills, fever and sweating which recur at regular intervals of 1, 2 or 3 days. There are 4 forms of malaria, Plasmodium Vivax is the most common; it is a chronic, debilitating disease that is difficult to cure. Plasmodium Falciparum is more virulent; it may be fatal if not quickly treated. The parasite goes through several stages in infecting the body. Depending on the stage, 4 types of drug therapy can be used: symptom suppressive, curative and transmission preventative (20).

Malaria was common in Eastern Canada during the early 1800s. Many of the laborers who built the Rideau Canal suffered from "ague". This was eventually eliminated by habitat control and the cool Canadian climate (21). Today it is a major problem in Central and South America, Central Africa, India, Pakistan, Sri Lanka, Turkey, Southern China and the South Pacific Islands (21). DDT was used in the WHO-sponsored eradication campaigns of the 1950s and early 1960s with remarkable success. With the disease nearly eradicated, many programs were halted in the early 1960s. Malaria has now come back to afflict some 200 million people and threaten over a billion (7). Aside from human suffering, malaria lowers agricultural and economic production , hindering the goals of food self-sufficiency and development (20).

The WHO admitted in 1968 that global eradication of malaria was not possible and set more limited goals. These goals are complicated by the appearance of drug-resistant forms of the disease, lack of drug research, resistance of mosquitoes to DDT and the expense of alternative pesticides (7). Attempts are underway to produce a malaria vaccine by genetic engineering (22).

REFERENCES

1. Dunlap, T. R., "DDT: Scientists, Citizens and Public Policy", Princeton University Press, Princeton, New Jersey, 1981.
2. Moore, J. W. and Moore, E. A., "Environmental Chemistry", Academic Press, New York, 1976.
3. Mitler, G. T. Jr., "Living in the Environment: Concepts, Problems and Alternatives", Wadsworth Publishing Co., Belmont, California, 1975.
4. Bryan, R., "Much is Taken, Much Remains", Duxbury Press, North Scituate, Mass., 1973.
5. "Guide to Chemicals Used in Crop Protection", 6th edition, Agriculture Canada, 1973.
6. Pryde, L. T., "Environmental Chemistry: An Introduction", Cummings Publishing Company, Inc., Menlo Park, California, 1973.
7. Agarwal, A., "Malaria Makes a 'Comeback'", New Scientist, Feb. 2, 1978. "Science is Losing to Mosquitoes", The Globe and Mail, Toronto, Oct. 11, 1983.
8. Carson, R., "Silent Spring", Fawcett Publications, Inc., Greenwich, Conn., 1962.
9. Jukes, T. H., "DDT: Bystander or Participant", Nature, 259, Feb. 12, 1976.
10. Beatty, R. G., "The DDT Myth: Triumph of the Amateurs", The John Day Company, New York, 1973.
11. Wagner, R. H., "Environment and Man", 3rd edition, Norton & Company, New York, 1978.
12. Lawless, E. W., "Technology and Social Shock", Rutgers University Press, New Brunswick, New Jersey, 1977.
13. "Safe Use of Pesticides", World Health Organization Technical Reports Series, No. 513, 1973.
14. The Journal, CBC-TV, June 16, 1982.
15. Wolfe, N. L., Zepp, R. G., Paris, D. F., Baughnam, G. L. and Hollis, R. C., "Methoxychlor and DDT Degradation in Water: Rates and Products", Environmental Science and Technology, 11, 1077, 1977.
16. Perfect, J., "The Environmental Impact of DDT in a Tropical Agro-ecosystem", Ambio 9, 16, 1980.
17. Stalker, J. M., "Regulatory History of DDT Under the Pest Control Products Act, 1968-1976", Agriculture Canada, PA834.2 DDT, June 2, 1977.
18. "DDT Scare in Alabama", Chemical Engineering, July 12, 1982.
19. Fletcher, W., "Pesticides or Disease?", New Scientist, Sept. 30, 1976.
20. "Kirk-Othmer Encyclopedia of Chemical Technology", 1st edition, Interscience Encyclopedia Inc., New York, 1952.
21. Dorozynski, A., "Malaria Returns", Science Forum, Sept./Oct., 1978.
22. "Malaria Vaccine Engineered Genetically", New Scientist, Jan. 15, 1981.
23. Immen, W., "A Year for Mosquitoes", The Globe and Mail, Toronto, July 18, 1983. "Scientists Fear Manitoba Mosquito Spraying Will Harm People", ibid, July 22, 1983.

RECOMMENDED READING

A brief but thorough history is found in (12), while (1) examines DDT in detail as a case history of public response to a hazardous substance. Reference (21) provides a good summary on malaria.

DIOXINS

The chemicals known as dioxins are some of the deadliest poisons known and can occur as impurities in some chemicals. It is now believed that traces of dioxins are also a by-product of combustion.

The ICMESA (Industrie Chimice Meda Societa Anonyma) plant in Seveso, Italy employed about 200 people in the production of 2,4,5-trichlorophenol for the Swiss-based Givaudan Corporation, a subsidiary of Hoffman-LaRoche. On Saturday, July 10, 1976, a safety disc in the reactor ruptured, releasing a cloud of chemicals containing sodium hydroxide (lye), trichlorophenol and an estimated 0.5 to 5 kg of the contaminant TCDD (see below). As a result of the accident, animals died and many people experienced nausea, headache, and skin irritation. Many cases of chloracne, a skin disease associated with exposure to chlorinated chemicals, were observed. Eventually, the town was evacuated (1,2).

THE CHEMISTRY OF 2,4,5-TRICHLOROPHENOL AND TCDD

TCDD is 2,3,7,8-tetrachlorodibenzo-para-dioxin (see below).

Dioxin isomer numbering

It is a by-product of the chemical process in which tetrachlorobenzene is converted to 2,4,5-trichlorophenol, an intermediate chemical used in the production of herbicides, disinfectants and wood preservatives. The process is performed at high temperatures and under pressure. Careful control of the temperature is necessary to prevent formation of TCDD and some contamination of trichlorophenol and its commercial issue can occur. TCDD is stable to heat, acid and alkali; it is virtually insoluble in water but quite soluble in chlorinated organic

solvents. It is 500 times more poisonous than the better known
poison strychnine and 10,000 times more poisonous than cyanide
(3), at least for guinea pigs (see Appendix). Nevertheless, no
human deaths have as of 1983 been attributed to dioxin
poisoning (4) in industrial accidents.

TCDD is the most toxic of a family of 75 compounds known
as polychlorinated dibenzo-p-dioxins, having from 1 to 8
chlorines in a structure comprising 2 hexagonal benzene rings
(see Benzene) joined by 2 oxygen bridges (see figure). The
numbers 1, 2, 3, 4, 6, 7, 8 and 9 indicate the positions where
chlorine can attach. TCDD's extreme toxicity is in part related to its shape; it has 2 reactive chlorines at each end.
TCDD exhibits a wide range of toxicity in laboratory animals,
varying with species, strains within a given species, and
method of administration. The LD_{50}, the dose that will kill

50% of a test population, was reported to range from 0.0006 mg/kg (milligram per kilogram) body weight for male guinea pigs to 3 mg/kg for hamsters (5). More recent data (4) give the LD_{50} levels as 0.001 mg/kg for guinea pigs, 5.0 mg/kg for hamsters and 0.115 mg/kg for rabbits (see Appendix).

As the mechanism of TCDD's toxicity to animals is poorly understood, extrapolations to humans vary widely. The fact that no one in Seveso died outright of TCDD poisoning leads a number of scientists to conclude that human toxicity should be modelled on less sensitive animals (2).

Trichlorophenol is used in the production of the herbicides 2,4,5-T and Silvex (2,4,5-TP, also known as fenoprop), and the disinfectant hexachlorophene. As indicated, these end products can be contaminated with TCDD.

HEXACHLOROPHENE

Hexachlorophene is used for the treatment of acne, the cleansing of intact skin around burns or wounds, pre-surgical washing, the cleansing of new-born infants, the control of staphylococcal diseases and as a preservative in the cosmetics industry (7). Ironically, the most common symptom of dioxin contamination in humans is a form of acne, called chloracne.

In the late 1960s some experiments were carried out on hexachlorophene by the United States Food and Drug Administration (FDA) (a division of the U.S. Department of Health, Education and Welfare established in 1906 to protect the public from unsafe food, drugs and cosmetics). The results indicated that the substance is absorbed through the skin and can cause significant brain damage (8). Before that time it had been known that only oral doses could be fatal. A dramatic illustration of the damage occurring as a result of absorption through the skin took place in France in 1972. Talcum powder, which was liberally applied to babies under their diapers, had been accidentally contaminated with 6% hexachlorophene. This caused 35 infant fatalities, as well as an outbreak of the symptoms of fever, lethargy, and severe convulsions (9).

In 1972, hexachlorophene was banned as a non-prescription drug in the U.S.. The FDA requires that a product containing

hexachlorophene be sold by prescription only, and that label-
ling state that it should not be used on premature babies. In
Canada, the same regulation was adopted under the Food and
Drug Act. The regulation is enforced by the Health Protection
Branch of Health and Welfare Canada (10).

It is suggested (7) that the medical industry would find
it quite easy to dispense with hexachlorophene altogether. A
new bactericide, chlorhexidene, has been cleared in the U.S.
It is effective as a surgical wash, skin cleanser and wound
sterilizer. Since the 1972 baby talc incident in France, the
risk associated with hexachlorophene baby washes has been
considered greater than the staphylococcal infections it was
used to prevent. Nurseries can rely on alcohol, either used
alone or with chlorhexidene.

2,4,5-T

2,4,5-trichlorophenoxyacetic acid is an agricultural
herbicide used as a weed killer to control woody brush. It was
originally developed in the military laboratories of the U.S.
and Britain and was the first herbicide sprayed for military
purposes (by Britain in Malaya in the early 1950s). Its full
potential in this capacity was not realized until the
Americans used it as a defoliant in Vietnam. Combined with
another herbicide 2,4-D (2,4-dichlorophenoxyacetic acid, see
2,4-D), it was internationally known as Agent Orange (11). It
was contaminated with TCDD at levels varying from 0.1 to 47
ppm (part per million), the average being 1.86 ppm (12). The
defoliation program, (known first as Operation Hades and later
as Operation Ranch Hand (13)), lasted from 1961 to 1970, with
1966 to 1969 being the most active years (12). Six percent of
South Vietnam was sprayed (12), an area equivalent to the
state of Massachusetts (13). It is estimated that 110 kg of
TCDD was unintentionally applied (12) and that 1 to 10% of the
Vietnamese population was exposed to TCDD by Operation Ranch
Hand (9). Its effect on people is a matter for debate, but
there have been consistent reports of child deaths, skin
rashes, diarrhea, abdominal pain and birth defects (11,17).

The use of Agent Orange as a defoliant must have been
seen as an atypical military use of herbicides which are
beneficial to agriculture. Agent Orange was a 50/50 mixture of

the n-butyl ester formulations of 2,4-D and 2,4,5-T. These are active and highly volatile alcohol-based formulations of the herbicides. Agent Orange was sprayed from planes in an undiluted form (i.e., 100% active ingredient) at an average rate of 32 pound per acre. If the spray plane was attacked, the spray apparatus was switched to a dump mode, increasing the application rate 10 times. Areas were sprayed repeatedly, some on a monthly basis, others weekly (13). By comparison, agricultural application of the less active and non-volatile amine-based 2,4-D to wheat, oats and barley is done once a season at a rate of 0.5 pound per acre. For general weed control, about one pound per acre is applied in spring or fall. In both cases, the herbicide is applied in a dilute form (14).

On Mar. 1, 1979, the U.S. Environmental Protection Agency (EPA) severely restricted the allowed uses of 2,4,5-T (15). The only uses remaining are for applications in rice fields and rangeland (16), where the herbicide kills weeds that are toxic and teratogenic to cattle (17). In Canada, 2,4,5-T was used to control roadside weeds and to suppress shrubs along railway and hydro rights-of-way (10). Although still registered for use in Canada, many provinces have banned or restricted its use. The Quebec Government decided against use of 2,4-D and 2,4,5-T in control of underbrush in forests (46). In Nova Scotia, however, the Supreme Court ruled that landowners protesting the use of that mixture failed to prove that there was a health hazard and awarded Nova Scotia Forest Industries Ltd. damages that could amount to $500,000 (49).

Subsequent to this court decision, the only North American manufacturer of 2,4,5-T, Dow Chemical announced a decision to abandon attempts to convince the U.S. EPA to remove restrictions placed on the sale of the chemical. Since it is not economical to produce 2,4,5-T for the smaller remaining markets, Canadian users of the herbicide must find a new herbicide or find an alternate supplier (53).

The maximum permissible level of TCDD in 2,4,5-T in Canada is 0.1 ppm under the Pest Control Products Act. Monitoring and regulation enforcement are carried out by the Pesticides Division of Agriculture Canada. The testing for dioxin in 2,4,5-T is done annually by the Laboratory Services

Division of Agriculture Canada (10). The Ontario Research
Foundation also has facilities for accurate analysis of
2,4,5-T and other pesticides (18).

The available alternatives to 2,4,5-T in the U.S. or
Europe are Amcide, Glyphosphate and Krenite, the latter being
available only in the U.S. and West Germany. All 3 are effective brushwood killers and are much less toxic than 2,4,5-
T. The production process for Amcide, which has been available
in Britain since the 1960s, does not present any of the potential hazards associated with trichlorophenol production. Even
though similar information is not available for Glyphosphate
and Krenite production, the EPA regards Krenite's manufacturers as conforming with accepted safety standards. Because
of its relatively low toxicity, its use is allowed even on
land adjacent to domestic water supplies. The principal disadvantage to the alternatives is cost. Not only are the herbicides' themselves more expensive than 2,4,5-T but also, in the
case of Amcide, labour costs are considerably higher: instead
of being absorbed through the leaves it must be applied to cut
surfaces on the plants (7).

There is considerable discussion as to whether the adverse health effects of 2,4,5-T are actually due to the substance itself or to the impurity, TCDD, which is often
associated with it. In 1969, the Bionetics Research Laboratories, under contract to the National Cancer Institute, studied
the teratogenicity of pesticides. The results of the study
have been used to show that 2,4,5-T is a teratogen (19).
However, it was found that the 2,4,5-T used was contaminated
with 30 ppm TCDD, and it has been reported (20) that purified
2,4,5-T containing 1 ppm TCDD is not teratogenic. The National
Academy of Sciences also conducted a study on the effect of
herbicides in South Vietnam. The study "could find no conclusive evidence of association between exposure to herbicides
and birth defects in humans" (17). This conclusion is supported in a report produced by the U.K. Forestry Commission
(22). Since the controversy is by no means settled, those
medical effects of TCDD which are known, are presented here.

HEALTH EFFECTS OF TCDD

TCDD residues accumulate in liver and fat cells. Clinical
symptoms associated with exposure to the chemical include:

atrophy of the kidney, degenerative changes of the liver,
ulceration of the stomach, haemorrhages of the gastrointestinal tract and other organs, and atrophy of the thymus
and lymphoid organs and tissues. Because of the difference
between being exposed over a long period of time and being
exposed all at once, occupational exposure can lead to
symptoms of systematic poisoning: cirrhosis of the liver;
damage to heart, kidney, spleen, central nervous system, and
pancreas; memory and concentration disturbances, emphysema and
depression (10). The skin disease chloracne (23) is caused by
the body trying to rid the poison through the skin (see PCB).
It is extremely contagious and can pass rapidly through a
worker's family, simply from contact with contaminated
clothing. The metabolization of dioxins has been found to be
slow (25) and represents a small fraction of that ingested
(26). In general most is excreted quickly or stored in fat,
then excreted gradually (26).

TCDD is a proven teratogen in animals, causing major
birth defects in the offspring of those exposed to it (6). In
Vietnam, birth defects such as cleft palates and kidney weaknesses were observed (9), but it cannot be stated conclusively
that the herbicide was responsible. TCDD is also listed (6) as
a suspected carcinogen. The substance causes malignant tumours
in rats (24), but there is still disagreement about the
carcinogenicity of dioxin to humans (51). U.S. Vietnam
veterans are however claiming damages for injuries they say
were caused by the dioxin in Agent Orange (29).

The most extensive human epidemiological data come from
workers in trichlorophenol plants who have been subjected to
TCDD exposure, usually as a result of releases due to excessively high reaction temperatures. This occurred in the U.S.
(1949, 1964), West Germany (1953), Holland (1963), and Britain
(1968). The commonest complaint was chloracne (4,9,23).

The event which has received most attention is the accident in Seveso in 1976 (1,2,3). The Seveso population is being
observed for the effects of dioxin exposure. Of the 730
pregnant women affected there, the 250 who were in the first
trimester applied for abortions, and the public called for a
reform of abortion laws. The Seveso women were given permission by the government, in the face of strong opposition from
the Vatican, to undergo the operation (7). It is known that

the less developed the organism, the more susceptible it is to toxic substances, so it is the children of Seveso who are being watched most carefully. A mass screening of 42,000 children of the area has revealed about 600 suspected and 134 confirmed cases of chloracne (30).

Except for a substantial number of animals that died or had to be killed to prevent the consumption of contaminated meat, no human fatalities have been conclusively caused by the TCDD release. In addition, 29 of the 30 fetuses from abortions following the accident were found on examination to be normal; the 30th was too badly damaged to tell (52). Some trends seem to be emerging, notably the increase in spontaeous abortions and impairment of the peripheral nervous system, but the epidemiological data from monitoring Seveso residents is incomplete and inconclusive (2). One Italian scientist estimated that another 10 years of monitoring would be needed to get any definitive results (2).

The ecological effects of the accident are yet to be determined. In Britain and the U.S., as well as in Italy, scientists have been engaged in decontamination research. Various methods were suggested: treatment with an emulsion of olive oil which acts as a hydrogen donor to facilitate the photoreduction of TCDD to a compound which is less harmful (31); incineration of contaminated soil which would mean removal of about 50 cm of soil (32); and bacterial degradation (32). The fate of some contaminated material from Seveso which was shipped away ended its scandalous journey in a French slaughterhouse (47) showing up weaknesses in toxic waste regulations in Europe. TCDD is disappearing from the topsoil, possibly due to degradation caused by sunlight. That found below the surface has a 10-year half-life in that particular soil (2). Zone A, the most contaminated area, was evacuated. Of those 700 residents, 300 had returned by 1981 (2).

Hoffman-LaRoche announced that the company will pay for all material damage due to the accident and it has established an $11 million fund to pay compensation to individuals and firms (30). Following 6 years of investigations, 5 people employed by Icmesa Chemical Co., and Givaudan S. A. were put on trial on charges of culpable negligence in disasters, injury; and omission of security against accidents. All 5 were convicted in Sept. 1983 (27).

TCDD IN THE ENVIRONMENT

Problems of TCDD contamination in trichlorophenol (TCP) and regulations on the TCDD content of commercial chemicals mean that the contamination must be reduced or the TCP must be discarded. Either way TCDD-contaminated waste requires disposal. The Love Canal was one such disposal site, containing 200 tonne of such waste (33). The acceptability of the Love Canal area for human habitation is still not determined as of 1983 (45). The Hyde Park site in Niagara Falls, New York, contains 3300 tonne of TCP, believed to be the largest known store of chemical (33).

Hyde Park and other sites are known to be leaking TCDD into the Great Lakes system, Lake Ontario in particular (25). These and other leaking waste repositories in the Niagara, New York, region are considered responsible for the TCDD detected in herring gull eggs on the Canadian side of the Great Lakes at levels ranging from 44 to 64 ng/kg (34). (One nanogram per kilogram (ng/kg) is equal to one part per trillion (ppt) or 0.001 part per billion (ppb)). Monitoring of fish found Lake Ontario to be the problem area. TCDD levels in sports fish were highest in the salmon at 20-25 ppt; in commercial fish, eels and smelt levels were less than 20 ppt (25). Recently, it was reported that 19 ppt TCDD was detected in a cadaver tissue sample from the Kingston area, the first such finding in Canada. The source is not known (35).

One part per trillion (ppt) is a very small amount; it is equal to one drop of water in 2000 railway tank-cars (36). Permissible levels of TCDD in fish have been set by Health and Welfare Canada at 20 ppt. This is based on an annual consumption of 13 pound of fish and provides a safety factor of 2000 from first measurable effects of teratogenicity and carcinogenicity (25). The U.S. Food and Drug Administration has developed a guideline of 50 ppt. For sport fish, the New York guideline is 10 ppt for 6 ounce per week consumption; Ontario's is 20 ppt for 4 ounce weekly (37).

The long-term leakage of TCDD from waste disposal sites in the Niagara, New York region poses a potential threat to the 5 million people who draw drinking water from Lake Ontario (38). TCDD has yet to be detected in North American drinking water (24,25). The detection limit in water is 0.01 ppt (25).

Several Canadian citizens' groups were granted "friend of the court" status by the Judge presiding over the Hyde Park landfill case. A settlement was reached Apr. 30, 1982. The view has been expressed that the clean-up plan to be implemented will only slow down the rate of chemical seepage (38).

There are other potential problems with dioxin residues. It was reported that traces of trichlorophenol were found in the dump of the Uniroyal plant in Elmira, Ontario, but no TCDD was detected (39). The spraying of waste oil contaminated by dioxins for dust control on roads and horse arenas in Missouri has led to numerous animal deaths and human illness (48). The problem of decontamination of up to 100 such sites in Missouri has not been solved (48). The EPA has decided to buy all the homes and businesses in the town affected worst, Times Beach. The plan is to raze the buildings but the eventual fate of the contaminated soil has not been decided upon (50).

In the early 1970s, TCDD and all the dioxin isomers were considered synthetic chemicals that resulted as unwanted contaminants from several chemical manufacturing processes. Dow Chemical's 1978 study, The Trace Chemistries of Fire, changed that view. Initially criticized (40), the study caused many researchers to examine the trace by-products of combustion. By 1981, other research studies supported Dow's hypothesis (25). Dioxins were found in incinerator fly ash, fireplace soot, motor vehicle exhaust systems and cigarette smoke. Along with dioxins there are other chlorinated aromatics: furans, which have one less oxygen than dioxin molecules; PCBs, which have no oxygen, but instead a direct bond across the phenyl rings; and polychlorinated terphenyls (5). Their production essentially depends on the type of material burned and the conditions of combustion (5). These trace chemicals are usually absorbed by particulate matter, which carry them into the environment. Thus, emission controls are important for large incinerators and power plants. The emission of dioxins varies widely, the concentrations ranging from 0.001 to 1100 ppb (24).

The National Research Council estimates that up to 1.5 tonne of dioxins enter the Canadian environment annually (5). The major source is pentachlorophenol which can contain dioxins as impurities and is used as a wood preservative by the forestry industry (5) (see PCP). The dioxin family consists of 2 monochloro, 2 dichloro, 14 trichloro, 22 tetra-chloro, 14 pentachloro, 10 hexachloro, 2 heptachloro, and one octachloro isomers (5). Toxicity of the dioxins is believed to vary substantially, but complete information is not available. Stability and lipophilicity are known to increase with the number of chlorines (5). Hence, concern about the health and environmental effects has tended to focus on the higher chlorinated ones, tetra through octa. It is suggested that the lower chlorinated dioxins may be more readily broken down by bacteria and sunlight (5). However, dioxins in landfills are not subject to these mechanisms.

None of the recent flurry of research into dioxins would be possible without the analytical technologies that have been developed in the past 3 decades. Methods include gas-liquid chromatography (41,42), mass spectrometry (43,42) and capilla-ry column gas-chromatography (42). Considerable advances have been made in analytical capabilities in recent years. The detection limits for TCDD have gone from 0.050 mg/kg in 1970 to 1 ng/kg in 1978, a factor of 50,000. Some researchers have reportedly advanced this limit to 100 femtograms/kg (1fg=0.000001 ng) (44). Needless to say, standardization of analytical procedures and extraction/preparation of samples is extremely important. The word used to describe the required cleanliness is "ultraclean". This type of analysis calls for highly skilled people and extensive capital investment. One problem impeding progress is producing pure compounds for use as calibration standards (42,43).

REFERENCES

1. "Le Nuage qui tue", Paris Match, Aug. 14, 1976.
   "Les enfants Martyrs de Seveso", ibid, Dec. 31, 1976.
2. Dagani, R., "Seveso: Five Years Later, Questions Remain", Chemical and Engineering News, June 29, 1981.
3. Jaubert, A., "Le poison de Seveso", La Recherche, 7(71), 868, 1976.
4. "Dioxin Report" Chemical and Engineering News, June 6, 1983.
5. "Poly-chlorinated Dibenzo-p-Dioxins: Criteria for Their Effects on Man and his Environment", National Research Council of Canada, Associate Committee on Scientific Criteria for Environmental Quality, NRCC No. 18574, Ottawa, 1981.
6. "Suspected Carcinogens: A Sourcebook of the Toxic Effects of Chemical Substances", E. J. Fairchild, Editor, Castle House Publications, 1978.
7. Hay, A., "Seveso: the Aftermath", Nature, 263, 538, 1976.
8. "After Seveso, What?", Comment, New Scientist, Aug. 12, 1976.
9. McGinty, L., "The Graveyard on Milan's Doorstep", ibid, Aug. 19, 1976.

10. Nichols, A., "Dioxin in Canada", A report prepared for the Science Council of Canada, Nov. 8, 1976.
11. "Vietnam Herbicide Controversy", Research Reporter, Chemistry, 47(6), 23, 1974. Norman, C. "Vietnam's Herbicide Legacy", Science, 219, 1196, 1983.
12. Que-Hee, S. S., and Sutherland, R. G., "The Phenoxyalkanoic Herbicides", Chemistry, Analysis and Environmental Pollution, Vol. I, CRC Press Inc., Boca Raton, Florida, 1981.
13. Whiteside, T., "The Withering Rain", E. P. Dutton & Co., Inc., New York, 1971.
14. "Guide to Chemical Weed Control, 1981", Ontario Ministry of Agriculture and Food, Publication 75.
15. "EPA Bans use of 2,4,5-T", Chemical and Engineering News, Mar. 5, 1979.
16. "Producers, Users Protest Ban of 2,4,5-T", Chemical and Engineering News, Mar. 19, 1979.
17. Cranston, R. S., "Claims False, Say Agrologist", Dow Canadian Insight Edition, 1(1), 3, 1978. "Agent Orange was Safe" New Scientist, Mar. 10, 1983.
18. "Pesticide Residue and Trace Contaminant Analysis", Ontario Research Foundation, Mississauga, Leaflet T-14.
19. Bryan, R., "Much is Taken, Much Remains", Duxbury Press, North Scituate, Mass., 1973.
20. Gribble, G. W., "TCDD. A Deadly Molecule", Chemistry, 47(2), 15, 1974.
21. "The 2,4,5-T Rumble--What is it All About?", Dow Canadian Insight Edition, 1(1), 9, 1978.
22. Hay, A., "Informing on 2,4,5-T", Nature, 269, 749, 1978.
23. "Chloracne: the Chemical Disease", New Scientist, Apr. 13, 1978.
24. "Second Annual Report on Carcinogens", U.S. Department of Health and Human Services, Dec., 1981.
25. Somers, E. and Douglas, V. M., "Dioxins and Related Compounds as Issues of International Concern", Paper for the International Symposium on Chlorinated Dioxins and Related Compounds, Arlington, Virginia, 1981.
26. "Digesting Dioxin", Sciquest, Feb. 1982.
27. "Dealing Escalates as Seveso Trial Opens", New Scientist, Apr. 21, 1983. "Dioxin Accident Trial Finds Defendants Guilty", Chemical and Engineering News, Oct. 3, 1983.
28. Hay, A., "Vietnam's Dioxin Problem", Nature 271, 597, 1978.
29. "Dioxin Poisons Vietnam Veterans", New Scientist, Apr. 13, 1978. "Lawyers Reveal Conspiracy of Silence on Dioxin", New Scientist, Aug. 4, 1983.
30. Walsh, J., "Seveso: The Questions Persist Where Dioxin Created a Wasteland", Science 197, 1064, 1977.
31. "Cleaning up Seveso: Science, Politics and Chaos", Research Reporter, Chemistry, 50(9), 21, 1977.
32. "Too Late to Clean up Seveso's Poisoned Land", New Scientist, Nov. 4, 1976.
33. Brown, M., "Laying Waste: The Poisoning of America by Toxic Chemicals", Washington Square Press, New York, 1981.
34. Ogilvie, D., "Dioxin Found in Great Lakes Basin", Ambio, 10(1), 1981.
35. "Dioxin Discovered in Human Tissue Test", The Globe and Mail, Toronto, June 25, 1982.
36. Baeder, D. L., "Chemical Waste: Fact and Perception ", Vital Speeches of the Day, 46, June 1, 1980.
37. "Report on Great Lakes Water Quality, 1981", International Joint Commission, Ottawa/Washington, D.C.
38. Vigod, T., "Hyde Park Landfill Settlement Ratified: Future of Niagara in Doubt", Canadian Environmental Law Association Newsletter, 7(3), June 1982.
39. "Plant Monitors its Toxic Time Bomb", Kitchener-Waterloo Record, Aug. 9, 1980.
40. Rawls, R. L., "Dow Finds Support, Doubt for Dioxin Ideas", Chemical and Engineering News, Feb. 12, 1979.

41. Considine, D. M., Editor-in-chief, "Chemical and Process Technology Encyclopedia", McGraw-Hill, 1974.

42. Personal Communication, Judith Lockwood, Farrington, Lockwood Company Limited, Ottawa, Aug. 20, 1982.

43. "Kirk-Othmer Encyclopedia of Chemical Technology", 2nd edition, Interscience Publishers, 1967.

44. "Polychlorinated Dibenzo-p-Dioxins: Limitations to the Current Analytical Techniques", National Research Council of Canada, Associate Committee on Scientific Criteria for Environmental Quality, NRCC No. 18576, Ottawa, 1981.

45. Sun, M. "Love Canal Is in Limbo Again", Science, 221, 136, 1983.

46. Drouin, L. "Aerial Spraying Plans Abandoned", The Citizen, Ottawa, June 16, 1983.

47. Norman, C. "The Embarrassing Odyssey of Seveso's Dioxin", Science, 220, 1362, 1983.

48. Sun M., "Missouri's Costly Dioxin Lesson", Science 219, 367, 1983.
Sun M., "Dioxin's Uncertain Legacy", Science 219, 468, 1983.

49. Steed, J., "Spray Unleashes a Forest of Fear", The Globe and Mail, Toronto, Nov. 26, 1983. "Homes, Land Saved in Herbicide Spraying Case", ibid, Dec. 10, 1983.

RECOMMENDED READING

The history of Seveso is discussed in a readable, quite complete manner, in French in references (1) and (3). The situation is updated in (2). Reference (20) is a good technical account of the formation and properties of TCDD. Reference (25) surveys the health, environmental and regulatory aspects of the dioxins issue. A summary of the trace chemistries of fire theory can be found in (5), along with an exhaustive survey of the literature. A good general reference on dioxins is the special issue of Chemical and Engineering News (4) published by the American Chemical Society. Copies of a recent report "Dioxins in Canada: The Federal Approach" are available from the Environmental Protection Service, Environment Canada.

FENITROTHION

Fenitrothion is an insecticide which is used worldwide on a variety of crops. In Canada it is applied by aerial spraying to control the spruce budworm, but there are claims that the formulated spray mixture is harmful to humans.

DEVELOPMENT, PROPERTIES, USES, APPLICATION AND ACTION

Fenitrothion is one of many organophosphorus insecticides which were developed for use as alternatives to organochloride compounds, such as DDT. The synthesis of the first organophosphate occurred in 1854 but, as with DDT, its potential as an insecticide was not realized until the late 1930s (1). In 1959 it was introduced as an experimental insecticide by the Sumitomo Chemical Company in Japan (2). There are now about 40 organophosphorus insecticides available commercially; the most common in Canada are malathion, fenthion, phosphamidon, ronnel, Abate, diazinon and fenitrothion. Fenitrothion is also known as sumithion, folithion and novathion (3). At room temperature, it is a yellowish brown liquid with an unpleasant odour, insoluble in water but soluble in most organic solvents (2).

Fenitrothion is a broad spectrum insecticide, meaning it is toxic to a wide variety of insects (2). It has a low mammalian toxicity compared to other organophosphorus compounds (2) and a rapid degradation rate compared with organochlorine insecticides. However, organophosphates in general have a higher initial toxicity than organochlorines and must be handled with care to avoid exposure (4). The use of fenitrothion as a pre-harvest treatment in agriculture is worldwide on a variety of crops such as rice, wheat, barley, vegetables, cotton, cocoa, tea, coffee and fruits, for the control of insects including borers, fruit flies, mites, lady beetles, caterpillars and soft scale insects. In Canada, fenitrothion is limited to the following uses: on apples to control plum curculio and tarnished plant bug; and in woodlands and forests to control fall cankerworms, jack pine budworms, sawflies, spruce budworms and eastern and western hemlock loopers (3).

In some parts of the world, fenitrothion is used in

post-harvest treatment of grains such as rice, wheat and barley against weevils and beetles, and it has public health uses in controlling malaria and in killing flies, cockroaches and bedbugs. Finally, because of its low mammalian toxicity, fenitrothion is a useful veterinary insecticide for the control of lice, flies, mites and ticks on domestic animals and poultry (2,5).

The key to the insecticidal action of fenitrothion is its phosphorus content, which acts as a neurotoxin, causing poisoning of nerve endings. Symptoms of this poisoning are hyperactivity, tremors, paralysis and eventual death by respiratory failure (4). Stronger organophosphates are toxic to man as well, and have been developed as "nerve gases" for military purposes (4).

ENVIRONMENTAL EFFECTS

Fenitrothion used in Canadian forests has been targeted chiefly at the spruce budworm, the larva of which feed on the new shoots of spruce and fir trees, mainly mature ones (2). In nature, the spruce budworm is useful in that it kills off old trees, clearing room for new ones (6). The main argument for fighting the spruce budworm is that the vital forest industry would suffer if the budworm were not controlled. Fenitrothion is used because it has been shown to kill the spruce budworm, and because it is of low hazard to wildlife. Fenitrothion is used only in New Brunswick and Quebec at present (7), and since the New Brunswick government started using it in 1969, there have been concerns about the biological side effects of fenitrothion.

It has generally been found that fenitrothion begins to degrade immediately upon application, although some reports (8) have suggested that fenitrothion can persist in the environment for 2 years. It has been recommended (9) that more attention be given to degradation products of fenitrothion, particularly those which, because of their structure, are potential carcinogens. Another way fenitrothion degrades is through its metabolism by plants and animals. The resulting by-products are mostly non-toxic, with the exception of a by-product called fenitrooxon, which because it is itself highly unstable, does not damage the biota (10).

Another concern is that environmental conditions can result in certain areas receiving high concentrations of sprayed fenitrothion (or any other sprayed insecticide). Because the cloud of sprayed insecticide can be carried in a bundle by wind, deposits can vary from 0.3 to 12 ounce of active ingredient per acre. Most of the deposit is intercepted by the upper canopy, with possibly not more than 5% reaching the forest floor (9); wildlife inhabiting the upper canopy will be exposed to more of the pesticide.

Flora are very vulnerable to fenitrothion, but when the pesticide is applied at the recommended rate, flora protected by the crown canopy do not appear to be affected (9). With insects such as spiders and flies, it appears that for a few days after spraying, there is a high mortality rate, but that in most cases, the species recover their population numbers in the next generation (11). There is concern that pollinating insects are adversely affected by fenitrothion, and because pollinators are important to the blueberry crop of New Brunswick, an alternative insecticide, trichlorfon, is applied in forest areas surrounding blueberry fields (8,10,12).

Studies have also been done on the higher animals. Studies of frog, toad and salamander populations have indicated that fenitrothion is not lethal at conventional dosage (10,12). Salmon, trout and crayfish have also been shown to survive application, but because fenitrothion temporarily reduces food supplies by killing aquatic insects, some fish may show lower growth rates for about a month after spraying (9,10). It is generally agreed that fenitrothion is only toxic to mammals at high dosages (10,12), and it has been observed that mammals quickly learn to avoid food sprayed with fenitrothion (9). Thus fenitrothion is thought to be one of the safer pesticides when used correctly, but there is concern that the effects of the solvents, emulsifiers and diluents are not understood (13). Also, it has been recommended (9) that the effect of perennial application of fenitrothion on flora and fauna be studied further.

EFFECT ON HUMANS

The medical debate surrounding fenitrothion began in 1972 when a 10-year-old boy died from Reye's Syndrome. The illness, which was first defined in 1963 by Dr. R. Reye at the Royal

Alexandria Hospital for Children in Sydney, Australia, almost exclusively attacks children, usually following some minor viral infection. The symptoms are first observed when, as the child is beginning to recover, uncontrollable vomiting and high fever develop followed by central nervous system disorders ranging from irritability and depression, through hysteria to convulsions and coma. With early diagnosis and treatment (dialysis, exchange transfusion and assisted ventilation) survival rates of 34-75% can be achieved, although in a significant number of cases there is brain damage. If the illness is not treated, the mortality rate may reach 100%. Although the progression of the syndrome is not clearly understood, it is known that two primary disorders are involved: swelling of the brain and widespread fatty changes in the liver, heart, muscles and kidneys (14).

The cause of Reye's Syndrome is not known but research indicates that it could be one or a combination of agents. There is evidence that viral infections such as Influenza B and chicken pox play important roles in producing the syndrome. A second suggestion is that children suffering from the illness have an inborn error of metabolism that makes them more susceptible to viruses or toxic substances. Finally it is possible that an external toxic agent is a contributing factor to Reye's Syndrome. Several compounds have been implicated; warfarin (a rat poison), fungal toxins (aflatoxins), and pesticides. Most recently, it has been reported, but the evidence is not conclusive, that with children recovering from influenza, chicken pox and other viral infections, Reye's Syndrome has a greater likelihood of occurring if the child receives ASA (known as aspirin) (15).

The relations between Reye's Syndrome and pesticides have been studied chiefly by Dr. J. Crocker and colleagues of Dalhousie University, Halifax, Nova Scotia. The research team examined a number of cases of Reye's Syndrome and carried out experiments on mice to see if they could simulate the illness using the chemicals involved in the spray program. The report (16) suggested that, in mice, the insecticide may have a priming effect to increase viral susceptibility and it cautiously concluded that "the part that this interaction (between insecticide and virus) played in the Reye's-like disease of the children that stimulated this work is still hypothetical but it is now a theory which is chemically and virologically possible" (16).

The result of this publication was that the controversy surrounding fenitrothion in anti-budworm spraying programs focused on human health; citizens groups launched protests to governments, particularly in Eastern Canadian provinces. Governments in turn tried to produce sufficient data to assure the public that the spraying programs were safe. Numerous reports on the subject appeared, and still do appear, in the press. One article states, "Stories about the spruce budworm spray program usually begin with the death of children and this one is going to be no exception". The article then details the 1979 painful death of a boy suffering from Reye's Syndrome and proceeds to link the disease to the spraying program (6).

A more recent study by a Dalhousie University research group (17) has found that in Atlantic Canada, the populace of neighbouring unsprayed forests has a significantly lower incidence of Reye's Syndrome than the populace of the sprayed areas. The report of the Brunswick Task Force on the Environment and Reye's Syndrome reached a different conclusion (18). It said that in the published report of the Dalhousie study, only 1 of the 5 patients described was a resident of New Brunswick; 2 were from Nova Scotia and 2 were from Michigan -- areas where regular extensive forest spraying has not been conducted. As well, the Task Force conducted its own study, and concluded that there was no basis, at the present time, for concluding that a relationship existed between aerial forestry spray programs and Reye's Syndrome in New Brunswick. However, although the Task Force's own data did not reveal that any emulsifier used in New Brunswick increased the incidence of Reye's Syndrome, it recommended that one of the emulsifiers (a chemical used in formulating the spray mixture) Atlox 3409, should be replaced because animal studies have made it suspect (18).

ALTERNATIVE METHODS OF SPRUCE BUDWORM CONTROL

Other than spraying with chemical insecticides there are 2 alternative methods of controlling the spruce budworm. These are biological control and forest management.

Biological control includes the propagation of disease-causing organisms such as viruses, bacteria, microsporida and fungi; manipulation of parasites and predators; and

interference with the behaviour and physiology of the insect
(19,20). Provided that enough is known about their effects on
other species, disease organisms could be useful in controlling pests. Generally viruses have been the most successful
agents, but only bacteria (Bacillus thuringiengis, Bt) have
been successfully used in large biological spraying programs
against the budworm. The Quebec Government is planning to
spray 500,000 hectares (1.2 million acres) with Bt in 1984
(26). The use of viruses, microsporida and fungi are all
limited at present because they do not cause a sufficiently
high mortality rate and they are difficult to test on a large
scale.

Parasites and predators can sometimes be introduced as
useful methods of control but so far attempts to naturalize
exotic insects for budworm control have failed (19). The
method has recently received attention from home gardeners
trying to control aphids with ladybugs or praying mantis.

It is also possible to develop chemicals which will alter
the spruce budworm's behaviour. For example, there is a
synthetic pheromone (sex attractant) which simulates the scent
emitted by the female moth trying to attract a mate. If the
environment is saturated with this or similar chemicals, then
the male budworm may get confused, and breeding may be
prevented (21).

Good forest management may be another tool in fighting
the spruce budworm (22). The idea is to make the forest less
susceptiple to the budworm. Characteristics of a forest which
make it susceptible include a high percentage of fir, red
spruce and white spruce trees, a large continuous area of
susceptible trees, and a considerable amount of "sunlight"
foliage (i.e., needles growing in full sunlight) (22). Forest
management thus requires a shift in the type of trees grown,
making it a slow, labour-intensive, and thus, expensive
method. New Brunswick continues to use fenitrothion in its
battle with the budworm since it considers it the only viable
short-term option (25).

The spruce budworm does not respect international
boundaries, and in light of this the Canada-United States
Spruce Budworm Program (CANUSA) was established in 1977. Run
jointly by the forest services of the Canadian and American

governments, CANUSA coordinates research, development and application efforts in order to provide forest management alternatives for controlling the budworm (21). CANUSA has set several goals in its fight against the budworm, including evaluation of budworm population and damage, greater knowledge about the host trees being attacked, evaluation of the economic impacts of the budworm, and evaluation of the methods of control (23). This emphasizes the need for research to protect the forests and to resolve the conflict of the needs of man and the health of the ecosystem.

REFERENCES

1. Bryan, R., "Much is Taken, Much Remains", Duxbury Press, North Scituate, Mass., 1973.
2. Krehm, M. S., "Fenitrothion", Chemical Control Research Institute, Ottawa, Information Report CC-X-39, 1973.
3. Information from Pesticides Division, Agriculture Canada, Dec., 1980.
4. Pryde, L. T., "Environmental Chemistry; an Introduction", Cummings Publishing Company, Menlo Park, California, 1973.
5. Fontaine, R. E. and Pull, J. H., "Malaria Control: Field Testing of a New Insecticide", World Health Organization Chronicle, Mar. 1977.
6. Thurston, H., "The Enemy Above", Harrowsmith, Apr./May, 1982.
7. Interview with Mr. E. Caldwell, Agriculture Canada, July 29, 1982.
8. Lesiak, C., "Spruce Budworm Spraying", Canadian Consumer, Feb. 1978.
9. "Fenitrothion: the Effects of Its Use on Environmental Quality and Its Chemistry", Associate Committee on Scientific Criteria for Environmental Quality, National Research Council, Ottawa, NRCC No. 14104, 1975.
10. Varty, I. W., "Forest Spraying and Environmental Integrity", Forestry Chronicle, 51(4), 12, 1975.
11. "Fenitrothion: The Long-Term Effects of Its Use in Forest Ecosystems. Current Status", Associate Committee on Scientific Criteria for Environmental Quality, National Research Council, Ottawa, NRCC No. 15389, 1977.
12. Buckner, C, J., "The Biological Side-Effects of Fenitrothion in Forest Ecosystems", Chemical Control Research Institute, Ottawa, Report CC-X-67, 1974.
13. Pollack, J. D., Burech, D. and Hamparian, V. V., "The Role of Chemicals in Potentiating Viral Infections and Reye's Syndrome", Not dated.
14. "Forest Spray Program and Reye's Syndrome", Report of the panel convened by the Government of New Brunswick, Apr. 1976.
15. "Aspirin Products Must Carry Warning Label" Chemical and Engineering News, June 14, 1982.
16. Crocker, J. F. S., Ozere, R. L., Rozee, K. R., Digout, S. C. and Hutzinger, O., "Insecticide and Viral Interaction as a Cause of Fatty Visceral Changes and Encephalopathy in the Mouse", The Lancet, Vol. II (7871), 22, 1974.
17. Rozee, K. R. et al, "Is a Compromised Interferon Response an Etiologic Factor in Reye's Syndrome?" Canadian Medical Journal, 126, 1982.
18. "First Report", New Brunswick Task Force on the Environment and Reye's Syndrome, Apr. 28, 1982.
19. Miller, C. A. and Varty, I. W., "Biological Methods of Spruce Budworm Control", Forestry Chronicle, 51(4), 16, 1975. "Biological Control of Forest Insects and Pests", Update, Environment Canada, 4, 8, 1983.

20. Weatherston, J. and Retnakaram, A., "The Potential of Autocides and Microorganisms as Ecologically Acceptable Agents for the Regulation of Spruce Budworm Infestations", J. Environ. Qual., 4(3), 294, 1975.
21. "The Spruce Budworm Program in the East", Canada-United States Spruce Budworm Program, Date unknown.
22. Baskerville, G. L., "Spruce Budworm--The Answer Is Forest Management--Or Is It?", Forestry Chronicle, 51(4), 23, 1975.
23. "CANUSA Program Activity Schedule: Master Plan for Coordination and Cooperation", CANUSA, Oct., 1981.
24. Varty, I. W., "Credibility of the NRCC 'Current Status' Report, 1977, on Fenitrothion", Canadian Forestry Service, Department of Fisheries and the Environment, Information Report M-X-79, 1977.
25. Mail, P., "N.B. Unveils $14-Million Spray Plan", St. John Telegraph Journal, Apr. 14, 1983.
26. "Quebec to Battle Bugs with Biological Spray", The Globe and Mail, Toronto, Dec. 19, 1983.

RECOMMENDED READING

The NRC Associate Committee for Environmental Quality reports (References (9), and (11) together with reference (2)) give thorough discussions although reference (11) has been seriously criticized (24). References (10), (19) and (22) are available in a reprint which is interesting to read. Reference (12) is a useful account of the biological effects of fenitrothion.

FLUORIDES

Industrial processes release fluorides into the environment, damaging plants and animals. Meanwhile, the controversy over the fluoridation of drinking water continues.

Fluorides, which are compounds containing the element fluorine, occur naturally and are widely distributed in the earth's crust. Fluorine is found in 3 important minerals; fluorspar, cryolite and fluorapatite. Fluorspar is mined chiefly for use in steel production to increase the fluidity of the slags. Cryolite is used in the production of aluminum. Although cryolite used to be obtained from large natural deposits in Greenland, it is now produced synthetically. Fluorapatite is used in the manufacture of phosphate fertilizers (1).

There are many other uses of compounds containing fluorine. These include: etching (for example, etching to produce the frosted inner surface of light bulbs using hydrofluoric acid); the separation of isotopes of uranium hexafluoride; the production of special glasses, such as the enamel coating on metals; the production of high temperature plastics such as Teflon (registered trademark); the manufacture of fluorocarbons used in air conditioners, refrigerators and spray cans (see Fluorocarbons); the manufacture of brick, tile, pottery and cement; petroleum refining, where hydrogen fluoride is used as a catalyst in the production of high octane gasolines; metal casting and welding; the manufacture of pesticides; the manufacture of phosphors for cathode ray tubes; electroplating; leather tanning; and protection against tooth decay (1,2,3).

All of these processes result in the release of varying amounts of fluorides into the environment (1). Of the 16,000 tonne of fluorides released into the atmosphere by Canadian industry in 1972, about 57% came from primary aluminum production, 17% from phosphate fertilizer and elemental phosphorus plants, 16% from primary iron and steel production, 6% from power generation, and the rest from industrial and commercial fuel combustion, solid waste incineration, and miscellaneous industries (14). Fluoride emissions can be a transboundary problem as well. In 1977 it was reported that fluoride air pollution from an aluminum production company in New York State was causing severe adverse effects to animals and vegetation at an Indian reserve on Cornwall Island in the St. Lawrence River (5).

Fluorides can also be released into the environment through aqueous discharges and solid wastes (4) as indicated in the following figure.

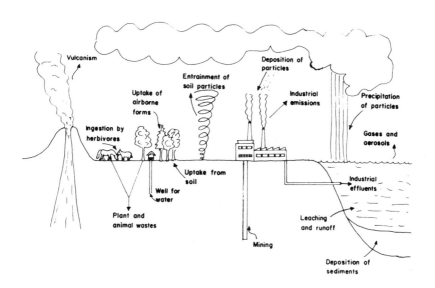

Fluorides in the Environment. After reference (1).

It has been calculated that if all North American plants discharge fluorides into the water at the 14 kg (kilogram) per tonne rate reported in a 1972 study, then the total discharge by the aluminum industry would exceed 63,000 tonne, or about 4 times the amount discharged into the atmosphere (4). Large quantities of fluorides are used as landfill or are buried. This practice is generally considered to be non-polluting, but there have been some reports of contamination of surface and

ground-waters by fluorides from solid wastes (4). Soils can
become contaminated with fluorides from air-borne emissions,
and from fertilizers containing fluorides (4).

Industry can limit fluoride emissions with control devices such as water scrubbers, spray towers, chemisorption
devices, electrostatic precipitators and bag filters, but the
reclaimed fluorides must still be disposed of or stored. In
addition to burying the reclaimed fluorides, companies can
store it in retaining ponds or convert it to useful materials
such as those used for fluoridation of water supplies (2).
There is also a natural background level of fluorides in the
environment provided by volcanoes, geysers, erosion and
leaching (2) as shown in the figure.

EFFECT OF FLUORIDES ON PLANTS AND ANIMALS

Plants absorb fluorides from the soil via roots and from
the air via breathing pores or stomata; however, the specific
mechanism of its actions is not clear (2). The fluorides can
reach the plants from industrial emissions, either in particle
or gaseous form, or from applied uses of fluorides in insecticides or fertilizers (2). Once absorbed, fluorides can
accumulate in both terrestrial and aquatic plants (4). Fluorides can be transported by plants to the tip or leaf margin,
resulting in a yellowing, and eventual browning of the leaf.
An excess intake of fluorides by plants can result in poor
growth and premature fruit drop because fluorides inhibits
enzymes which are active in plant metabolism.

Some plants convert toxic levels of inorganic fluorides
to organic fluorides. These new fluorides are non-toxic to
plants but toxic when ingested by man or animals. One of these
organic fluorides, fluorocitrate, inhibits an energy-yielding
biochemical reaction involved in respiration. Thus, where
levels of inorganic fluorides of 40 ppm (part per million) may
be permissible in forage, the level of organic fluorides
tolerable would be much lower (2).

Cattle are the animals most often affected by fluoride
pollution, their major source of the chemical being high-
fluoride vegetation which when ingested in concentrations
exceeding 40 ppm can lead to fluorosis. Symptoms include
abnormalities in permanent teeth, osseous lesions, lameness

and loss of appetite, which result in decreased weight gain
and milk yield (1). Fluorides can accumulate in and have toxic
effects on other animal life as well, including fish, bees,
and a variety of other insects.

The health effects of fluorides on plants and animals
have been observed on Cornwall Island, Ontario. In 1959,
the Reynolds Metals Company in New York state began operations
next to Cornwall Island, part of the St. Regis Indian Reserve
(6). It was 3 years later that the first signs of cattle
disease appeared on the island. Cattle became so lame that
they lay down on pasture to eat, then crawled to the next spot
to eat lying down. With increasing age, the animals had difficulty drinking cold water. Pregnancy, delivery, and support of
calves became increasingly difficult. By 1971, the majority of
the farmers had switched from dairy to beef cattle. Studies in
the mid and late 1970s showed that the cattle had abnormal
fluoride levels in urine and bones. Vegetation was also affected. It was reported that on Cornwall Island, adverse effects
on plants included contamination of forage, garden vegetables
and farm crops, and damage to sensitive plant life (5). In
Apr., 1980, the Canadian government set up a study group to
determine the health effects on the inhabitants of their
exposure to fluorides, mercury, Mirex, and PCBs (7).

EFFECT ON HUMANS

The 3 main sources of fluorides are water, food and air.
It has been established that on average food contributes at
least 0.2 mg (milligram) of fluorides to the daily intake,
water contributes an amount depending on its fluoride concentration and volume consumed (usually about one milligram per
litre in fluoridated water). Air contributes amounts varying
from about 0.01 mg to 5 mg (for a person working in an atmosphere containing fluorides (1)). Cigarettes may be another
significant source of fluoride intake by humans. The average
American-made cigarette, according to one study, contains 0.16
mg fluorides.

The fatal dose of fluorides is difficult to establish.
From autopsy results, it has been claimed (1) that the small-
est absorbed lethal dose of fluorides is 105 mg for a 65 kg
person, although this is actually the amount of fluorides
remaining in body tissues at death. Symptoms of poisoning are

abdominal pain, diarrhea and vomiting, painful rib spasms and effects on the nervous system (1).

Long-term exposure to fluorides, that is, its chronic effect, has been blamed for an increased incidence of mongolism and a variety of vague symptoms such as headache, nausea, loss of weight, bone abnormalities such as osteosclerosis, and kidney and thyroid injury (1). There are disputed claims that fluorides are carcinogenic (8). Contrary to the findings of a U.S. study, a 1977 Health and Welfare Canada study could find no difference in death rates from all types of cancer between fluoridated and non-fluoridated water in Canadian municipalities (9). Generally it is thought that adequate dietary supplies of calcium, magnesium, and vitamin C are important factors in man's ability to tolerate long-term exposure to fluorides (2).

Recently, there have been concerns that the level of fluoride intake by humans is too high (10). There is evidence that people with kidney problems have a particular susceptibility to long-term health effects of fluoride ingestion at levels encountered in city life (11). There is concern that the modern-day tendency towards convenience beverages and foods ("just add water") is elevating the intake of fluorides from water supplies. And children who eat fluoride toothpaste "just like candy" (11) may be accumulating too much fluoride.

Purposeful ingestion of fluorides began with the fluoridation of drinking water after it had been noticed that, in cities where the concentration of natural fluorides was unusually high, the incidence of tooth decay was lower than average. It was found that the presence of fluorides was particularly effective in preventing tooth decay in young children. Widespread fluoridation followed this finding, and the fluoride concentration in drinking water was elevated to about one ppm (12). Fluorides act by chemically reacting with a calcium compound in teeth. The reaction makes the compound less likely to react with decaying food (12). Excessive amounts of fluorides, however, may damage teeth; for example, at relatively low doses such as 2 ppm, mottling or discolouration may occur on the surface of the teeth, and at higher doses the structure of the tooth may be affected. Both these effects occur only when excess fluoride is ingested as the teeth calcify, i.e., in children up to the age of 8 (1). There is still controversy regarding the fluoridation of drinking water, however (14).

The Canadian Guidelines for Drinking Water Quality (1978) specify a maximum acceptable fluoride concentration of 1.5 milligram per litre. Air quality standards for work areas specify threshold limit values (average workplace concentrations for an 8-hour day) in the U.S. of 0.1 ppm for fluorine gas and 3 ppm for hydrogen fluoride, with different values for the other fluorine-containing compounds (1). The Ontario Occupational Health Guideline for hydrogen fluoride in air is 3 ppm.

REFERENCES

1. "Biologic Effects of Atmospheric Pollutants. Fluorides", Committee on Biologic Effects of Atmospheric Pollutants, National Academy of Sciences, Washington D.C.,1971.
2. Marier, J.R. and Rose, D., "Environmental Fluoride", National Research Council of Canada, Ottawa, NRC Publication No. 12, 226, Dec. 1971.
3. Johnson, L.C. in "Fluorine Chemistry", Vol. 4, Eds. H.C. Hodge and F.A. Smith, Academic Press, New York, 1965.
4. "Environmental Fluoride 1977", National Research Council of Canada, Ottawa, NRC Publication No. 16081, 1977.
5. "Fluoride Pollution Hits Indians' Farms Close to U.S. Plant", The Globe and Mail, Toronto, Aug. 29, 1977.
6. Krook, L. and Maylin, S., "Industrial Fluoride Pollution", Cornell University, 1979.
7. "The St. Regis Health Study: What it is, What's Being Done, How It's Being Done." The St. Regis Health Study, Cornwall, Ontario.
8. "Cancer-Fluoridated Water Link Disputed", The Ottawa Journal, June 13, 1977.
9. "Fluoridation and Cancer", Health and Welfare Canada, 77-EHD-18, 1977.
10. Smith, G., "Fluoridation - Are the Dangers Resolved?", New Scientist, May 5, 1983.
11. Marier, J., "Comments on Magnesium Intake and Fluoride Intake in the Modern-Day World", Proc. Finn. Dent. Soc.,1980 and interview with Dr. John Marier, July 13, 1982.
12. Jones, M.M., Metterville, J.T., Johnston, D.O. and Wood, J.L., "Chemistry, Man, and Society", Second edition, W.B. Saunders Company, Philadelphia, 1976.
13. Groth, E., "Science and the Fluoridation Controversy", Chemistry 49(4), 5, 1976.
14. "Town Stops Adding Fluoride to Water", The Citizen, Ottawa, Apr. 16, 1983.

RECOMMENDED READING

References (1) and (4) are thorough accounts, with exhaustive bibliographies, of all aspects of fluorides. Reference (2) is an interesting review of "environmentally-relevant scientific literature". For a more detailed discussion of the fluoridation of drinking water, see references (10) and (13).

FLUOROCARBONS

In the early 1970s, it was realized that fluorocarbon propellents in spray cans might deplete the Earth's "ozone shield" and thus cause severe climatic changes.

During World War II, U.S. soldiers were spared discomfort and loss of life from sickness because of the appearance of a "bug bomb", a portable aerosol insecticide with a dispenser made from 2 shell cases welded together. These first aerosols were heavy, cumbersome and expensive (1). However, technological improvements made aerosol sprays attractive to the consumer so that by 1975, the Canadian aerosol industry employed thousands, and added about $90 million to the Canadian economy (2). Many of the aerosols used fluorocarbons as propellents. In 1980, the use of non-essential aerosols in Canada was phased out by law (3).

The reason for this phaseout is usually explained by the statement "...fluorocarbons may harm the ozone layer". An understanding of this statement requires blending together of many aspects: the properties of fluorocarbons, their use in aerosols, the composition of the atmosphere, the effect of fluorocarbons on the ozone layer, the importance of any changes in the ozone layer, some information regarding the economics of the fluorocarbon industry and possible substitutes.

FLUOROCARBONS AND THEIR USE IN AEROSOLS

In the 1920s the refrigeration industry was trying to find replacements for the toxic and corrosive compounds then in use as refrigerants, sulphur dioxide, SO_2 (see Sulphur Dioxide) and ammonia, NH_3. Almost by accident it was found that difluorochloromethane, CF_2Cl_2, was non-corrosive, had the correct thermal properties and had a very low toxicity. By 1929, Kinetic Chemicals Incorporated (a joint venture of DuPont and General Motors) was operating an experimental plant, and in 1931 began producing fluorocarbons under the trade name Freon (Registered Trademark). In 1949, DuPont took over the manufacture of Freons after which a number of other companies entered the market. There are now several manufacturing fluorocarbons, although DuPont is still the largest (4).

The use of the name "Fluorocarbons" to describe the Freons is really erroneous. Properly, the compounds should be called chlorofluorocarbons (CFCs). The ones used as propellents are mainly chlorofluoromethanes (CFMs), so-called as they contain only one carbon atom per molecule. Here, fluorocarbons (FCs) will be used synonymously with the other 2 terms. The industry has developed a system of nomenclature for its fluorocarbon products, according to which $CFCl_3$ is FC-11 and CF_2Cl_2 is FC-12. There are many other fluorocarbons in use, but the concern here is mainly with these 2.

Fluorocarbons in general are odourless, non-flammable compounds of low toxicity, miscible with organic solvents, with low solubility in water and possessing low boiling points (1). FC-11 has a normal boiling point of 24 deg. C; it is the least expensive of the CFMs and next to FC-12, is the most widely used. Its low vapour pressure (one atm (atmosphere) at 24 deg. C) makes it impractical to use alone so the most common propellent use is in a 50:50 mixture with FC-12. It is an excellent solvent and is useful where propellent compatibility could be a problem.

FC-12 was the first CFM to be used as an aerosol propellent. It has a low boiling point (-30 deg. C) and hence a high vapour pressure (about 5 atm) at room temperature. This compound is the second cheapest of the CFMs and the most widely used. It is stable to hydrolysis which means that it will not decompose in water and so can be used with water-based products. It has, however, too high a vapour pressure to be used alone and is thus generally used in conjunction with some organic solvent with a low vapour pressure or a CFC such as FC-11 or FC-114. FC-114 is also used as a propellent, but not so extensively as FCs 11 and 12. It is somewhat more expensive than the former two but has very little odour and hence is often used in perfume and cologne aerosol formulations.

Although fluorocarbons were initially developed for use as refrigerant fluids, their physical and chemical properties have made them useful for other applications, e.g., in fire extinguishers (5), as blowing agents for foamed plastics and thermal insulation (6). The main use of fluorocarbons was as propellents in aerosols. In 1974, only 28% of FC production in the U.S. was used for air conditioning and refrigeration, while 49% was used for aerosol products (6).

Much of aerosol technology preceded the development of
FCs in the late 1920s. Already in 1862, a patent was granted
to J. D. Lynde for a valve with a dip tube for the discharge
of aerated liquid from a bottle (7). Various chemicals including methyl chloride, CH_3Cl, carbon dioxide, CO_2, or ace-
tone, CH_3COCH_3 were suggested at various times for the aerosol
agents. In the 1930s, the properties making fluorocarbons good
refrigerants were soon recognized as making them good propellents too, so patents were issued for the use of these compounds as propellents in fire extinguishers. It was realized
that the combination of the propellent with several of the
fire fighting agents used produced a system with a constant
pressure during the unit's lifetime (i.e., did not need re-
charging with propellent).

The first aerosols for consumer use came out in 1947 when
an estimated 4.3 million cans were produced, mostly insecticide. The first "personal product" in aerosol form was a
hairspray which appeared in 1950. "Personal products" became
by far the largest sector of the aerosol market, comprising
49.8% of that market in 1973 (8). Products which used fluorocarbon propellents included deodorants, hairsprays, perfumes,
and pharmaceuticals, household goods such as polishes, waxes,
laundry products, some cooking products like cookware sprays,
insecticides, automobile and pet products (6).

There is some question regarding the danger of the use of
CFMs due to human toxicity. Ever since the introduction of the
product PAM (Registered Trademark), a spray-on cooking oil in
1968, there were deaths attributed to inhalation of it's
vapours, possibly in combination with other ingredients.

THE COMPOSITION OF THE ATMOSPHERE AND THE EFFECT
OF FLUOROCARBONS ON THE OZONE LAYER

During the decades of increasing use of fluorocarbons, no
serious thought was given to the eventual fate of the fluorocarbons emitted from aerosols, fire extinguishers, or scrapped
refrigeration and air conditioning equipment. In 1971,
measurements of FC-11 concentrations in the atmosphere over
Ireland were reported (9). These measurements were made in the
lower atmosphere or troposphere (see Figure next page).

This raised the curiosity of F. Rowland and M.J. Molina, 2 chemists at the University of California at Irvine who began research to determine what became of the lighter CFCs (FCs 11 and 12) after they were released to the atmosphere. Their conclusions, published in 1974 (10) catapulted the fluorocarbon and aerosol industries into a tremendous controversy. It was suggested that there was no natural "sink" (removal process) for the fluorocarbons in the troposphere because of their "desirable" qualities (unreactive, insoluble in water). The lighter fluorocarbons, FC-11 and FC-12 were slowly drifting up into the upper atmosphere (the stratosphere, see Figure), where they were being bombarded by ultraviolet light (UV) of sufficient energy to cause them to break up. Such UV radiation is not present in the troposphere because the stratosphere filters it out. The product of this "photolysis" then catalyzed a reaction (shown in the Figure), the result of which lowered the total ozone concentration in the stratosphere. A lowering in the amount of ozone would decrease the UV filtering ability of the stratosphere, and would thus result in a greater in cidence of skin cancers among humans and have unknown worldwide consequences for the whole ecosphere and for the climate.

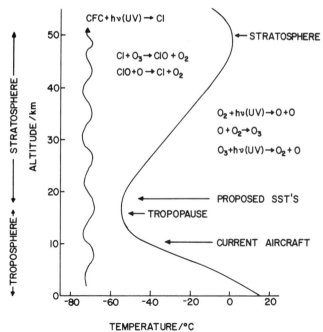

It is important to note that at lower levels of the atmosphere, ozone (O_3) is not a desirable chemical (see Nitrogen Oxides), as it causes damage to humans, vegetation, and materials. Normally, ozone is not present to any great extent in the troposphere, which extends up to about 11 km (kilometre). This is a region of swirling air masses, warm and cold fronts and cloud formations; it is the zone in which the weather occurs. It contains almost all the atmospheric water vapour and comprises 80% of the atmospheric mass (11). It is marked by a temperature decrease of about 6.5 deg. C/km altitude due to the increasing distance from the sun-warmed earth. The tropopause at the top of the troposphere is a small region of constant temperature, about -56 deg. C.

Above the tropopause lies the stratosphere, marked by a temperature increase with altitude. It extends from about 11 to 50 km above the earth's surface and is very calm compared to the troposphere. The temperature rises from minus 50 deg. C to about zero deg. C in this region due to the presence of ozone. The total atmospheric pressure in the stratosphere is very much less than in the troposphere, but the concentration of ozone is greater. It is this stratospheric ozone which is very important to us.

At the altitude of maximum concentration (25 to 30 km), ozone has a concentration of 10 ppm (part per million) as compared to 0.04 ppm in the troposphere. Even though the quantity of stratospheric ozone is still not very great, it is enough to somewhat shield the earth from ultraviolet UV-B radiation (of wavelengths 290 to 320 nanometres) by absorbing it. It is the only chemical present in the stratosphere which absorbs in part of this UV region (12). The energy absorbed by the ozone, O_3, causes it to break up into molecular oxygen (O_2) and oxygen atoms (O). This dissociation reaction, coupled with some other ozone and oxygen reactions in the stratosphere, is responsible for the stratospheric absorption of solar energy which goes into warming the surrounding atmosphere, giving rise to the statospheric temperature inversion (see Figure).

The natural ozone concentration in the stratosphere is kept fairly constant with time as the formation and destruction reactions shown on the right of the figure have the same overall rates. As indicated, in the natural stratosphere the primary destruction mechanism is by nitric oxide, NO (13). The effect of the 2 sets of reactions, formation and destruction, can be compared to pouring water into a bucket with a small hole in it. If the rates of entry and exit of water remain constant, the level of water in the bucket stays the same. Similarly, if the rates of formation and destruction of ozone remain constant, the amount of ozone stays constant. If one now "pokes another hole in the bucket" by injecting man-made ozone destroyers into the stratosphere, the amount of ozone drops to a lower steady-state value. Because the new rates of formation and destruction are again balanced, the amount of ozone remains steady, but it is less than it was originally.

This reduction of the "steady state" concentration of ozone is what sparked the outcry against Supersonic Transports (SSTs), as it was discovered that these planes, which would be flying in the stratosphere, would have NO emitted from their exhausts, and this would increase the rate of destruction. Similarly, chlorine atoms, another ozone-destroying species, were postulated to be released from CFCs which had migrated into the stratosphere and absorbed UV radiation present there, causing dissociation to chlorine atoms and other products. The chlorine atoms can then react with the ozone as shown in the left of the figure. This sequence of reactions is an example of a "chain reaction". A product of the first reaction (ClO) provides a reacting species for the second reaction, which gives a product (Cl) to start the first over again. A chain, once started, will continue until one or more of the reacting species is removed.

The chlorine-catalyzed ozone degradation chain continues to destroy ozone until either the ClO species diffuses to the troposphere, or the Cl atom abstracts a hydrogen atom from some source and the HCl thus formed diffuses to the troposphere. In the troposphere ClO and HCl can be removed by weathering processes, e.g., by dissolution in water droplets or ice crystals.

Since 1974, many studies have been carried out to discover a "sink" for fluorocarbons. For example, in 1976, it was proposed (14) that the chlorine oxide formed reacted with nitric oxide to yield chlorine nitrite (ClONO). This idea caused great excitement, as it would result in the removal of

2 harmful species. However, recalculations did not support the proposal (15). Recently, the Manufacturing Chemists Association initiated an ambitious and expensive project to see if there are any tropospheric sinks which remove CFCs before they can reach the stratosphere (16).

There are other sources for chlorine entering the stratosphere. Eruptions of volcanoes can inject chlorine compounds directly into the stratosphere. It has been estimated that in 1976, the Augustine volcano in Alaska introduced an amount of chlorine into the stratosphere which may be as much as a third of the 1975 world production of chlorine in CFCs (17). These most recent estimates of the importance of natural sources make the effect of anthropogenic sources less serious.

Even though there have been a number of experimental observations consistent with the original hypothesis of Rowland and Molina, the uncertainties in the observations are great enough to leave many questions. The rates of many stratospheric reactions have been recalculated and the roles of many species which may or may not be important have been questioned. But above all, the fact has been stressed that very little is known about stratospheric chemistry.

There is a disagreement over the amount of destruction of ozone by CFMs. Rowland and Molina originally claimed that the damage may be as high as 13%, but Dr. J. Peter Jesson of DuPont gave an estimate for depletion of 2% by the year 2100 at current growth rates of atmospheric release (18). The National Academy of Sciences (NAS) report on the effects of CFMs, released in Sept. 1976, is quoted as saying (19) "It is inevitable that CFMs released to the atmosphere do destroy stratospheric ozone. The more difficult problem is evaluating such effects quantitatively". The panel who wrote the report estimated an ozone reduction of about 7% based on 1973 production figures. However, it noted that the effect could be as small as 2% or as large as 20%. The time estimated to reach half the steady-state value (3.5% reduction) was 40-50 years. A recent National Aeronautics and Space Administration and World Meteorological Organization report released in Jan. 1982, estimated the reduction after several centuries to be 5% to 9% percent (20).

A major snag in dealing with ozone depletion is the

measurement of that depletion. The concentration of ozone in any one place varies daily and seasonally and is believed to follow the 11-year sunspot cycle (13). Any man-made change would have to be of the order of 10% before it could be noticed against the natural variation. Another problem is that of the time delay between release of CFMs into the lower atmosphere and their arrival in the stratosphere. Fifteen years has been estimated as the length of time required for CFMs to diffuse from their release sites to the stratosphere (21). Thus any decision taken today to ban fluorocarbons will not be reflected in the stratosphere for some time to come.

CFMs are not the only substances which could harm the ozone layer. As mentioned previously, SSTs produce nitric oxide, which also destroys ozone, in their exhausts. Nitrogen fertilizers also have been implicated in ozone destruction (22). The claim has been made that nitrogen oxide compounds present in fertilizers could deplete the ozone layer by as much as 15% over a century (23). This problem, if real, would present a much tougher problem for legislators to deal with than the fluorocarbon one. As indicated above, however, the effects of nitrogen oxides and chlorine are not additive (20).

MEDICAL AND CLIMATIC EFFECTS OF STRATOSPHERIC OZONE DEPLETION

There is a strong, though not conclusive, connection between UV-B radiation and incidence of non-melanoma skin cancer in humans. This is a generally non-fatal cancer, but there is some evidence to support a connection between that type of radiation and melanoma skin cancer which is a more frequently fatal form of the disease. The NAS report (24) concluded that there would be "an increased incidence of malignant melanoma, a serious form of skin cancer, frequently causing death and thus an increase in mortality from this cause" (21). It is argued that a 10% reduction in stratospheric ozone would result in a 20% increase in both forms of skin cancer.

This view has not gone uncontested. First it is said that the skin cancers only affect fair-skinned people, because the pigmentation of darker-skinned people protects them from such a fate. Also, it has been argued that the projected depletion of ozone will result in an increase in UV-B radiation the same

as that which one would experience moving south. The increase
in UV intensity in going from sea-level to the altitude of
Denver, Colorado is 125% and yet the citizens of Colorado have
one of the lowest skin cancer fatality rates of all the
states, 1.69 deaths per 100,000 as compared to the national
average of 2.40 per 100,000 (25).

The effects of UV-B radiation on other constituents of
the ecosystem are virtually unknown. The Environment Canada
report on CFMs states: "...our knowledge of the effects of
UV-B on the entire ecosystem is extremely limited and it is
precisely what we don't know that causes this committee great
concern" (21).

The climatic effects of CFMs are even more speculative
than the medical effects. There are 2 ways in which CFMs can
alter the world's climate. First, they are strong infrared ab-
sorbers; they can absorb the infrared (heat) radiation given
off by the earth, and thus warm the atmosphere in the same
manner as does carbon dioxide (the greenhouse effect, see
Carbon Dioxide) (21). It has been calculated that this effect
could, for a concentration of 2 ppb (part per billion) of
FC-11 and FC-12, raise the average global temperature one deg.
C (26).

The second climatic effect is caused by a decrease in
ozone. Because the ozone layer warms the stratosphere, any
decrease in the ozone should cause a decrease in the stratospheric temperature. This temperature drop could be as much as
5 to 10 deg. C. There is no way of telling what the effect of
such a decrease would be in the troposphere, but it would be
reasonable to expect some effect. Its nature and magnitude
can only be guessed at, as the coupling between troposphere
and stratosphere is poorly understood. Possible effects could
be a raising or lowering of the tropospheric temperature, a
change in wind and weather patterns, or any combination of
these. It should be noted that a global (tropospheric)
temperature difference of only one deg. C marks the difference
between the Little Ice Age and our present-day climate (21).

The Environment Canada report (21) concluded that because
of our geographical location, skin cancer increase may not be
the serious problem in Canada that it may be further south.
Because of the shorter growing season and the sharp northern

limits on most commercial crops, however, it is not possible
to predict the effects of a climatic change. A change for the
worse could have drastic social and economic consequences; the
chance, concluded the Report, is not worth taking. It must be
remembered that the FCs already released will have some
effects in future decades. However, a total ban on any futher
use of FCs is difficult to conceive because of the economic
disruptions which would result.

ECONOMIC AND POLITICAL ASPECTS OF BANNING CFCs

Fluorocarbons are manufactured in about 24 countries by
about 40 companies (8). In Canada, they are made by DuPont of
Canada and Allied Chemicals. About one-half of the fluorocarbons made in Canada went into aerosol propellents; an
outright ban on these translates into a loss of about $12
million in sales each year (21). There is a capital investment
of some $60 million in the Canadian aerosol industry and the
amount injected into the economy yearly through wages, profits
and taxes was about $90 million in the 1970s.

The figures for the U.S. are even more impressive. For
1974, the fluorocarbon-industry-dependent employment was
estimated at close to 600,000, or 0.7% of the total U.S.
employment. A possible additional 900,000 were indirectly
dependent on the industry for their livelihood. An American
Department of Commerce report (6) on the fluorocarbon industry
dated 1975 said "with respect to aerosols, 55% of the 28,100
employed in formulation are fluorocarbon dependent...". This
large industry contributed an estimated $8 billion in 1975 to
the U.S. economy, of which a quarter was from fluorocarbon
propellents (27).

The refrigeration and air conditioning industry in the
U.S. accounted for 28% of the fluorocarbon production in 1974.
In the same year 16% of Canadian-produced fluorocarbons went
to refrigerant uses. The U.S. fluorocarbon-dependent refrigeration industry employed about half a million people, with an
annual payroll of some $5.2 billion. The foamed plastics
industry sector has a total employment of about 57,000 producing goods valued at around $930 million in 1973 (6).

The American aerosol industry was affected by threats of
a ban on fluorocarbon propellents and an economic recession

which caused sales to drop steadily since 1973 (28). Although there has been an increase in some markets (insect sprays, coatings, finishings and some others) the 2 largest markets, personal and household products, together comprising two-thirds of total production, had gone down even before a ban went into effect. Since Apr. 15, 1979, manufacture and inter-state shipment of CFCs for use in non-essential aerosol sprays has been forbidden in the U.S.. Some minor uses (pharmaceuti-cals, insecticides) have been allowed to continue (29).

There are some replacements possible for CFCs as aerosol propellents. There has been a gradual and difficult change to hydrocarbon propellents such as butane and propane; this has resulted in new growth in the aerosol industry (30). The disadvantage of hydrocarbons is their flammability. A flame suppressant, methylene chloride, has been added to the hydro-carbons, but it is now under attack because it has been found to cause cancer in rats and mice (31). Many "personal" pro-ducts can also be packaged in a non-aerosol form, for example, roll-on instead of spray deodorants. Many such products are also considered non-essentials; this has been put forward as one of the reasons for the decline in sales during economic recessions.

Legislation introducing some restrictions on CFCs in aerosols is thus feasible. Control of CFCs introduced into the atmosphere from air conditioning and refrigeration equipment may prove more difficult. Because of the mixing of air in the troposphere, the fluorocarbon problem also cannot be tackled on a regional, or even national scale; it must be faced by all members of the global community. Only if the release of CFCs worldwide is controlled will a satisfactory solution be achieved.

REFERENCES

1. Sanders, P. A., "Principles of Aerosol Technology", Van Nostrand, New York, 1970.
2. Whittington, L. "The Canadian Price of Regulation of Fluorocarbon Use", Financial Times of Canada, 65(18), 8, 1976.
3. News Release, 23-4-80, Environmental Protection Service, Environment Canada, 1980.
4. Sherwood, M., "The Rise of Fluorocarbons", New Scientist, Oct. 2, 1975.
5. Bichowsky, R. R., U.S. Patent No. 2,021,981, 1935.
6. "Economic Significance of Fluorocarbons", Office of Business Research and Analysis, Bureau of Domestic Commerce, U.S. Department of Commerce, 1975.
7. Lynde, J. D., U.S. Patent No. 34,894, 1862.
8. "Fluorocarbons and the Environment", U.S. Federal Task Force on Inadvertent

Modification of the Stratosphere, GPO Stock No. 038-000-00226-1, U.S. Government Printing Office, Washington, D.C., 1975.

9. Lovelock, J. E., "Origin and Movement of Fluorine Compounds", Nature, 230, 379, 1971.

10. Molina, M. J. and Rowland, F. S., "Stratospheric Sink for Chloro-fluoromethanes", Nature, 249, 810, 1974.

11. Vaughan, W.W. and Devries. L.L., Eds., "The Earth's Atmosphere", American Institute of Aeronautics and Astronautics, New York, Selected Reprint Series Vol. 13, 1972.

12. "Fluorocarbons and the Environment (A Literature Review)", Ontario Ministry of the Environment, Report No. ARB-TDA-14-75, 1975.

13. Rowland, S., "Chlorofluoromethanes and Stratospheric Ozone--a Scientific Status Report", Fluorocarbon File, New Scientist, Oct. 2, 1975.

14. "Aerosols and Ozone--Good News and Bad", New Scientist, May 20, 1976.

15. "Upper Atmosphere Chemistry: the Arguments Continue", New Scientist, June 10, 1976.

16. "Chlorofluorocarbon Study Launched by MCA", Chemical and Engineering News, Feb. 6, 1978.

17. Johnston, D. A., "Volcanic Contribution of Chlorine to the Stratosphere", Science, 209, 491, 1980.

18. "Chlorofluorocarbon Issue Swirls On", Chemical and Engineering News, Sept. 13, 1976.

19. "Uncertainties Remain in Ozone Controversy", Chemical and Engineering News, Sept. 27, 1976.

20. Josephson, J., "Stratospheric Ozone: Changing Forecasts", Environmental Science and Technology, 16, 328A, 1982.

21. "Anthropogenic Modification of the Ozone Layer--the CFM Effect", A report by the AES Advisory Committee on Stratospheric Pollution, Fisheries and Environment Canada, 1977.

22. "Agriculture May be Worse than Fluorocarbons", New Scientist, June 24, 1976.

23. "Will Fertilizers Harm Ozone as Much as SSTs", Science, 195, 658, 1977.

24. "NAS Waffles a Bit on Aerosol Problem", Chemical and Engineering News, Sept. 20, 1976.

25. Jones, A., "Ozone Depletion and Cancer", Fluorocarbon File, New Scientist, Oct. 2, 1975.

26. Ramanathan, V., "Greenhouse Effect Due to Chloroflourocarbons: Climatic Implications", Science, 190, 50, 1975.

27. "At Issue: Fluorocarbons", Kaiser Aluminum and Chemical Corporation, Center for Technology, Pleasanton, California, 1975.

28. "Aerosol Producers Have Another Bad Year", Chemical and Engineering News, May 23, 1977.

29. "Chlorofluorocarbons Phaseout Begins", ibid, Oct. 23, 1978.

30. "Aerosols Slowly Making a Comeback", ibid, Sept. 13, 1982.

31. "Methylene Chloride May Cause Cancer", ibid, Oct. 4, 1982.

RECOMMENDED READING

There is a vast amount of literature covering fluorocarbons of which only a few references are cited in this chapter. The Ontario Ministry of the Environment Report (12), presents a clear, unbiased and readable background. The Fluorocarbon File (references (4), (13) and (24)), presents the viewpoints of various authors. There is also a recent book, "The Ozone War", by L. Dotto and H. J. Schiff, published by Doubleday Canada, Ltd., 1978. An update on stratospheric science can be found in "Stratospheric Science Undergoing Change", Chemical and Engineering News, Sept. 13, 1980.

FORMALDEHYDE

One of the uses of formaldehyde is in "UFFI", a home insulation. Concern about the health effects of formaldehyde has many Canadian homeowners worried.

Formaldehyde has never had an attractive public image; it has been associated with funeral homes and with storeroom bottles in biology class (1). But used in business, formaldehyde ranks 25th among all commercial chemicals in terms of volume produced (1). It is used in the production of particle board, fertilizers and textiles (3). It is found in building materials, combustion products and tobacco smoke (4). It even occurs naturally in air and in our bodies. In Canada in 1980, about 109,000 tonne of the aldehyde were produced, worth roughly $78 million (2).

Probably no commercial application of formaldehyde has done as much to bring the chemical to the public's attention as has its use in home insulation. Urea formaldehyde foam insulation (UFFI) was introduced in Canada in the early 1960s, and by 1981, it was in 80,000 homes (5). Formaldehyde gas was known to be toxic at high concentrations, causing adverse health effects ranging from eye irritation to pneumonia (4). In 1980, however, exposure of rats to high concentrations of formaldehyde was linked to cancer (6). These potential health hazards, combined with indications that under some circumstances UFFI could break down and formaldehyde could infiltrate into the living space, influenced the Canadian government to ban the material (5).

In Feb. 1982, the Consumer Product Safety Commission of the U.S. also banned UFFI from use in American homes, but this ban was overturned in Apr. 1983 by the Court of Appeals (18). Because of the widespread use of formaldehyde, there is now much research into the chemical processes and health effects of formaldehyde.

PROPERTIES, PRODUCTION AND USE

The aldehydes, of which formaldehyde is the most common and important member, are a class of organic compounds characterized by the presence of one carbon, one hydrogen and one oxygen atom in a group (denoted as CHO) (4). What distinguishes one aldehyde from another is the molecule or atom which is attached to the CHO group. With formaldehyde, known as the first member of the aldehyde family, that attached atom is hydrogen (thus, denoted as HCHO).

Formaldehyde was discovered in 1859 (3). It is a colourless gas, has a pungent odour and is highly irritating to the exposed membranes of the eyes, nose and upper respiratory tract (4). A highly reactive chemical, formaldehyde is very soluble in water and combines readily with many substances (3).

Formaldehyde is marketed principally as an aqueous solution, called formalin. Methanol is added to the solution to suppress polymerization. Formalin is clear, and has the strong pungent odour of formaldehyde. Because formaldehyde is stored in solution, wherever it is transported, water and methanol must be transported as well. Thus, costs for transporting formaldehyde are high, and generally it is transported only over short distances (4). Paraformaldehyde is a solid form of formaldehyde. None is produced in Canada, and in 1980, less than 1,000 tonne were imported for use where very high concentrations were required (2).

In Canada, in 1980, over 60% of the formaldehyde produced was consumed in the production of urea formaldehyde and phenol formaldehyde resins (2). Urea formaldehyde is used in the production of particleboard glues, hardwood plywood, furniture glues, textile finishes, fertilizer, thermal insulation, baking enamels, electrical parts, buttons and wet-resistant paper. Phenol formaldehyde is used to make softwood and plywood glues, waferboard glues, hardboard binder, decorative laminates, foundry sand binder, thermal insulation, brake linings, auto parts, varnishes and electrical parts. There are other formaldehyde-based resins as well, used in the production of dishware, rubber-tire adhesive and marine plywood glues (2). Non-resin forms of formaldehyde are used to make many of the items just listed, and as well, explosives, inks, synthetic drying oils, pharmaceuticals, corrosion inhibitors, disinfectant, germicides, embalming fluids and preservatives.

HEALTH EFFECTS

Formaldehyde has been implicated in a wide range of health problems. It has been linked at varying levels and durations of exposure to illnesses from throat irritation to bronchial pneumonia to nasal cancer (6). Yet, the National Academy of Sciences (NAS) in the U.S. has cautioned that "there is an urgent need for research to resolve several important questions related to the health effects of formaldehyde" (4). The following summarizes the current state of knowledge regarding the health effects, but several of the findings are only of a preliminary nature.

In general, no ill effects of formaldehyde in the air have been reported at levels below 0.05 ppm (part per million)(4). (The formaldehyde level in ambient outdoor air usually ranges from 0.005 to 0.06 ppm, depending on the location (7)). At levels between 0.05 and 0.5 ppm, formaldehyde can produce eye irritation in some people (4). In one study, eye, nose and throat irritation was reported by 3 of 16 subjects exposed to 0.2 ppm of formaldehyde 5 hours a day for 4 days. At a level of 0.7 ppm, 15 of 16 subjects reported similar irritation (4). The odour of the gas can be detected in the concentration range 0.1 to 1.0 ppm, depending on the individual. With concentrations above 1 ppm, increased thirst, dizziness, headache, tiredness, and difficulty in sleeping have been reported. At concentrations reaching 5 ppm, nose, throat and bronchial irritation have been readily reported by subjects. At concentrations greater than 50 ppm, pulmonary edema and pneumonia can occur (4). And at 100 ppm, formaldehyde exposure has been reported to be fatal (4).

The health effects of formaldehyde vary not only with the level of exposure, but as well with its duration. For example, one cannot take a short-term study and derive conclusions on the health effects on persons who live in homes where there is a continuous low-dose exposure (4). Some people can develop a tolerance to formaldehyde after several hours of exposure, while in others not previously sensitized to formaldehyde, repeated exposure results in the development of hyper-sensitivity (4).

Another variable is the susceptibility of the individual who is exposed. Certain individuals, particularly those with a history of respiratory allergy, appear to be acutely sensitive to formaldehyde (7). NAS has identified a need to explore whether children, pregnant women, older persons, and persons with specific medical conditions have increased susceptibility (4). As well, the response to formaldehyde can be modified by other factors, including smoking habits, pre-existing disease, and interactions with other pollutants and aerosols (4).

Formaldehyde, a very reactive chemical, combines readily with chemicals present in living organisms, including proteins, amino acids, DNA and RNA (4,19). High levels of formaldehyde have been found to be mutagenic in a variety of in vitro and in vivo tests. Although formaldehyde can produce both gene mutations and various types of chromosome aberrations, it has been described as only giving "weak responses" in many laboratory organisms (8).

Formaldehyde has not been shown to be teratogenic in animals (4). There were no abnormalities reported in the offspring of pregnant dogs fed diets containing formaldehyde; nor were there abnormalities in the next generation offspring (4). Rats exposed to 0.8 ppm of formaldehyde over 20 days produced normal offspring, although there was an increase in gestation time (4).

Recent tests have linked formaldehyde to nasal cancer in animals. The first was a 2-year inhalation study on rats and mice, sponsored by the Chemical Industry Institute of Toxicology, released in 1980 (7). In that study, rats exposed to 15 ppm of formaldehyde 6 hours a day, 5 days a week, developed nasal cancer (7). Other studies with a different strain of rat have supported this finding (6).

In man, however, the carcinogenicity of formaldehyde has not been established. A 1980 epidemiological study of cancer mortality among Du Pont employees who had worked with formaldehyde showed no excess in cancer deaths compared with other employees (9). A British epidemiological study revealed that patholgists, who have higher than average exposure to formaldehyde, had a longer life expectancy, a lower mortality rate, and as well, a lower incidence of respiratory disease than the general population (7). On the other hand, a January 1982 report in the U.S. documented that 5 workers occupationally exposed to formaldehyde developed nasal cancer, which occurs only rarely in man (8).

EXPOSURE

In the body, formaldehyde is formed in many biochemical processes, and is a normal metabolite of the cell (3). It is active in the formation of amino acids and other chemicals essential for life (7). Formaldehyde readily oxidizes to formic acid and several enzymes which catalyze this reaction have been identified in the body (3).

In the environment, formaldehyde occurs in the natural unpolluted atmosphere. For example, in 1968, formaldehyde concentrations of up to 0.01 ppm were reported in Antarctica (4). In urban atmospheres, aldehydes are among the most abundant of the carbon-containing pollutant molecules (4). Formaldehyde enters the atmosphere whenever the incomplete combustion of hydrocarbon fuels occurs. Thus, formaldehyde is produced from automobile exhausts, cigarette smoking, fire places, gas cooking stoves, combustion based heating appliances, power generating plants that burn fossil fuels, forest fires, and the open burning of wastes (3,7). Urban levels of formaldehyde usually range from 0.005 to 0.06 ppm, with the upper levels found near industry and busy highways (7). The availability of natural sinks for formaldehyde also determines its concentration: wind conditions affect the dispersion of formaldehyde; formaldehyde is highly soluble in water so that rain and standing water are good sinks; sunlight causes photodecomposition of formaldehyde; and higher air temperature increases the chemical reactions which remove formaldehyde (4).

In the workplace, the Dangerous Substances Regulations under the Canada Labour Code specify both an 8-hour time weighted average and a ceiling limit of 2 ppm of formaldehyde in the air (2). This regulates exposure in federal facilities only, and as such, each province, with the exceptions of Manitoba and Prince Edward Island, has its own regulations (2). In the United States, the Occupational Safety and Health Administration (OSHA) standard for formaldehyde allows an eight-hour time-weighted average concentration of up to 3 ppm, and a ceiling concentration of 5 ppm (3). This is currently being challenged by The United Autoworkers Union which has filed suit in Washington, D.C., to force OSHA to reduce permissible workplace levels of formaldehyde (10).

Formaldehyde exposure concentrations vary from one work-place to another. Workers in plants producing plywood or particleboard, and using one of the formaldehyde resins, have been exposed to formaldehyde levels reported as high as 10 ppm (4). For these workers, variables determining the concen-tration of formaldehyde include ventilation, the amount of free (unattached) formaldehyde in the resin, the moisture content of the wood, the humidity of the air in the plant, and the processing temperatures (4). (The higher the humidity and/or temperature, the more likely formaldehyde is to be removed from the resin and enter the atmosphere (6)). In the U.S. selected sampling of other workplaces revealed different ranges of formaldehyde concentration: up to 2.7 ppm of formaldehyde at textile plants; 0.9 to 2.7 ppm at garment factories; 0.9 to 3.3 ppm at a clothing store; 0.04 to 10.9 ppm at laminating plants; and 0.09 to 5.26 ppm of formaldehyde at funeral homes (4).

The primary sources of formaldehyde in non-occupational indoor air are building materials, combustion appliances, tobacco smoke, and a large variety of consumer products (4). Studies in Denmark, Sweden, West Germany and the United States, concentrating on indoor formaldehyde emissions from particleboard and plywood furnishings, have found that indoor concentrations often exceeded 0.1 ppm (4). Gas stoves emit substantial amounts of formaldehyde, having been measured at approximately 25 mg/hr (milligram per hour) for the oven and 15 mg/hr for each top burner (4). It has been estimated that cigarette smoke can contain as much as 40 ppm of formaldehyde (5). One study measured the amount of formaldehyde in tobacco as 0.02 to 0.04 mg of the chemical in the smoke of a cigarette (4). But it has been the application of formaldehyde as a component of a home insulation material that has given the chemical its current notoriety.

UREA FORMALDEHYDE FOAM INSULATION

Increased heating costs have made home insulation popu-lar. Insulation slows the process whereby warm air inside the house loses its heat to the cold air outside. One possible consequence of insulation is the creation of "tight" houses, in which the indoor air cannot escape (see Radon). In these houses, pollutants generated within the home, such as formal-dehyde, can build up in the air. When the federal government

measured formaldehyde levels in insulated houses, it found
that 2.6 % of the houses with insulation other than UFFI had
formaldehyde concentrations of at least 0.1 ppm (11). A
further source of formaldehyde can exist, however, when the
insulating material itself -- UFFI -- gives off formaldehyde.

The UFFI Information and Coordinating Centre of the
Department of Consumer and Corporate Affairs, describes UFFI
as "a low-density foam prepared at the installation site from
a mixture of urea formaldehyde resin, an acidic hardening
agent solution, and a propellent, usually compressed air. The
mixture is pumped through a tube into the cavities of a wall,
where it hardens. At the time it is pumped in, the material
looks and feels like shaving cream" (12).

The resin used in producing UFFI contains free formaldehyde, much of which is released shortly after installation
(13). Chemical reactions involved in the formulation of UFFI
can reverse, causing a degradation (hydrolysis) in the UFFI
and thus a decrease in the effective thermal resistance of the
UFFI and a liberation of formaldehyde gas (13). Increased
temperatures and/or increased humidity substantially contribute to the hydrolysis of UFFI, increasing the rate of degradation of the material and the release of free formaldehyde
and other gases (7,13). The gas can be carried away to the
outside immediately by air movement, or it may get stored in
the wall, entering the home by air movement or diffusion (13).
If the insulating cavity is not dried properly after installation, fungus may grow on the foam or on other materials. The
fungus spores can infiltrate the living space, and some can
cause allergic reactions (14).

The levels of formaldehyde infiltrating the indoor air
vary widely from one UFFI insulated house to another. There
are cases of UFFI being installed in houses with aluminum
siding, for example, which doesn't permit the escape of free
formaldehyde to the outdoors (15). Some houses allow rain to
leak into the insulating cavity, causing moisture build-up and
thus the increased release of formaldehyde gas (13). Another
variable is the make-up of the wall separating the indoor air
and the insulating cavity. In Britain, UFFI can only be put
into houses in which the wall is made of brick or masonry to
reduce formaldehyde infiltration (16). The expertise of the
installer, and the particular formulation of UFFI used can

also affect the amount of formaldehyde released (5). The
National Research Council has summarized "that every situation
is unique and must be considered separately" (14).

This variation is reflected in the results of a fed-
erally-sponsored national testing survey (11). Of 1,146 houses
insulated with UFFI under the Canadian Home Insulation Program, 37.4% had maximum formaldehyde levels not exceeding
0.025 ppm, 39.9% had maximum levels between 0.025 and 0.055
ppm, a further 18.7% had maximum levels between 0.05 and 0.1
ppm, and a final 5.1% had levels in excess of 0.1 ppm. Since
formaldehyde is present in particleboard glue and other construction materials, high formaldehyde levels may in some
cases be due to the presence of such materials rather than
UFFI.

The federal government conducted tests upon request in
houses insulated with UFFI. If a house contains an average
formaldehyde level of 0.1 ppm or over, or if persons living in
a UFFI insulated house can show evidence that their health is
affected by a low level of formaldehyde gas, then the government will provide up to $5,000 to cover the costs of remedial
action. Such action includes sealing walls and installing
ventilation systems (13). Only in rare occasions is it necessary or wise to have the UFFI completely removed (13).

The Canadian experience with UFFI began in the late
1960s when the Central Mortgage and Housing Corporation
approved the use of UFFI in Canadian homes. In late 1977,
with energy costs rising, the federal government established
the Canadian Home Insulation Program (CHIP) to aid homeowners,
and of the 80,000 to 100,000 homes insulated with UFFI in
Canada, 29,000 were insulated under the CHIP program. Insulation not performed under the program was less likely to con-
form to provisional UFFI standards at the time (2).

Soon after UFFI was approved in Canada, questions were
raised about the stability of UFFI, and about the toxicological effects of formaldehyde. In 1980, Health and Welfare
Canada decided to place a temporary ban on UFFI because of
concerns for health. Starting in June 1981, the Department of
Consumer and Corporate Affairs began its own investigation
into UFFI by conducting surveys of formaldehyde levels in UFFI
homes across Canada and by establishing a Hazardous Products

Act Board of Review to hear the view of both industry and consumers. The Board heard from possible victims of formaldehyde exposure, and this testimony made for prominent stories in the media (2).

Consumers formed groups. In Ontario, a group calling itself the Homeowners with Urea Formaldehyde Foam Insulation (HUFFI) marched on Queen's Park in Toronto demanding government action (2). It has been reported that in many instances, UFFI homes have decreased in property value, and this has won some UFFI home owners reductions in property taxes (17).

CONCLUSION

Research on formaldehyde continues. The American National Academy of Sciences has pointed out several areas which deserve further study, including: long-term effects of continuous low-dose exposure to formaldehyde; epidemiological studies of dermatitis due to formaldehyde; the effects of formaldehyde on nasal and lung defense mechanisms; the interactions of formaldehyde with other air pollutants; the mutagenic, teratogenic, and carcinogenic potentials of formaldehyde; and several other areas involving human health (4). With UFFI, there are suggestions that the adverse health effects suffered by some people who live in UFFI insulated houses are not directly attributable to formaldehyde (6). An article in the Canadian Journal of Public Health has observed, "Unfortunately, there are no studies in homes insulated with UFFI in which other gases were measured as well as the formaldehyde." (7).

The ban on UFFI has not yet resulted in a significant cutback in the consumption of formaldehyde, but has added to the unfavourable public opinion toward it (1). In the long-run, this could result in a drop in demand for the ubiquitous chemical, a drop which could be turned around or accelerated as further research results come in.

REFERENCES

1. "Effects of Foam Insulation Ban Far Reaching", Chemical and Engineering News, Mar. 29, p. 34, 1982.
2. "The Formaldehyde Issue", Editor: Lauzon, M., Corpus Information Services, Don Mills, Ontario, 1982.
3. "News About Chemicals. Special Report--Formaldehyde", International Register of Potentially Toxic Chemicals (IRPTC) Bulletin, p. 15, 1981.

4. "Formaldehyde and Other Aldehydes" National Academy Press, Washington D.C., 1981.
5. "News Release", Consumer and Corporate Affairs, No. NR-81-31, Dec. 23, 1981.
6. Somers, E., "Formaldehyde and Indoor Health Quality--The Health Issues", Corpus Forum, Toronto, May 4, 1982.
7. Wiberg, G. S. and Baranowski, E., "Health Implications of Urea Formaldehye Foam Insulation", Canadian Journal of Public Health, 72, 335, 1981.
8. "Report of the Federal Panel on Formaldehyde", Environmental Health Perspectives, 43, 139, 1982.
9. "No Cancer Link Found in Formaldehyde Study", Chemical and Engineering News, p. 8, May 31, 1982.
10. "Workers Sue over Formaldehyde Standard", Chemical and Engineering News, Aug. 30, 1982.
11. "The Report on the National Testing Survey to the Board of Review," by the Urea Formaldehyde Foam Insulation Information and Coordinating Centre, Consumer and Corporate Affairs, Dec.14,1981.
12. Information Bulletin from UFFI Information and Coordination Centre, Consumer and Corporate Affairs, Aug. 3, 1981.
13. Bower, R. P., Shirtliffe, C. J. and Chown, G. A., "Building Practice Note 23", Division of Building Research, National Research Council of Canada, Ottawa, Aug. 1981.
14. Chown, G. A., Bower, R. P. and Shirtliffe, C. J., "Building Practice Note 19: Urea Formaldehyde Foam Insulation", National Research Council of Canada, Ottawa, Apr. 1981.
15. "Final Report of the Department of National Health and Welfare Expert Committee on Urea Formaldehyde Foam Insulation", Apr., 1981.
16. New Scientist, Mar. 4, 1982.
17. "Niagara Owners of UFFI Homes Get 75% Tax Cut", The Globe and Mail, Toronto, June 24, 1982.
18. Sun, M., "Formaldehyde Ban is Overturned", Science 220, 699, 1983.
19. Grafstrom, R.C., Fornace, A.J. Jr., Autrup, H., Lechner, J.F. and Harris, C.C., "Formaldehyde Damage to DNA and Inhibition of DNA Repair in Human Bronchial Cells", Science 220, 216, 1983.

RECOMMENDED READING

Reference (4) provides a thorough discussion of issues related to formaldehyde, and (15) of the UFFI problem in Canada. A recent paper "Law and Science Policy in Federal Regulation of Formaldehyde", Science 222, 894, 1983 by N.A. Ashford, C.W. Ryan and C.C. Caldert as well as a recent book, "Formaldehyde on Trial: the Politics of Health in a Chemical Society", by L. Tataryn, document the history of the Formaldehyde and UFFI controversies.

LEAD

Lead is used in gasoline additives, and is therefore an ever-present pollutant in urban areas. There is much speculation about its effects on people.

THE METAL AND ITS USES

Lead is a soft, malleable, stable, heavy, bluish-grey metal. In air, its surface oxidizes quickly, increasing its resistance to corrosion. Lead has been used by man since approximately 2500 BC, but initially the main interest was in the silver which could be separated from lead after extraction from its ores. The principal ore is lead sulphide or galena, PbS (1). The Egyptians used lead-glazed pottery, the Romans used lead pipes to convey water and Ancient Greeks had the first lead-covered roofs (2).

In Canada, about 1.8 million tonne of lead are produced annually, only half of which is consumed by Canadian industry (3). About 43% of the amount used in Canada is used in the manufacture of lead-acid storage batteries for automobiles. Lead is also used in semi-finished products, such as pipes, sheets, foils and ammunition, and in other products, including solders, cable sheathing, and various alloys. About one-quarter of the lead produced annually is used in the manufacture of chemicals, the most important one being tetraethyl lead, an anti-knock additive for gasoline. Lead-based pigment was once widely used in exterior paints, but titanium has now replaced lead in most such paints (4).

SOURCES OF POLLUTION

The largest single global source of lead pollution in the air is leaded gasoline used in automobiles (1). In Canada, cars using leaded gas are the source of over 70% of the total airborne emissions of lead. Although groups like the World Health Organization have set acceptable levels of lead in the atmosphere, these levels are usually greatly exceeded in most cities during peak traffic flow (5). Lead is also introduced through the production of primary copper and nickel, and from lead mining, milling, smelting and refining operations (5). Much greater concentrations of lead are found in the vicinity of point sources, such as lead smelters, with the concentration decreasing exponentially as a function of distance from the source (3).

Lead can contaminate water, and the harder the water (i.e., the more calcium and magnesium in the water), the greater is the solubility of lead. Lead can reach the water by way of paints, old lead pipe installations (although almost all pipes now are plastic, copper or iron), lead solders, atmospheric washout, effluent from sewage treatment and agricultural run off from, for example, pesticides and agricultural limestone (1).

There are several other sources of lead. World-wide, lead emissions from the burning of coal were estimated to be 3.5 thousand tonne per year. Magazines and coloured paper wrapping can contain lead, as they are sometimes made from incinerated solid waste. Factories producing clay colours, television picture tubes and car batteries have all resulted in cases of elevated non-occupational exposure to lead (6). In Toronto, lead emissions have however decreased considerably since 1974 due to the greater use of lead-free gasoline and better pollution control in 2 smelters (12).

Lead occurs naturally as a minor constituent in soil and plants. The natural level in plants is estimated to be less that 5 ppm but variations occur depending on the time of year (2). Increased lead levels are evident in vegetation growing near highways or in densely populated areas (2). It has been shown (6) that plants can take in lead from soil, and that airborne lead deposits on, accumulates on, and is absorbed by plant leaves. Fish can absorb lead through the body and from food, and much of the lead put into the water near cities is from automobiles (6). Acute lead toxicity in fish can lead to impairment of gills causing death by asphyxia (6). Domestic livestock are subject to the same sources of lead pollution as humans are (1). In rats, it has been shown that lead can be transferred to the female's litter via lactation (6) .

A recent Italian study lasting 18 months and involving thousands of people suggested that at least 24% of lead in blood came from gasoline (13). This evidence has given added impetus to efforts to eliminate leaded gas in several countries (see Regulations) as it had previously not been possible to estimate the anthropogenic contribution of lead to humans with any certainty.

THE HEALTH EFFECT OF LEAD

The average total lead absorbed by adults in Canada is between 31 and 38 microgram per day. The contributers to this intake are air (30-45%), water (8-20%) and food (40-50%). This average intake is a factor of 2-3 below the level at which chronic lead poisoning occurs. However, if a person is occupationally exposed to lead, and if he or she consumes food and drink with above-average lead content, then this safety factor may not be present. A cigarette smoker takes in about 1 microgram of lead from each cigarette. Dust falling from walls covered with lead paint, and improperly glazed ceramic ware add lead to food (1). Because of concerns for health, some domestic uses of lead have now faded; for example, solder in some electric kettles can release lead, but it is reported that lead-free alloys are now being used (1).

At low levels of exposure, lead does not accumulate in the body, as daily intake is balanced by daily excretion through urine, sweating, hair, nails, and exhalation (1). However, if exposure levels are elevated, lead can become a "cumulative" poison (1). In adults, lead can accumulate in the bones. In later years as the bones gradually dissolve, high levels of lead can circulate in the body, attacking soft tissue. The liver is less able to metabolize certain drugs, the kidneys may become irreversibly diseased, the heart may be affected directly through disease or indirectly through high blood pressure, the lungs may be less able to rid themselves of dust and infectious agents, and the reproductive system can be adversely affected (6).

There is evidence that the widespread use of lead by Romans caused sickness and insanity (15). Analysis of bones of Romans showed lead levels considerably higher than that found in the bones of a modern North American. Some extremely high levels (2000 ppm as compared to the current level of about 30 ppm) may have been due to the use of lead acetate as a sweetener.

The main concern for young children exposed to elevated levels of lead is that lead can slow down the development of the brain. Mental retardation can result from acute lead poisoning in young children. As a result of moderate increases in lead levels, exposed children have displayed hyperactivity and decreased cognitive, verbal and perceptual ability (6,14). Because lead easily crosses the placenta, elevated exposure of a pregnant woman to lead can adversely affect the fetus. In general, children are more susceptible to lead poisoning than are adults for several reasons: a higher fraction of the lead in a child's body is found in the prone soft tissue; a child's fast growing tissue is more easily affected than an adult's slow growing tissue; and children ingest more lead per body weight than do adults (6).

Because lead can affect so many parts of the body, the symptoms of lead poisoning can be as varied. Early symptoms can include stomach ache, weakness, irritability and fatigue (4). In later stages, the victim may have headaches, loss of appetite, pallor, drowsiness, vomiting, cramps, clumsiness, convulsions and stupor (4). But lead is not the sole cause of these symptoms and disorders, and it is often not the major cause (6). Nevertheless, lead exposure is widespread, and in certain cases the exposure is high enough to represent an unacceptable risk to health (6). Those most likely to be affected are urban children, pregnant women, and persons living near busy highways and near smelters without proper emission controls.

REGULATIONS

The debate over lead pollution has become very intense in the 1980s in the United Kingdom (16). The anti-lead lobby group received some support from the Italian study (13) indicating the contribution of lead in gasoline to blood levels. As a result, The U.K. is the first country to announce the phase-out of leaded gasoline, by 1988-90 (17,18). However, after the U.K. decision, W. Germany decided to ban lead from gasoline by an even earlier date, Jan. 1986 (19). The U.S. Environmental Protection Agency stated its intent to phase out leaded gasoline (8) but finally decided to restrict the lead content of gasoline to 1.1 g (gram) of lead per gallon of gasoline (9). In Canada, the federal government has taken some steps to protect its citizens from lead poisoning. It has reduced the maximum allowable lead content of paints used in homes and schools (1). There are drinking water standards setting maximum acceptable concentrations of 50 microgram of lead per litre of water (7). Food and drug regulations have specified different limits for different foods (7). The Canadian limit for lead in gasoline in 1982 was 0.77 g per litre; but in Dec., 1983, Environment Minister Caccia announced plans to lower this limit to 0.29 g per litre by 1987 (11). One reason lead emissions from cars have been dropping on average is that air quality regulations for other emissions (such as nitrogen oxides) have brought about the catalytic converter, which lowers these emissions, but which cannot work with leaded gas (10). The fraction of cars sold in Canada which were made for leaded gas has however increased in the 1980s and stricter controls of lead content were considered advisable (11).

REFERENCES

1. Leah, T. D., "The Production, Use and Distribution of Lead in Canada", Environmental Contaminants Inventory Study No. 3, Report Series No. 41, Cat. No: En 36-508/41, Environment Canada, 1976.
2. "Lead in the Canadian Environment", Associate Committee on Scientific Criteria for Environmental Quality, National Research Council Canada, Ottawa, NRCC No. 13682, 1973.
3. "Effects of Lead in the Environment -- 1978", Associate Committee on Scientific Criteria for Environmental Quality, National Research Council of Canada, Ottawa, 1978.
4. "Chemical of the Month: Lead", Journal of Chemical Education, Sept. 1981.
5. Wessel, M. A. and Dominski, A., "Our Children's Daily Lead", American Scientist, 65, 294, 1977.
6. "Effects of Lead in the Canadian Environment, 1978, Executive Report", Associate Committee on Scientific Criteria for Environmental Quality, National Research Council of Canada, Ottawa, 1979.
7. Flanson, R. T., Lucas, A. R., Giroux, L. and Kenniff, P., "Canadian Law and the Control of Exposure to Hazards", Science Council of Canada Background Study, No. 39, Catalogue No. SS21-1/39, 1977.
8. Anderson, E. V., "Phasing Lead out of Gasoline: Hard Knocks for Lead Alkyls Producers", Chemical and Engineering News, Feb. 6, 1978.
9. "EPA Close to Adopting Tough Lead-In-Gas Rule" Chemical and Engineering News, Aug. 30, 1982 and Nov. 15, 1982.
10. Jaworski, J., National Research Council of Canada, Private communication, 1982.
11. Keating, M. "Ottawa Plans to Cut Lead in Gasoline", The Globe and Mail, Toronto, Mar. 10, 1983. "Lead in Gasoline Threat to Children, Roberts Tells Group", ibid, Apr. 9, 1983. "60% Cut Ordered for Gasoline Lead by Jan. 1, 1987", ibid, Dec. 22, 1983.
12. Laver, R., "Toronto's Air Pollution Shows Sharp Decline", The Globe and Mail, Toronto, July 8, 1983.
13. Price, D., "Censorship Hits Turin Lead Survey", New Scientist, Feb. 17, 1983. Keating, M., "Half of Lead in Human Beings from Gasoline, Official Asserts", The Globe and Mail, Toronto, Mar. 11, 1983.

14. "Lead and IQ Studies Inconclusive", New Scientist, Apr. 21, 1983.
15. Immen, W., "Age of Lead Helped Sink Romans", The Globe and Mail, Toronto, Mar. 12, 1983. "Lead Traces Found in Bones of Romans", ibid, June 13, 1983.
16. Eysenck, H., "How Scandalous is the Lead Scandal?", New Scientist, Apr. 14, 1983. Pearce, F., "Labs Accused of Deplorable Conduct in Lead Debate", ibid, Sept. 8, 1983.
17. Layman, P.L., "Use of Lead in Gasoline in Europe Heads for Possible Phaseout", Chemical and Engineering News, Apr. 4, 1983.
18. "The U.K. Intends to Eliminate Lead Additives in Gasoline", Chemical Engineering, May 2, 1983.
19. Stansell, J. and Milgrom, L., "Germany Accelerates its Lead-Free Drive", New Scientist, July 28, 1983.

RECOMMENDED READING

Reference (2) gives a thorough, technical review of lead in Canada, while reference (1) is somewhat less technical. A detailed technical report is available covering characteristics, monitoring and analysis of lead; transport and distribution; effects of lead; control strategies and economic aspects of control: "Lead in the Environment", Report prepared for the National Science Foundation, Research Applications Directorate, U.S. Government Printing Office, Washington, 1977.

MERCURY

Disasters due to the use of this metal have occurred throughout the world for centuries. Today some communities in Northern Ontario and Quebec are concerned with mercury in their diets.

PROPERTIES AND USES OF MERCURY

Mercury is a relatively rare element which is present in the earth's crust to the extent of 0.08 ppm (part per million) by weight (1). In nature it rarely occurs in a free form as it tends to form amalgams (alloys) with other metals such as tin, zinc, and copper. It also occurs in organic forms (2), but it is most commonly found in the form of compounds such as mercuric sulfide (HgS), the brilliant red mineral, cinnabar. The pure metal is obtained chiefly by primary extraction: cinnabar is heated in a current of air whereby the mercury in the cinnabar evaporates and is subsequently condensed and collected. The largest producer of mercury metal is the U.S.S.R. (3). Spain produces a substantial portion of the supply for non-communist countries (3).

When World War II prevented the Atlantic countries from obtaining their mercury from Spain (and Italy and Yugoslavia), Cominco Ltd. began production at Pinchi Lake and Takla Mines in British Columbia. After the war, production in Canada almost ceased because mercury was cheap on the international market. In the 1960s, the price of mercury rose sufficiently that Cominco reopened its Pinchi Lake mine and by 1968, Canada again produced most of the mercury it required. There has been no mercury output since 1975 however, and mining operations have been suspended indefinitely due to a decline in demand for mercury (3). Mercury is also obtained from redistilled stock reclaimed from products such as batteries, dental amalgams, and mercury sludge.

Mercury has certain physical and chemical properties which make it uniquely attractive: it is the only metal which is a liquid at room temperature and remains a liquid over a long range of temperatures; it has a lower freezing point (-39 deg. C) than any other metal; it has a high density, 13.59 g/cm^3 (gram per cubic centimetre); it is one of the best electrical conductors; it forms amalgams with other metals; it expands uniformly over a wide temperature range; and the metal and its compounds are toxic to bacteria, fungi and other living organisms (1,2).

Mercury compounds were initially used as medicines and were prescribed by Arab and Roman doctors for use as diuretics, antiseptics, and in the treatment of syphilis and ring worm. They were also used as preservatives in cosmetics, as colouring agents in the tanning industry, and by hatmakers in the treatment of fur and felt (2). At present, there are approximately 3000 uses for mercury, in its metal form, or as organic or inorganic compounds (1). Organic mercury compounds are used: as slimicides in the pulp and paper industry to kill bacteria, fungi and yeast-like organisms (2); in agricultural substances applied to leaves, soil and seeds to inhibit the growth of fungi (1); and in the manufacture of latex paints to restrict the formation of mildew.

The metal itself is used in 2 main areas: in the production of electrical goods such as mercury vapour lamps, electrical switches and batteries; and in the chlor-alkali industry which employs mercury as a cathode in the electrolysis of salt solution, $NaCl$, to produce chlorine, Cl_2, and sodium hydroxide, $NaOH$ (1,4). Most such mercury is recovered and re-used. Miscellaneous uses include mercury in dental fillings (5,6), in thermometers and as a catalyst in the plastics industry (7).

A certain amount of mercury in the environment is of natural origin, produced for example, by the weathering of rocks and minerals (1). Human activities can increase the amount entering the environment by an estimated 20,000 tonne per year. Industrial emissions during the production and use of the metal and its compounds are significant sources (2). The burning of coal and petroleum are also sources of mercury contamination (1,2). Environment Canada calculated that in 1970 about 80 tonne of mercury were released into the Canadian environment. Accidental spills of drug preparations and breakage of thermometers are said to account for the annual release of about 10 tonne.

TOXICITY OF MERCURY AND ITS COMPOUNDS

The toxicity of mercury and its compounds is dependent on whether they are organic or inorganic.

An organic compound may roughly be described as any substance which contains carbon. Compounds of the remaining elements together with some carbon-containing compounds such as those found in minerals (carbonates) are classified as inorganic compounds. The distinction between organic and inorganic compounds developed in the early 19th century when there was great interest in the origins of various substances. Those derived from living organisms became known as organic compounds and those that had not been associated with living organisms were labelled inorganic. Although it is now known that organic compounds can be created in a laboratory synthetically from inorganic compounds, the nomenclatures have remained. It is thought that carbon compounds outnumber the compounds of all the other elements put together. The ubiquitousness of carbon compounds is due to the carbon atom's ability to form strong bonds with atoms of other elements and with itself. When carbon atoms bond together, they form chains or rings varying in length from two atoms to thousands -- these are the molecular backbones of countless substances.

Inorganic mercury poisoning is primarily an occupational disease (2). In such cases, mercury tends to concentrate in the kidney. After prolonged exposure death may occur due to failure of the kidney to function properly (2). Metallic mercury vapourizes easily and diffuses through the lungs into the blood, then into the brain causing serious damage to the central nervous system (1). There are several examples of inorganic poisoning throughout history (8,9). It was recognized in the first century, AD; Pliny, in writing of the mercury mine at Almaden, Spain, told of the illness of the miners (Roman slaves) as well as of the dangers faced by Roman goldsmiths who used mercury to harden and purify gold. The mercury mine at Almaden is still the largest and most productive mine in the world. In 1665, a health law was passed there forbidding miners to work more than 8 days a month and 6 hours a day in the shafts and refinery. Although this law still stands, some workers continue to contract mercury poisoning as a result of mining (8).

Workers in the felt hat industry used mercury solutions to treat fur when shaping hats (2,9). Victims of mercury poisoning caused this way suffered "hatter's shakes" and even psychotic symptoms. The fact that hatters went mad may have inspired Lewis Carroll's "Mad Hatter" in Alice in Wonderland (10).

From 1955 to 1975, the Workmen's Compensation Board of Ontario paid compensation to 24 workers affected by mercury poisoning. They were invoved in such things as hat manufacturing, gold refining, fungicides, a dental laboratory, battery manufacturing, the electrical industry, and a chloralkali plant (8).

Of the organic substances, the alkyl mercury compounds, particularly methylmercury species such as CH_3Hg and $(CH_3)_2Hg$, are the greatest health hazards. They readily diffuse and accumulate in the brain. They are retained in the body for long periods of time as distinct from inorganic compounds which are rapidly excreted having a half life of about 70 days (11). Also, they can be produced from inorganic mercury compounds by the action of certain microorganisms (1).

Symptoms of methylmercury poisoning progress from numbness, constriction of the visual field, hearing difficulties, speech impairment, loss of motor coordination to paralysis, deformity, coma and death (2). These symptoms now constitute what is usually known as "cat dancing" or Minamata disease, so called because cats fed scraps of fish caught in Minamata Bay, Japan began jumping and twitching, running round in circles, finally throwing themselves into the water to drown. Humans also began showing signs of the disease in the 1950s. The cause of the outbreak appears to have been the releasing of methylmercury into Minamata Bay, beginning in 1932, by Chisso, an industrial chemical and fertilizer company. It is difficult to say how long and how regularly the residents ate fish from the contaminated bay before they showed signs of mercury poisoning (2).

A Canadian study showed that individuals who ate the equivalent of 320 g per day of fish containing 500 ppb (part per billion) Hg were developing definite signs of mercury poisoning after a six-month period (12). Methylmercury poisoning is especially hazardous to the fetus and the developing child. Methylmercury crosses placental and mammary barriers and may produce immediate or latent toxic effects in the offspring even when none was evident in the mother (12).

Mercury poisoning is usually diagnosed by determining blood levels of methylmercury through various analytical methods such as atomic absorption, gas chromatography, neutron activation and X-ray fluorescence. Usually, levels in excess of 100 ppb (or less in pregnant women and children) indicate a risk of poisoning (2). It is clear that, except for those exposed to high mercury levels in the workplace, the principal source of mercury is food, and the levels may become very high in regions where the metal or its compounds are used in agriculture or industry (2).

HISTORY OF MERCURY CONTAMINATION

The observations in Japan (described above) provided the first indication that mercury is an environmental hazard. Following the incidence of Minamata disease in 1953, 143 residents had died and 899 had been diagnosed as having Minamata disease by November 1975. There were other alarming incidents. In 1956 and 1960, methylmercury poisoning resulting in 450 deaths and over 6500 illnesses (2) occurred in Iraq. The farmers there, who had received grain seed treated with mercurial fungicides, had used it for making bread or ate livestock to which it had been fed (2). Similar outbreaks occurred later in Pakistan and Guatemala (13). In Sweden, poisoning of game birds by mercury-treated seed was noticed in 1960 and in 1967, the Swedish Medical Board banned the sale of fish from some lakes or rivers when it was discovered that the fish contained high levels of methylmercury (13). Minamata disease recurred in Niigata, Japan in 1965; again the cause was consumption of contaminated fish (2).

The demonstration in 1967 by Jernelov, a Swedish scientist, that inorganic mercury could be converted to organic mercury, raised the possibility that Canada may have an organic mercury problem (2). The first concrete evidence was the discovery of mercury in the sediment in Lake St. Clair (7). Evidence was then found of mercury-contaminated fish in Ontario lakes. The federal environmental authorities began a monitoring program of fish caught for commercial use and in 1969, banned commercial fishing in the South Saskatchewan

River. Restrictions on sale of fish were also imposed in many areas of the U.S., and in both countries action was initiated to control the discharge of mercury-containing wastes into lakes and streams (13).

Subsequent research revealed evidence of contaminated fish in many parts of Canada, and although concentrations vary greatly, many sources are apparent (7). For example, high concentrations of mercury originating from chlor-alkali plants in Sarnia, Ontario and Detroit, Michigan are found in Lake St. Clair (7). The English-Wabigoon River System downstream from the Dryden Paper Company in Northwestern Ontario (2) also was found to have high mercury concentrations.

The Canadians who are affected the most by mercury pollution are the native people, because they rely heavily on fish as a food and a source of income. To a lesser extent sports fishermen are exposed to mercury-contaminated fish and a substantial number of guides at fishing camps are exposed because of their occupations (2). Both federal and provincial governments have carried out surveys of mercury levels in the blood of groups of people most probably affected; residents of Northwest Territories, Northwestern Quebec and Northwestern Ontario have shown unacceptable levels of mercury in their bodies (2).

Between 1971 and 1978, the Medical Services Branch of Health and Welfare Canada had examined people in 350 communities across the country and had carried out over 35,000 tests of blood and hair samples. Approximately 2.5% of those tested were found to have mercury levels higher than 100 ppb, which put them at risk of having methylmercury poisoning. Those in the "at risk" range were encouraged to undergo detailed clinical examinations. Although milder forms of mercury poisoning were found possibly to be occurring, cases of Minamata disease, as described earlier, have not been found in Canada. The assessment of the Canadian situation has been complicated by the seasonal fluctuation of fish consumption -- highest in summer and fall, lowest in winter -- and thus, methylmercury exposure of the native population.

LEGISLATION

The legislation governing use, production, and monitoring

of mercury involves various government departments at both the federal and provincial levels (2). The federal role is shared by the following ministries: Environment; Health and Welfare; Agriculture; and Indian Affairs and Northern Development. At the provincial level, the following ministries are involved: Environment; Health; and Natural Resources.

The federal government acted quickly to restrict the release of mercury from industrial sources such as chlor-alkali plants. The regulations, imposed by Environment Canada in 1972, and revised in 1977, established a limit of 2.5 g per day per tonne of chlorine produced (14). Under the Clean Air Act, in 1977, emissions into the ambient air were limited to 1.68 kg per day. In 1970, the Department of Agriculture banned the sale of mercurial seed dressings. In 1977, the Foods Directorate of Health and Welfare recommended a ban on the sale or consumption of fish containing more than 500 ppb of mercury (15). Under the Hazardous Products Act, mercury compounds cannot be used as decorative or protective coatings on children's toys. Under the Ocean Dumping Control Act, mercury cannot be released into coastal waters (15). Under the Labour Code, a maximum exposure of 0.01 mg/m^3 (milligram per cubic metre) of air for alkylmercury and 0.05 mg/m^3 for all other mercury compounds was set for a 40 hour work week (16). Most provinces have established air quality and effluent guidelines and regulations (17).

The economic effects of some of these regulations and guidelines have been harsh. For example, the Matagami Indian fisheries in Northwestern Quebec, which employed about 200 people, had to close (2); chlor-alkali plants have, in many cases, been converted to the diaphragm process which does not involve the use of mercury (2); the Lake Erie fishing industry has declined (7) and fishermen in the Atlantic provinces and Manitoba have been put out of work (7). When commercial fishing was banned in the 1970s on the English-Wabigoon System, a lodge closed, costing Indians a further $300,000 in lost wages annually (18). Only in 1983 were the Indians involved given definite assurances of compensation (20).

Nevertheless, the regulations and guidelines have, to a large extent, been effective in reducing the amount of mercury being released into the environment. Environment Canada estimated that mercury losses to liquid effluents in 1977 were reduced by 99.5% since 1970 (16). Discharges from the chlor-alkali industries have either ceased due to shutting down of plants or decreased as a result of either recirculating waste water and installing lagoons and settling ponds in which the mercury collects, or a change of process (1). The pulp and paper industries have either discontinued the use of organo-mercury compounds or have installed waste treatment procedures to limit the amount of mercury released. The latter was the procedure adopted by the Dryden Paper Co. Slimicidal use of mercury has now been phased out completely in Canada (7). In the U.S., the Food and Drug Administration banned the use of these slimicides in any paper product which may come in contact with food (15). These changes have not always taken place smoothly. There have been long legal battles in which individuals and provinces have sued chemical companies (15).

The mercury released in the past is still present in the bottom mud of lakes and rivers and it is estimated that contamination of fish will probably continue for many years (7). Various task forces have been established to review the mercury problem (2). Methods for removal of mercury already in the environment have been suggested (1). These include dredging, conversion of the mercury to harmless compounds; covering the mercury with inert material, binding the mercury to inorganic material or increasing the pH of the water to facilitate formation of volatile dimethylmercury. In one operation, a river was diverted, sediment was carted away and the rocky river bed washed down (19). All of these suggestions are expensive and may cause other forms of damage (1).

Government agencies continue to monitor chlor-alkali plants (16). The Medical Services Branch continues a program of surveillance (close attention is being paid to the mercury levels in guides, pregnant women and newborn infants) and education on diet in the affected communities. Because levels of mercury were particularly high in the English-Wabigoon system, freezers were installed at Grassy Narrows and Whitedog reserves in order to facilitate shipping in and storing of frozen fish for the residents' consumption.

The mercury situation was concisely summarized in a paper presented to the Standing Committee on Mercury in the Environment in Ottawa on Mar. 21, 1975, by Dr. Miyamoto, who had more than 20 years experience with the Minamata problem:

"So perhaps our task -- the Japanese scientists' task -- is to make clear the fact that there is no technical solution, no monetary solution. The only solution is not to repeat the pollution anywhere." (2).

REFERENCES

1. Moore, J.W. and Moore, E.A., Environmental Chemistry, Academic Press, New York, 1976.
2. Charlebois, C. T., "An Overview of the Canadian Mercury Problem", Science Council of Canada Supplement to Science Forum, 10(5), 1977.
3. Hogan, J. J., "Mercury", Canadian Minerals Yearbook 1979, Department of Energy, Mines and Resources, Ottawa.
4. Schofield, M., "Mercury Scare", New Scientist, Mar. 2, 1978.
5. "Mercury Threat to Dentists", New Scientist, Feb. 10, 1977.
6. Treptow, R. S., "Amalgam Dental Fillings, Part II. Their Chemistry and a Few Problems", Chemistry, 51(4), 15, 1978.
7. Bryan, R., "Much is Taken, Much Remains", Duxbury Press, North Scituate, Massachusetts, 1973.
8. Troyer, W., "No Safe Place", Clarke, Irwin and Company, Toronto, 1977.
9. Mellon, E. K., "Alfred E. Stock and the Insidious Quecksilbervergiftung", Journal of Chemical Education, 54(4), 211, 1977.
10. Gardner, M., "The Annotated Alice", Penguin Books, New York, 1975.
11. "U of W Scientist Works on Mercury Antidote", Canadian Research, Mar.-Apr. 1976.
12. Jaworski, J. F., "Mercury", Executive Reports: Effects of Chromium, Alkali Halides, Arsenic, Asbestos, Mercury and Cadmium in the Canadian Environment, National Research Council of Canada, Ottawa, NRCC No. 17585, 1980.
13. Goldwater, L. J., "Mercury in the Environment", Chemistry in the Environment, Readings from Scientific American, 1952-1973, May 1971.
14. "Mercury in the Canadian Environment", Environment Canada, Environmental Protection Service, 1977.
15. Doern, G. B., "Regulatory Processes and Jurisdictional Issues in the Regulation of Hazardous Products in Canada", Science Council of Canada, Background Study No. 41, 1977.
16. "Status Report on Compliance with the Chor-Alkali Mercury Liquid Effluent Regulations", Environment Canada, Water Pollution Control Directorate, 1978-79.
17. Franson, R.T., Lucan, A. R., Giroux, L. and Kenniff, P., "Canadian Law and the Control of Exposure to Hazards", Science Council of Canada, Background Study No. 39, 1977.
18. Manlon, J., "Mercury and Trees", New Scientist, Oct. 28, 1976.
19. "Company 'Washes' River Bed, Removes Mercury Contamination", Chemecology, May 1983.
20. White, S., "Millions in Compensation No Help: Chief", The Citizen, Ottawa, Dec. 14, 1983.

RECOMMENDED READING

Reference (8) is an interesting, somewhat sensational and emotional book. Reference (2) is an excellent presentation of factual information with a good summary of many aspects of the mercury problem. Associated with reference (2) is another Science Council paper prepared by C. T. Charlebois, "Three perspectives on Mercury in Canada: Medical, Technical and Economic", 1976. Reference (15) contains good chronological accounts of the Grassy Narrows and Whitedog cases. These 3 and reference (7) contain extensive bibliographies. There has recently been a suggestion of a connection between acid rain (see Sulphur Dioxide) and high mercury levels in fish from some lakes (see Keating, M., "Acid Rain Tied to Mercury in Park", The Globe and Mail, Toronto, Apr. 17, 1984).

NITRITES AND NITRATES

Nitrite is used as a meat preservative. Bacon is a particular problem because cooking accelerates formation of carcinogenic chemicals.

For many years it has been known that preseved meat would
keep its attractive pink colour if the curing brine contained
some saltpetre or potassium nitrate, KNO_3. In the late 19th
century it was found that the nitrate ion, NO_3^-, was converted
to the nitrite ion, NO_2^-, by bacteria in the food and it was
the nitrite which preserved the pink colour in the meat (1).
However, in 1959, Health and Welfare Canada prohibited the use
of nitrite in curing fish products. In 1975, a legal limit of
200 ppm (part per million) (i.e., 200 mg (milligram) of $NaNO_2$
per kg (kilogram) of meat) for products such as hotdogs,
sausages and packaged luncheon meat, and 150 ppm for bacon was
established (2).

It is now known that, as well as improving the colour of
cured meats, nitrite also contributes to the flavour, inhibits
the reaction of oxygen with fats and oils, thus preventing a
rancid taste and odour, and prevents the growth of bacteria,
in particular those which cause botulism (1).

The exact reaction mechanism by which the pink colour of
preserved meats is formed is not fully known, but in some way
the nitrite generates nitric oxide which reacts with myoglo-
bin, the red pigment in the meat, to give nitrosylmyoglobin, a
stable red-pink compound. The "cured meat flavour" is due to
the action of the nitrite on the meat components but little is
known of the details. It has been reported (3) that the desired flavour can be obtained with nitrite in lower concentrations than the legal limit. The antibacterial effect of the
nitrite is also not clearly understood (3) but the growth of
Clostridium botulinum appears to be a complicated process
dependent upon the number of spores present, the amount of
heat applied, the concentrations of sodium chloride and sodium
nitrite and the pH of the meat product -- the lower the pH,
i.e., the more acidic the "surroundings", the greater is the
antibacterial effect (3). Preserved fish such as salmon, tuna,
halibut and cod also contain nitrite to control the growth of
Clostridium botulinum.

In addition to nitrite deliberately added to food, some can be produced by the reduction of nitrate in foods. The nitrate itself is not harmful, but during storage and shipping, enzymes or bacteria can convert nitrate into nitrite. In addition, bacteria in the human digestive tract can make this conversion after the food has been eaten (1). Some vegetables e.g., spinach, beets and rhubarb, accumulate nitrate from the soil as they grow. Levels of nitrate in vegetables grown with intensive fertilization can have especially high levels.

Nitrate can also enter the food supply from water supplies (4). Levels of nitrate in some wells have increased by as much as 30 times concomitant with the application of nitrogeneous fertilizers. Runoff from livestock or poultry manure is also rich in nitrates and may decrease groundwater quality if excessively applied, or applied in the wrong season (5).

There are 2 ways in which nitrites may affect human health. The proven toxicity is due to interaction in the bloodstream with hemoglobin, the substance which transports oxygen. The hemoglobin contains iron (II) and if nitrite is present, it can oxidize hemoglobin to methemoglobin, a brown compound, which contains iron (III) ions and is itself reduced. Methemoglobin cannot transport oxygen because of the change in the oxidation state of the iron. When the methemoglobin concentration exceeds 70%, asphyxia occurs. Infants are more susceptible to methemoglobinemia than adults, one reason being that the lower stomach acidity permits the growth of bacteria which can reduce nitrate to nitrite. As a result, giving infants water or food (such as spinach) with a high nitrate content can be hazardous (2). The incidence of nitrite poisoning of adults is low and reported cases have usually been due to accidental addition of nitrite to the food (2).

The second hazard associated with nitrite is that it can combine with amines (see Nitrogen Oxides) to form nitrosamines. Animal studies have shown that there are more than 100 known carcinogenic nitrosamines (6,7) which are organ selective depending on their exact structure (6,8). It is reported that many nitrosamines are also mutagenic (6) and may be teratogenic (2). Nitrosamines have been found in a number of foods and a correlation between these substances and tumour formation in animals has been shown (2). Although there is some suggestion that the combination of nitrite (and nitrate) and amines may be responsible for high incidences of cancer, it has not yet proven to be carcinogenic in humans (9).

Both Health and Welfare Canada and U.S. National Research Council recommend that nitrite added to cured meat be reduced "to the extent that protection against botulism is not compromised" (2,10). However a U.S. study which reports that approximately 79% of nitrite that the average person is exposed to comes from vegetables, as compared to 10% from cured meats.

The U.S. study also investigated alternatives to the current use of nitrite. A promising alternative is biological acidification -- the fermentation of sucrose by lactobacilli (bacteria) to form lactic acid. This process tested on bacon proved to give protection against botulism and to retain the colour and flavour of consumer expectation. Ionizing radiation in small doses with a reduced amount of nitrite to retain flavour was also investigated. This process destroyed microorganisms without causing the food to become radioactive and without destroying nutrients. Other chemical alternatives tested were potassium sorbate, sodium hypophosphite and fumarate ester alone and in combination.

All of the above need to be evaluated further for toxicity arising from long-term exposure and certain cooking and storage conditions. The U.S. study committee recommends that, until an effective and safe substitue is found, additions of Vitamins C and E to block formation of nitrosamines be continued (10). Meanwhile, refrigeration, freezing and sterilization are effective in inhibiting botulism. Refrigerated nitrite-free frankfurters are available at a limited number of markets and so far no botulism has arisen.

It is clear that further research is necessary before the potential hazard of nitrate, nitrite and nitrosamines can be completely evaluated and before any action to eliminate the use of nitrate and nitrite can be justified.

REFERENCES

1. Jacobson, M.F., "Don't Bring Home the Bacon: How Sodium Nitrite Can Affect Your Health", Center for Science in the Public Interest, Washington, D.C., 1973.
2. "Canadian Position on Nitrite in Cured Meats", Food Directorate, Bureau of Chemical Safety News Release, Aug. 17, 1978.
3. Wolff, I. A. and Wasserman, A. E., "Nitrates, Nitrites and Nitrosamines", Science, 177(4043), 15, 1972.
4. Jacobson, M. F., "Eater's Digest: The Consumers Factbook of Food Additives", Doubleday and Company, Garden City, New Jersey, 1972.
5. Webber, L. R., "Nitrogen Inputs to Ground Water from Livestock Wastes", Identification and Measurement of Environmental Pollutants, National Research Council of Canada, Ottawa, June 1971.
6. Magee, P., "Nitrosamines: Ubiquitous Carcinogens?", New Scientist, Aug. 23, 1973.
7. Walters, C. L., "Nitrosamines--Environmental Carcinogens?", Chemistry in Britain, 13(4), 149, 1977.
8. Lijinsky, W., "How Nitrosamines Can Cause Cancer", New Scientist, Jan. 27, 1977.
9. Shapley, D., "Nitrosamines: Scientist on the Trail of Prime Suspect in Urban Cancer", Science, 191, 268, 1976.
10. "Alternatives to the Current Use of Nitrite in Foods", Part 2 of a 2-part study, Committee on Nitrite and Alternative Curing Agents in Foods, National Academy Press, 1982.

RECOMMENDED READING

Reference (1) summarizes the nitrite controversy. Information about nitrosamines can best be found in references (3), (6), (7) and (9).

NITROGEN OXIDES (NOx)

Automobile exhausts contain nitrogen oxides, which can be responsible for the formation of smog in urban areas and can contribute to acid rain.

The most abundant element in the earth's atmosphere is nitrogen. Nearly all this nitrogen is in the form of N_2, but a small portion of it exists in forms such as ammonia (NH_3), nitrous oxide (N_2O), nitric oxide (NO) and nitrogen dioxide (NO_2). Biological action in the soil results in the decomposition of nitrogen-containing compounds, such as proteins or other amines, with the resultant global emission of about 900 million tonne of NH_3, 350 million tonne of N_2O and 200 million tonne of NO per year (1).

Nitrogen is also being removed continuously from the atmosphere by various means. The nitrogen oxides are removed by biological processes, or through eventual formation of nitric acid (HNO_3) in rain. Ammonia can return to the soil or water directly from the gas, but it also comes down in the form of precipitation, usually in the form of a nitrate or a sulfate salt. Thus its presence in the atmosphere is of importance in moderating the acidity of rain (see Sulphur Dioxide). A natural "nitrogen cycle" occurs in the environment resulting in steady state concentrations of ammonia and the nitrogen oxides.

The activities of modern man introduce an additional source of nitrogen oxides into the atmosphere, of the order of 10% of the natural sources (1). They result from the combustion of nitrogen-containing material, e.g., cigarettes, or of nitrogen (N_2) in high-temperature flames. Most such emissions are in the form of nitric oxide.

It has been estimated (2) that 2 million tonne of nitrogen oxides were emitted in Canada in 1979, and that 20.2 million tonne were emitted in the U.S. in 1980. About 40% of the total came from the internal combustion engines of transportation vehicles. Another 30% came from various industrial, commercial and residential activities. Even though the NO_x introduced by man is a small fraction of the total NO_x production, it is concentrated in urban areas.

Nitrous oxide (N_2O) is not known to be toxic to humans. It is sometimes called "laughing gas" due to its effect when present in large amounts, and is used as an anaesthetic. Nitric oxide (NO) is the major component of NO_x from combustion. If emitted into the stratosphere, it can cause depletion of the ozone layer (see Fluorocarbons). It is converted to NO_2 in air by a complex sequence of reactions, although this may take some time (hours or days) if the effluent gases from a flame are cooled rapidly. It is the NO_2 which is the most toxic NO_x component. Acute exposure of humans to NO_2 (>150 ppm (part per million)) can cause death from pulmonary edema. Lower levels of exposure lead to an increase in the resistance of air passages in lungs, but the effects seem to be reversible (3,4). NO_2 also causes injury to vegetation and fading of dyes (5).

The secondary effects of NO_x are, however, more damaging. Under certain chemical reactions, NO_x can lead to the formation of 3 other chemicals which have adverse health effects. These chemicals discussed below are: ozone, PAN (peroxyacetylnitrate) and nitrosamines.

Ozone (O_3) is formed in small quantities from electric discharges in the air (for example, lightning) and gives the air what is considered a "fresh" smell. Larger amounts of ozone can, however, be quite harmful. Ozone has the same type of toxic effects as nitrogen dioxide (NO_2), but to a considerably greater degree (6). Both ozone and nitrogen dioxide presumably oxidize biological compounds such as fatty acids (5). Ozone also attacks rubber and causes injury to vegetation (5).

The main source of larger concentrations of ozone seems to be the "photolysis" of nitrogen dioxide (7,8). Photolysis is a process by which nitrogen dioxide absorbs visible radiation from the sun, causing the release of an oxygen atom (O). The oxygen atom is then free to react with O_2 to give ozone (O_3). One way in which ozone is broken down is by a reaction with nitrogen oxide (NO), which produces nitrogen dioxide (NO_2) and O_2.

These various reactions, which either create or break down ozone, give rise to an interesting phenomenon. In the immediate vicinity of NO_x emissions, there is a predominance of nitric oxide (NO), which breaks down ozone, thus causing a decrease in the amount of that toxic molecule. However, in regions downwind from the NO_x source, the nitric oxide has converted to nitrogen dioxide, which causes an increase in the O_3 level (7). It is important to note that the discussion here is regarding ozone near sea level. Ozone also exists at higher levels where it can be broken down into O_2 and O by ultraviolet radiation (see Fluorocarbons).

NO_x and O_3 are 2 components of photochemical or "Los Angeles-type" smog (9). Such smog results when NO_x and hydrocarbons (e.g. unburned gasoline) are emitted in high concentrations, and meteorological conditions do not allow for dispersal in the air. In addition, the presence of hydrocarbons renders other photochemical reactions possible (reactions where solar radiation is involved). Some of the compounds subsequently formed can be strong eye irritants. One of these is PAN (peroxyacetylnitrate). PAN is also extremely toxic to plants and damage usually appears as a silvery or bronzed colouration on the lower leaf surface (10,11). Recent reports indicate that PAN can be present in clean air, e.g. over the Pacific Ocean (15).

Neither nitric oxide nor nitrogen dioxide has been demonstrated to be carcinogenic. Yet a correlation has been noted between incidence of cancer and high levels of NO_x. The cancer may be caused by nitrosamines. Nitrosamines are formed by a reaction of nitrous acid (which itself is formed by NO_2 or NO) and amines (for example, ammonia, NH_3). Dimethylnitrosamine (DMN) is a proven potent carcinogen in animals. Nitrosamines have been detected in places where considerable traffic is the only known source (e.g. 0.8 microgram per cubic metre on an expressway in New York City) (12), but it has not been demonstrated conclusively that nitrosamines are formed following inhalation of nitrogen dioxide (8). Nitrosamines can also occur in the preservation of foods (see Nitrites) and in tobacco smoke (see Tobacco).

Another controversy involving nitrogen oxides emissions is the link to acid rain (see Sulphur Dioxide). Nitrogen oxides, travelling over distances of up to thousands of kilometres, can be transformed into nitric acid, which falls to the ground during precipitation (2). Because nitrogen is an essential plant nutrient, some plants have shown increased yields when exposed to slightly acidic precipitation. Other plants, however, have shown decreased yields, and in the long-term, acid rain has the cumulative effect of increasing soil acidity (see Sulphur Dioxide for further effects of acid rain) (2).

Regions where conditions for photochemical smog are more common, as in some big American cities, have had legislation regarding limits of NO_x and other automobile emissions (hydrocarbons (HC), carbon monoxide (CO)) for some years. California set emission standards in 1966, with standards on NO_x set first in 1971 at 4.0 g (gram) of NO_x per mile of travel. The Environmental Protection Agency (EPA) in the U.S. recommended a standard of 2.0 g/mile of NO_x for 1977 (3).

Simultaneous control of HC, CO and NO_x is considerably more difficult than control of HC and CO emissions only, as both HC and CO, but not NO_x can be controlled by using high air/fuel ratios and catalytic converters (16). Systems of control of all 3 may be less economical in terms of energy consumption. The standards in the U.S. are in a very flexible state depending on degrees of concern for the environment, energy conservation, cost of automobiles, and technological advances (1).

In Canada, a multitude of federal and provincial departments, associations, unions, and industries must be involved if NO_x is to be considered comprehensively (3,13). NO_x has generally not been perceived as a major hazard. It was only in 1975 that NO_x levels began to be monitored all across Canada in 44 cities. The Canadian Clean Air Act establishes 0.05 ppm (part per million) as the ambient maximum level of NO_2, with a 0.2 ppm maximum for one hour exposures (14). Ontario, Saskatchewan and British Columbia are 3 provinces that have set limits of 5 ppm on NO_2 concentrations in the workplace, and New Brunswick has set a maximum permissible level of 10 ppm for the NO_2 concentration in mines (3).

Compared with other substances, oxides of nitrogen have not been regarded as high priority hazards. Further research into their secondary and synergistic effects may lead to a change in attitude.

REFERENCES

1. Moore, J. W. and Moore, E, A., "Environmental Chemistry", Academic Press, New York, 1976.
2. "Still Waters", Sub-Committee on Acid Rain of the Standing Committee on Fisheries and Forestry, Ministry of Supply and Services, 1981.
3. Basuk, J. and Nichols, A., "An Overview of the Oxides of Nitrogen Hazard in Canada", Prepared for the Science Council of Canada, Committee on Policies and Poisons, 1977.
4. "Air Pollutants--Good News and Bad", Chemistry, 51(6), 24, 1978.
5. "Photochemical Air Pollution: Formation, Transport and Effects", Associate Committee on Scientific Criteria for Environmental Quality, National Research Council of Canada, Ottawa, NRCC No. 14096, 1975.
6. Federal Register, 36(105) as quoted by Innes, W. B., "California Smog", Environmental Science and Technology, 11, 738, 1977.
7. Pitts, J. N., Jr., "Keys to Photochemical Smog Control", Environmental Science and Technology, 11(5), 456, 1977.
8. "Nitrogen Dioxide and Nitric Oxide/Recommendations for Occupational Exposure", Health and Welfare Canada, Ottawa, 1977.
9. Hanst, P. L., "Noxious Trace Gases in the Air. Part I. Photochemical Smog", Chemistry, 51(1), 8, 1978.
10. Pryde, L. T., "Environmental Chemistry, An Introduction", Cummings Publishing Company, Menlo Park, California, 1973.
11. Pyle, J. L., "Chemistry and The Technological Backlash", Prentice-Hall Inc., Englewood Cliffs, New Jersey, 1974.
12. Shapley, D., "Nitrosamines: Scientists on the Trail of Prime Suspect in Urban Cancer", Science, 191, 268, 1976.
13. Doern, G. B., "Regulatory Processes and Jurisdictional Issues in the Regulation of Hazardous Products in Canada", Science Council of Canada Background Study No. 41, Catalogue No. SS21-1/41, 1977.
14. "The Clean Air Act--Compilation of Regulations and Guidelines", Environment Canada, Apr. 1981.
15. "PAN Measured in Clean Tropospheric Air", Chemical and Engineering News, Apr. 4, 1983.
16. Stansell, J., "Clean-Air Cars Reach a Crossroads", New Scientist, Nov. 24, 1983.

RECOMMENDED READING

Reference (1) gives general overviews of the NO_x and smog problems at a reasonably simple level. Reference (6) is written at a more specialized level, and reviews toxic effects of NO_x, ozone etc., thoroughly, including effects on vegetation. Regulatory aspects for Canada are thoroughly discussed in references (4) and (14). Reference (4) also includes a broader discussion of NO_x in cigarette smoke. Reference (9) considers oxides of nitrogen as occupational rather than environmental hazards. Reference (10) is a very interesting article on photochemical smog.

POLYCHLORINATED BIPHENYLS (PCBs)

The great chemical stability of PCBs has made them useful for several industrial purposes. This stability now poses a problem as harmful effects of PCBs have been discovered. Although their use is discontinued PCBs will persist in the environment for years.

Polychlorinated biphenyls (see figure) were first identified in 1881 and first used in 1929. They are a class of chemical compounds containing biphenyl to which a number of chlorine atoms are attached (see figure). There are about 210 possible PCBs of which around 102 are probable (1). PCB formulations do not consist of just one of these possible polychlorinated biphenyls; they are a mixture with a fixed percent by weight of chlorine. Monsanto Ltd., the only North American producer of PCBs, has a 4 digit numbering system for its products giving the type of compound (first 2 numbers) and its percent by weight of chlorine (last 2 numbers). Thus Arochlor (a trade name for PCBs) 1254 represents a chlorinated biphenyl containing 54% chlorine and 18 distinct PCBs.

A typical PCB   Furan

PCBs are inert chemically and have high dielectric constants, properties which explain their suitability for many industrial purposes. They are not soluble in water and are unaffected by acids, bases or corrosive chemicals. They have high boiling points and may be heated and boiled without decomposing but can degrade into polychlorinated dibenzofurans (furans)(see figure) under conditions of prolonged high temperatures (2). They are related to DDT (see DDT) but are even less biodegradable than that substance, presumably because in

PCBs the 2 benzene rings are directly bonded (see figure) (3). Thus, although their stability makes them ideal for many industrial uses, this same stability makes them very persistent in the environment.

The major use of PCBs in industry was in the electrical industry as a dielectric fluid for industrial capacitors and transformers. Because they combine the qualities of high dielectric constant and low flammability, they were until recently in great demand for such purposes. These constituted the only important Canadian applications (4). They were used also as heat-transfer and hydraulic fluids; in carbonless copying paper; as dust suppressors on roads; as plasticizers in synthetic resins, rubbers, paints, waxes and asphalts; as flame retardants in conjunction with polyvinylchloride, and in lubricating oils (3).

PCBs IN THE ENVIRONMENT

PCBs were first recognized as environmental contaminants in 1966, having been detected in eagle feathers in Sweden (3). They may, in fact, have been present before that time but any PCB would have been interpreted as being part of the DDT (see DDT) searched for at the time. This was due to the state of analytical technology which was not then capable of resolving closely-related compounds (see Dioxins). Some of the adverse effects blamed on DDT may actually be due to PCBs (5).

Since then, PCBs have been found widely dispersed (even in Antarctica (6)), in many fish and birds, in human and animal fat tissue, in milk, in food (6), in planktons, in snow, in industrial waste discharges, in river-bottom sediments (8) and in nursing mothers' milk (9). The PCBs in the environment bioaccumulate because they are lipophilic, preferring organic media such as body fats.

PCBs enter the environment through leakages from electrical transformers and power capacitors (10), through run-off from roads on which PCBs have been sprayed for dust-suppression, from burning of carbonless copy paper, from landfill leachate, from leaking transport trucks (11), from derailments (12) and by other accidental causes such as an Ontario Hydro electrical transformer fire in Toronto in 1977 (13). PCBs were used to suppress the vaporization and so extend the active life of insecticides such as aldrin, dieldrin and chlordane (2); hence they also entered the environment through insecticide run-off.

Recently there has been concern over the levels of PCBs in indoor air. A study shows that indoor air, whether commercial, industrial or residential, contains levels of PCBs at least one order of magnitude higher than outdoor levels (14). Defective fluorescent light ballasts and video display terminals have been suggested as sources of PCBs (14,15).

HEALTH EFFECTS

The health effects of PCBs have been studied in animals and, to some extent, observed in humans. In several animal species (birds, monkeys) reproductive processes have been shown to be affected; the livers, enzyme systems and immunities of some animals are also affected (8). Cancers of the liver have been observed in rats fed PCB-containing diets (16). However tests conducted by the National Cancer Institute did not show Arochlors to be carcinogenic (17). The only human health effects revealed by epidemiological studies are chloracne (see Dioxins) and mild liver abnormalities (18). No substantial adverse human health effects seem to have resulted from exposure to PCBs in the U.S. as of 1983 (42).

The effects of PCB ingestion in humans first became evident in Japan in 1968 when, on the island of Kyushu, many cases of chloracne, eye discharges, headaches, vomiting, fever, and visual disturbances were reported. The cause of the epidemic (1057 patients had been reported by 1971) was traced to a leak in the heating system of a rice oil producer in Kitakyushu City. On analysis, samples of the rice oil were found to contain from 2,000-3,000 ppm (part per million) of Kanechlor 400, a Japanese PCB used in the plant's heating system. Because the epidemic was associated with the rice oil product, the disease has become known as Yusho, or oil disease (1,19). A mass poisoning of 20,000 people in Spain in 1981 showed symptoms similar to those of the Yusho incident. In this case however, cooking oil had not been contaminated by PCBs, but had been heated to remove denaturing agents (48).

Testing of Yusho oil 10 years later found it to be contaminated with several highly toxic furans. Most prominent was

the 2,3,7,8 tetra-isomer, the furan analog of TCDD, but significant quantities of 1,2,3,7,8 and 2,3,4,7,8 penta-isomers
were present. The researchers say the toxicity of these furans
is comparable to TCDD. Used PCBs from a transformer were also
tested; furans were found to occur in very similar concentrations to the Yusho oil (20). Strikingly similar concentrations of these furans were related to toxic effects in
European workers in 1970 (2). Laboratory tests have indicated
that PCBs can degrade to furans at prolonged exposure to
temperatures of 300 deg. C. Such conditions can occur in
transformer "hot spots" (2). This evidence suggests that PCBs
were not directly the culprit in the Yusho incident.

CONTROL OF PCBs AND THEIR CURRENT STATUS

There have been 2 kinds of response to the PCB problems.
First, a voluntary response by manufacturers; and second, a
response by various government agencies. Monsanto Ltd.
initiated a sales program which was fully implemented in 1972
(21). Under this program, production of PCBs was curtailed for
"open applications" which are those most likely to lead to
losses in the environment. Production was cut by 20,000 tonne
per year, amounting to one-half of the PCBs manufactured.
Affected by this withdrawal were carbonless copy paper,
hydraulic fluid, heat transfer fluid and plasticizer uses. The
company supplied PCB dielectric fluids for closed uses only,
where environmental contamination was unlikely.

In Oct. 1976 (22) Monsanto announced plans to cease
production of PCBs by the fall of 1977. It was expected that
their stockpiles of PCBs would be depleted by the spring of
1978 (23). Several companies have announced their intentions
to switch to PCB substitutes for electrical purposes (24).
Nevertheless, the PCB problem continues because it is such a
stable chemical (25) and because there are still many
transformers filled with PCBs in existence. The replacement of
PCBs in such transformers was estimated to take 20 years, but
the program may be accelerated (43).

In 1973 the U.S. Food and Drug Administration (FDA) set
maximum limits for PCBs in food and food-packaging material
(8). These ranged from 0.2 ppm in infant and junior food to
2.5 ppm in milk and dairy products, to 5.0 ppm in poultry and
fish to 10.0 ppm in paper food packaging (8). Lower maximum

levels have recently been proposed by that agency (26). Various states have initiated legislation concerning PCB levels(8,27).

The U.S. Environmental Protection Agency (EPA) was recently ordered to issue regulations requiring 1.5 million pieces of electrical equipment containing Askarel (a brand name for PCB insulating fluid) to be replaced over the next 6 years. The court order to the EPA concerned areas where the public may be exposed to leaks from capacitors and areas where contamination of food or animal feed would result. Both the utilities and the environmentalists are unhappy with the order (30).

In Canada, PCBs were the first substances studied with respect to regulation under the Environmental Contaminants Act, proclaimed in 1975 (28). Initially their use was restricted to new electrical equipment, then to servicing of existing electrical equipment. All use of PCBs was finally stopped on July 1, 1980 (29).

Internationally the Organization for Economic Cooperation and Development (OECD) recommended in 1973 that its member countries restrict the use of PCBs to closed systems (8). Of the countries involved, only Japan had eliminated nearly all uses of PCBs (8).

Such measures have been successful in reducing the number of people having high levels of PCBs in their bodies, at least in the U.S. (43). The fraction of the population with levels greater than 3 ppm was 2.7% in 1972, increased to 8% in 1977, but then declined to 1% in 1981.

Disposal of PCBs is a problem. Incineration is one possible method, but the stability of PCBs means that combustion temperatures must reach 1000 deg. C. The U.S. EPA approved 2 incinerators for PCB destruction in early 1981 (34), and ocean incineration has proven successful (44). A special incineration ship incinerated PCB wastes with an efficiency of 99.99% at a site in the Gulf of Mexico.

In Ontario, the Ministry of the Environment conducted plant trials in a modified cement kiln and approved the process (31), but public protest prevented full-scale use (32). Concerns over emissions of PCBs by cement kilns are

valid, but the trials in Mississauga achieved 99.986%
destruction (31). Such concerns also ignore the production in
nature of PCBs, furan and dioxin traces (36)(see Dioxins).
When a Canadian firm developed a promising method using an
industrial diesel engine, details of a trial run were witheld
to prevent the NIMBY ("not in my backyard") syndrome (33).

A chemical process for removing PCB residues was approved
by the EPA in 1981 (34), and was planned to start in Canada in
1983 (46). There is also the possibility that microorganisms
can be designed to degrade PCBs and other industrially
produced chemicals (47).

THE PBB TRAGEDY

The bromine analog of PCB is PBB, or polybrominated
biphenyl, and sometimes confused with it. PBB was used as a
fire-retardant under the name "Firemaster" by the Michigan
Chemical Co.; the same company also produces a food additive
under the name "Nutrimaster". A mix-up resulted in
"Firemaster" (i.e.,PBB) being added to animal feed in a feed
mixing plant.

The result was the destruction of 30,000 cattle, 1.5
million chickens and numerous other farm animals which caused
on the order of $ 100 million in damages (37, 38, 39, 40). In
addition about 8000 people on Michigan farms who had eaten
PBB-tainted food suffered adverse effects such as damaged
livers, swollen joints and extreme fatigue.

This incident reached such proportions because the cause
for the initial symptoms in cattle (in Sept. 1973) was difficult to find; it took several months before PBB was identified (Apr. 1974) (38). A study carried out by the Mount Sinai
School of Medicine found that 97% of the state's population
had been contaminated (41). Levels in men and children were
found to be higher than in women. Farmers had the highest
concentrations and will likely be the first to contract cancer
if the risk estimated from animal studies is correct (41).

In Canada, regulations banning the use of PBBs were
announced on Apr. 1, 1978 as a result of a report on polybrominated biphenyls in the environment submitted to the Joint
Environment/Health and Welfare Contaminants Committee (29).

REFERENCES

1. National Technical Information Service Washington, D.C.: Polychlorinated Biphenyls and the Environment. COM-72-10419, May, 1972.

2. Webber, I., "The Degradation of Polychlorinated Benzenes in Electrical Equipment", IEEE/PES Conference, New York, 1982.

3. DiNardi, S. R. and Desmarais, A. M., "Polychlorinated Biphenyls in the Environment", Chemistry, 49(4), 14, 1976.

4. "Background to the Regulation of Polychlorinated Biphenyls (PCBs) in Canada", A report of the Task Force on PCB to the Environmental Contaminants Committee of Environment Canada and Health and Welfare Canada, Technical Report 76-1, Apr. 1, 1976.

5. Jukes, T. H., "DDT: Bystander or Participant", Nature, 259, 443, 1976.

6. "PCBs in Antarctica", Science News, 111(3), 44, 1977.

7. Highland, J., "PCBs in Food. What is Acceptable?", Environment, 18(2), 12, 1976.

8. Ahmed, A. K., "PCBs in the Environment: The Accumulation Continues", Environment, 18(2), 6, 1976.

9. Information Supplemental to the CTV Reports Inquiry "The Failing Strategy", broadcast Sunday, Dec. 11, 1977, on the CTV Network, 42 Charles St. E., Toronto.

10. Resource Planning Corporation, "Major Findings of the Study of PCBs in Equipment Owned by the Electric Utility Industry", Washington, D.C., Mar. 30, 1982.

11. "Truck Leaks PCBs from Crack", The Globe and Mail, Toronto, June 30, 1977.

12. "Ministry to Remove PCB-Polluted Soil near Sudbury", ibid, Sept. 7, 1977.

13. "Fire on Adelaide Releases PCBs into the Air", ibid, Dec. 15, 1977.

14. Macleod, K.E., "Polychlorinated Biphenyls in Indoor Air", Environmental Science and Technology, 15(8), 927, 1981.

15. "Unionist Links PCBs with Use of VDTs", The Globe and Mail, Toronto, Sept. 30, 1982.

16. International Agency for Research on Cancer, IARC Monographs on the Evaluation of the Carcinogenic Risk of Chemicals to Humans (1978), Volume 18, Polychlorinated Biphenyls, Lyons, France.

17. "Hexachlorophene, PCB not Carcinogenic", Government Concentrates, Chemical and Engineering News, Apr. 24, 1978.

18. "Recent Advances in Exposure, Health and Environmental Effects Studies of PCBs", A Symposium for Scientific Information Exchange, ICAIR Systems Division, Life Systems Inc., under contract to EPA, Bethesda, Maryland, May, 1982.

19. Environmental Health Criteria 2, "Polychlorinated Biphenyls and Terphenyls", World Health Organization, Geneva, 1976.

20. Buser, H. R., Rappe, C. and Gara, A., "Polychlorinated Dibenzofurans (PCDFs) Found in Yusho Oil and in used Japanese PCB", Chemosphere, 5, 1978.

21. "Polychlorinated Biphenyls: a Risk/Benefit Dilemma", Monsanto Company, St. Louis, Jan., 1976.

22. "Monsanto to Shut Down PCB Unit, Exit Business by Oct. 31, 1977", Monsanto Press Release, Oct. 5, 1976.

23. "The Evidence Mounts Against PCBs", Business Week, 2449, 39, Sept. 13, 1976.

24. Chemical and Engineering News: "PCB Substitutes are Getting an Important Market Boost", Sept. 13, 1976. "PCB Substitute is Safe for Environment", Dec. 8, 1975. "Westinghouse Will Phase out PCBs", July 26, 1976. "PCB Users Looking Hard for Ideal Replacement", May 9, 1977.

25. "PCB Levels Persist Despite Limited Use", Chemical and Engineering News, Dec. 1, 1975.

26. "FDA Proposes Lower PCB Levels in Foods", ibid, Apr. 11, 1977.
27. "PCBs Would be Banned in Illinois...", ibid, May 31, 1976.
28. "End Near for Electrical Uses of PCB", Energy Analects, 5(24), 5, 1976.
29. Canada Gazette Announcements--Environmental Contaminants Act, Environment Canada, Environmental Protection Service, Apr. 1981.
30. "New Final Rules Set for PCBs", Chemical and Engineering News, Aug. 30, 1982.
31. "Burning of Chlorinated Hydrocarbon Wastes", Chemistry in Canada, p. 16, Apr., 1978.
32. "Ministry to Provide $400,000 to Test Plasma Torch on PCBs", The Globe and Mail, Toronto, July 11, 1980.
33. "Burning of PCBs in Diesel Engine Found Promising", ibid, Aug. 16, 1980. "Residents not Told of PCB Burn Plans", ibid, Apr. 20, 1982.
34. "First PCB Disposal Facilities", Chemical and Engineering News, Feb. 16, 1981.
35. "PCB Destruction Process Backed Nationwide", ibid, June 7, 1982.
36. "Polychlorinated Dibenzo-p-Dioxins: Criteria for their Effects on Man and his Environment", Associate Committee on Scientific Criteria for Environmental Quality, National Research Council of Canada, NRCC No. 18574, 1981.
37. Carter, L. J., "Michigan's PCB Incident: Chemical Mix-up Leads to Disaster", Science, 192, 240, 1976.
38. Emshwiller, J., "A Chemical Horror Study in Michigan", Business and Society Review, 17, 5, 1976.
39. McGinty, L., "How a Fire Retardant Polluted Michigan", New Scientist, Dec. 22/29, 1977.
40. Robertson, L. W. and Chynoweth, D. P., "Another Halogenated Hydrocarbon", Environment 17(6), 25, 1975.
41. "Chemical Mix-up Contaminates Michigan People", New Scientist, May 6, 1982.
42. Miller, S., "The PCB Imbroglio", Environmental Science and Technology 17, 11A, 1983. "Scientist Says not to Worry About PCBs", Chemical Engineering, Jan. 9, 1984.
43. Sun, M., "EPA, Utilities Grapple with PCB Problems", Science, 222, 32, 1983.
44. Trewhitt, J., "Drop in PCB Level Seen as Joint Accomplishment", Chemical Engineering, July 11, 1983.
45. "Shipboard PCB Destruction is Successful", Chemical and Engineering News, May 30, 1983.
46. "Chemical Destruction of PCBs to Begin Soon", The Globe and Mail, Toronto, Apr. 6, 1983.
47. "Microbial Dustmen Clean up Toxic Waste", New Scientist, May 5, 1983.
48. MacKenzie, D., "Japanese Clue to Spanish Cooking Oil Disaster", New Scientist, Oct. 13, 1983.

RECOMMENDED READING

References (1,4,19) give a thorough, technical view of the PCB problem. There are also several more readable articles, e.g. references (3,7,8). Reference (42) is a recent updating of issues relating to PCBs. The PBB tragedy is described in a human interest style in reference (38). Additional reading: National Research Council, "Polychlorinated Biphenyls", 1978, NRCC No. 16077.

PENTACHLOROPHENOL (PCP)

PCP has been used for years as a wood preservative. Doubts have now arisen about its safety.

Pentachlorophenol (PCP), a synthetic chemical, has been associated since 1936 with wood preservation (1). PCP can contain various toxic dioxins, and is itself toxic. As well, there have been well-publicized cases of PCP entering the food chain. In 1977, the state of Michigan banned PCP after the chemical was found in cows which had either licked PCP-treated wood or had breathed the fumes (3). In Canada, also in 1977, a shipment of feed grains for consumption by livestock became contaminated with PCP because the railway boxcar, which had previously carried PCP, had been improperly cleaned. The result was a partial feed refusal by livestock and the withholding of livestock and milk from market (2). Then in 1980, on the heels of a highly toxic dioxin being found in herring gull eggs off the Canadian Great Lakes, other dioxins, traced to PCP-treated wood, were found in some Guelph Ontario chickens (4). In 1981, Agriculture Canada placed tight restrictions on the uses of PCP (5).

PROPERTIES, PRODUCTION, AND USES

The chlorophenols (CPs), of which PCP is one of the most commonly manufactured members, are synthesized chemicals made by attaching chlorine atoms to a phenol (a benzene ring with an hydroxyl (OH) group attached) (2). Pentachlorophenol has 5 chlorine atoms attached. Pure PCP forms colourless crystals with a phenolic odour (1); it is non-flammable and is soluble in most organic solvents (1). Because the oil used to dissolve PCP can cause rapid deterioration of rubber, synthetic rubber is used for equipment parts and protective clothing which will come in contact with the solution (1).

Most of the chlorophenols, including most PCP, are marketed as a complex mixture of CPs, not just as one single chemical (6). Thus technical, as opposed to pure, PCP contains up to 12% tetrachlorophenol (4 chlorine atoms attached) (6). In 1976, approximately 1.7 million kg (kilogram) of PCP, plus an additional 180 tonne of PCP salt, were used in Canada (2). Thirty-two percent of this was imported; there is now only one

producer of CPs in Canada, that being the Uniroyal Chemical
Division of Uniroyal, located near Edmonton (2).

In 1976, almost 95% of the PCP produced in Canada was
used for wood preservation. PCP is used as a bactericide,
slimicide, fungicide, herbicide, and insecticide, in paints,
drilling muds, photographic solutions, hides and leathers,
textiles, industrial cooling systems and pulp and paper mill
systems. PCP is also used in health care and veterinary products and in disinfectants. In the wood protection industry,
there is now a trend to substitute kiln drying methods for
CPs. The reasons for the shift are that wood with less moisture content is cheaper to ship, and that new U.S. regulations
require kiln dried lumber for wood house construction (2).

HEALTH EFFECTS

There are 2 sources of adverse health effects associated
with PCP use. The first source is the PCP itself. In general,
the toxicity of CPs increases with an increase in the number
of chlorine atoms attached to the phenol (2). Thus, PCP is
expected to be the most toxic of the CPs (6). The second
source of adverse health effects is some of the impurities in
PCP which are formed during its manufacture. During the latter
stages of PCP production, elevated temperatures are needed,
and this favors the formation of PCDDs (polychlorinated
dibenzo-p-dioxins), PCDFs (polychlorinated dibenzofurans), and
other impurities (2). Such impurities may become a problem if
the PCP is misused or mishandled.

Chlorophenols are toxic in that they interfere in the
mode by which the body utilizes energy; this can lead to death
from energy starvation (6). The lethal dose of PCP is similar
for a wide range of organisms including mammals and fish, and
is in the order of 100-200 ppm (part per million) (6). Pure
PCP is more toxic to a fetus than is PCP that contains impurities such as PCDDs (6). Although this appears to be an
anomalous observation, it can be explained because the PCDDs
act to attract enzymes which break down PCP (6).

PCP has not been shown to cause cancer; a 2-year study of
the effect of PCP on rats did not find PCP carcinogenic when
administered orally on a chronic basis at dose levels

sufficiently high to cause mild signs of toxicity (2). Only at high levels in animal studies has pure PCP been found to produce chronic effects, such as decreased body weight.

It is widely agreed that the causes of long-term adverse health effects of CPs are contaminants such as various PCDDs. A 1980 study using cattle compared the toxicity of technical and analytical grades of PCP (6). The lower grade technical PCP produced health effects in cattle including increased liver and lung weight, decreased thymus weight and an abnormal functioning of the gall bladder. Except for minor symptoms, cattle receiving higher grade (analytical) PCP (less PCDDs) were comparable to the unexposed control group of cattle (6).

In humans, PCP dust and vapour is irritating to mucous membranes, and may provoke violent sneezing (1). In solid form, and in water solutions stronger than 1% concentration, PCP is irritating to the skin (1). Some effects on workers exposed to PCP include corneal numbness and damage, blind spots, and autonomic nervous system impairment (7).

EXPOSURE

PCP can enter the environment both intentionally and accidentally. Intentional disposal of PCP (although perhaps through ignorance) can occur in the manufacturing process, at wood treatment plants or during on-site treatments with wood preservatives (2). Accidental dispersal can occur from manufacturing mishaps, such as spills from ruptured processing equipment, or from broken storage containers. It has been noted that although these accidental spills contribute an overall small volume of PCP, they can be significant in the immediate vicinity of the accident (2). In 1972 in British Columbia, a hydro pole was treated in place with a PCP preservative. A nearby stream received a shock load of PCP, killing fish for a distance of 800 metre downstream (2).

There are several wood-protection facilities which dip wood into solutions containing various CPs. Environment Canada has identified some of these facilities in British Columbia as being serious environmental hazards because of inadequate design and operation and because many such facilities are located at environmentally-vulnerable sites (2). CPs can be accidentally mixed with food or ingested by animals, as was documented at the beginning of this chapter. Chlorinated water can also be a source of PCP. It has been shown that chlorine can react with naturally occurring phenol to produce CPs (2).

PCP has the highest bioaccumulation potential of the CPs, although even it accumulates to only 1000 times its concentration in water in the worst situations (6). It is therefore not anticipated that there will be the same problem of bioaccumulation in the food chain as there is with other chemicals, such as DDT. On the other hand, the National Research Council warns that not enough basic data on the properties of CPs exist to predict their environmental fate (6).

A recent discharge of wood-impregnating solution containing CPs, in Sweden, provided more information and warnings regarding longer term effects of CPs (8). The CPs were rapidly distributed in the river system, and even after 2 months, CPs could still be detected in the livers of fish caught 15 km from the discharge point. Microbial action added methyl groups to the CPs to give chlorinated anisoles. These chemicals were found to be more bioaccumulating than their parent compounds (8).

CPs and their impurities have been described as "probably ubiquitous" in the Canadian environment (2). It has been estimated that the average American has 0.02 to 0.08 ppm of PCP in urine samples (2). No similar Canadian study exists. Trace amounts of PCP have been found in potatoes and other crops and CPs have been found in the water and in sediment samples (2).

Some people risk greater exposure to PCP than others. A U.S. study published in 1975 reported exposures to CPs in wood treatment plants of up to 0.015 mg/m^3 (milligram per cubic metre), although on average, the levels were probably below 0.002 mg/m^3 (6). People who are in houses which have just had PCP-containing wood preservers applied can be exposed to PCP vapours for several days after treatment (6). Babies who crawl on floors excessively treated with PCP, and workers who handle wood with PCP-containing preservative, can risk dermal absorption (6).

REGULATIONS

Products containing PCP and PCP salt have been registered for use in Canada since 1949 (5). In 1981, Agriculture Canada, under the authority of the Pest Control Products Act, announced revisions to use standards for the chlorophenols (5). There is a ban on several CP-containing products labelled for use in the home or on the farm in wood preservation. Included in this ban are CP-containing wood preservatives and wood stains for indoor use, and PCP-containing wood preservatives for use on above-ground interior woodwork of farm buildings, such as on chicken roosts. There is a ban on CP-containing products labelled for a variety of uses such as herbicides, fungicides, and soil sterilants. As well, the new regulations limit the use of CPs as additives to textiles. Products for use on textiles now must contain the warning, "Do not incorporate into materials of which end use will result in prolonged direct skin contact, e.g. life jackets, sleeping bags, sports equipment."

(As a final note to this chapter, one should not confuse PCP the wood preservative, with PCP the mood altering drug. The latter PCP stands for 1-(1-phenylcyclohexyl)piperidine, but is better known as "angel dust", "embalming fluid", and "killer weed" (9).)

REFERENCES

1. "Guide to Chemicals Used in Crop Protection", 6th edition, Agriculture Canada, 1973.
2. "Chlorophenols and Their Impurities in the Canadian Environment", Economic and Technical Review Report, EPS 3-EC-81-2, Environment Canada, 1981.
3. "Michigan Bans PCP Wood Preservative", Chemical and Engineering News, Mar. 21, 1977.
4. "Dioxin Traces Found in Chicken Livers", The Globe and Mail, Toronto, Dec. 9, 1980.
5. "Canada: Changes in the Regulatory Status of the Chlorophenols", International Registry of Potentially Toxic Chemicals (IRPTC), p. 28, Aug. 1981.
6. "Chlorinated Phenols: Criteria for Environmental Quality", Associate Committee on Scientific Criteria for Environmental Quality, National Research Council, 1982.
7. "Neurotoxic Follies", Psychology Today, June 1982.
8. Renberg, L., Marell, E., Sundstrom, G. and Adolfsson-Erici, M., "Levels of Chlorophenols in Natural Waters..", Ambio, 12, 121, 1983.
9. "PCP Hazards Prompt Tough Federal Action", Chemical and Engineering News, July 3, 1978.

RECOMMENDED READING

A complete description of PCP -- sources, environmental impacts, uses, toxicology -- can be found in reference (2). Also, reference (6) is a complete technical assessment of environmental and toxicological effects.

PHOSPHATES

Phosphates are introduced into lakes and rivers by inadequate treatment of sewage. In excess, they promote the
growth of algae, accelerating the natural aging of a lake.

Phosphorus is found in all living organisms as it is
essential to the use of energy by the cell and in genetic
mechanisms. Like other essential elements it follows a natural
cycle in the environment (1). Man's actions have caused an
imbalance in this cycle, especially in the amount of phosphorus available to aquatic plants, which need the nutrients
carbon, nitrogen and phosphorus in the approximate ratio of
100 to 15 to 1 (2). The nutritive properties of excess
phosphorus are considered to be responsible for accelerated
eutrophication of lakes as normally the availability of phosphorus governs the growth rate. Eutrophication is the excessive growth of aquatic vegetation such as algae which hastens
the natural aging of a lake (3).

Phosphates enter waterways from 2 types of sources: point
and non-point. Municipal and industrial wastewaters are
examples of point sources while urban and agricultural runoff,
shoreline erosion and atmospheric deposition are examples of
non-point sources. Prior to 1970 it was estimated that in
North America, 30-70% of the phosphate input resulted from the
use of phosphate detergents, which have been widely used since
1946 (4). In the late 1960s it was realized that phosphates
were responsible for the deterioration of freshwater lakes
(3).

Detergents have 2 major components: a surfactant and a
builder. The surfactant is the suds-producing ingredient which
dissolves grease and stains and holds them in solution (5).
The builder acts as a water conditioner, trapping hard water
ions and making the water alkaline to promote dirt removal and
prevent redeposition (6).

Before 1965 the chief problem with detergents was the
slow biodegradation of the branch-chained form of the surfactant alkylbenzene sulphonate. This resulted in highly visible
foam pollution. Since 1966 all Canadian detergents have been

required to contain the straight chain alkylbenzene sulphonate, which is more easily broken down by bacteria (7).

The next concern centered on the builders, the most common being the polyphosphate group, which made up as much as 66% of the weight of the detergent (6). In 1970 the Phosphorus Concentration Control Regulations (8) of the Canada Water Act (9) reduced the maximum permissible content to 20% expressed as phosphorus pentoxide, P_2O_5, on the principle that this was the fastest and most economical approach for reducing the amount of phosphorus entering waterways. The U.S. did not follow this action immediately, thus continuing the problem in Lakes Erie, Superior, and Ontario (10). However, the following states banned phosphates totally in the years noted: Indiana, 1973; Michigan, 1977; Minnesota, 1979; New York, 1973; Vermont, 1978; and Wisconsin, 1979, (rescinded 1982)(11). The city of Chicago, the major Illinois source, adopted a 0.5% limit. However, the remaining Great Lakes Basin states, Ohio and Pennsylvania, have no regulations (12).

The 1972 amendment to the Phosphorus Concentration Control regulations further reduced the phosphorus content of Canadian detergents to 5% in phosphorus pentoxide equivalent. Laundry detergents containing less than 1% can be described as phosphate free. However, these regulations do not apply to detergent boosters, dishwashing detergents or special purpose compounds which may contain 5-45% phosphate (13). Countries outside North America are also concerned. In 1983, Switzerland announced a ban on phosphates in all washing powders, even though the cost of washing powder was estimated to rise 20% (24).

Even with the restriction on the phosphate content of detergents, municipal sewage contains considerable amounts of phosphate. The Canadian and U.S. governments first attempted to control this in Apr. 1972 by signing the Great Lakes Water Quality Agreement. This required that the phosphorus content of effluents from all large municipal waste treatment plants discharging into Lakes Erie and Ontario and the international section of the St. Lawrence River be limited to 1 mg/L (milligram per litre)(expressed as phosphorus)(14). In 1976 the International Joint Commission (IJC), which considers problems related to boundary waters, suggested that the 1 mg/L limit be extended to all point source discharges of phosphorus in the Great Lakes system. The IJC phosphorus management strategies also considered industrial point sources and changes in land use and farming practices that would reduce non-point sources (15).

A January, 1981 supplemental report recommended that the phosphorus concentration limit of effluent entering Lakes Superior, Michigan and Huron remain at 1 mg/L, with a more stringent target of 0.5 mg/L for discharges into Lakes Erie and Ontario (16). This is an expensive proposition but there is suitable evidence from aerial photographs to suggest that sewage treatment can lead to revitalization of eutrophic water (17).

The result of these phosphorus management strategies has been substantial reductions of municipal effluent phosphorus loads, particularly to Lakes Erie and Ontario. From 1972 to 1976 there were 54% and 67% reductions, respectively. By 1980, the overall reductions from the 1972 estimates were 76% and 74%. Control of point sources of phosphorus has had some immediate results, notably in Lake Huron's Saginaw Bay and Lake Ontario's Bay of Quinte. However, the response in Lake Erie has been poor, possibly due to its relative shallowness. The recovery of Lakes Erie and Ontario is now seen as a long-term process. The lack of significant overall improvement makes it clear that these lakes are complex ecological systems (12).

The action to remove phosphate from detergents was controversial. The detergent industry argued that suitable replacements were not available, so that the cleaning power of detergents would be greatly reduced (18). Several alternative builders were considered; sodium citrate; sodium carbonate; organic polyelectrolytes and nitrilotriacetic acid (NTA). The most promising appeared to be NTA. Originally there was concern about the chelating properties of NTA. Chelation is the ability to dissolve heavy metals such as cadmium and mercury. It was also suspected that breakdown of NTA might produce carcinogenic nitrosamines (see Nitrites and Nitrates)(1).

NTA was approved for use in Canadian detergents. However, American detergent manufacturers were requested by the Surgeon General to withdraw NTA from their formulations or it would be regulated (20). In mid-1980, the Environmental Protection

Agency decided not to regulate the compound. Detergent manufacturers then began using NTA for detergent destined for
states that had regulated phosphate content. Consumer groups
and unions expressed concern that an alleged "carcinogen" was
approved for use in detergents (21).

The concern is centered around the question of NTA in
drinking water. It was found to cause urinary tract tumours in
laboratory rats and mice given large doses over their lifetime
(19). Canadian limits are set at 0.050 mg/L. The range detected in the drinking water monitoring program during 1976 and
1977 was up to 0.020 mg/L with the average being 0.003 mg/L
(22). The maximum cancer risk associated with consumption of
water containing 0.050 mg/L of NTA was estimated at 1 in
2,000,000 in 1977 (19). More extensive studies concluded that
a 1.0 mg/L level would pose the same risk. However, as the
more stringent standard is being met, it will not be relaxed
(23).

One benefit of the phosphorus-content regulation is that
it has bought time for provinces that do not have extensive
sewage treatment facilities. While the best way to prevent
phosphorus from entering our lakes and rivers is sewage treatment, the regulation of phosphates in detergents has been
successful.

REFERENCES

1. Bryan, R., "Much is Taken, Much Remains", Duxbury Press, North Scituate,
    Massachusetts, 1973.
2. "Restoring Damaged Lakes", Science, 203, 425, 1979.
3. Prakash, A., "NTA (Nitrilotriacetic acid) - an Ecological Appraisal",
    National Research Council of Canada, Ottawa, no. 15023, 1976.
4. Miller, G.T. Jr., "Living in the Environment. Concepts, Problems and
    Alternatives", Wadsworth Publishing Company, Belmont California, 1975.
5. J.W. Moore and E.A. Moore, "Environmental Chemistry", Acedemic Press Inc.,
    New York, 1976.
6. Stoker, H.S. and Seager, S.L., "Environmental Chemistry: Air and Water
    Pollution", Second edition, Scott, Foresman and Company, Glenview,
    Illinois, 1976.
7. Pryde, L.T., "Environmental Chemistry: an Introduction", Cummings
    Publishing Company, Menlo Park, California, 1973.
8. "Canada Water Act. Phosphorus Concentration Control Regulations Amendment",
    Canada Gazette Part II, 106(20), 1820, 1972.
9. Canada Water Act, 18-19 Elizabeth II, Chapter 52, page 1097, 1970.
10. Moriber, G., "Environmental Science", Allyn and Bacon, Inc., Boston, 1974.
11. Personal Communication, Soap and Detergents Association, New York, July 19,
    1982.
12. "1981 Report on Great Lakes Water Quality", Report to the International
    Joint Commission, Washington D.C./Ottawa.

13. "Laundry Detergents and other Cleaning Compounds", Information Sheet from
     Environment Protection Service, Mar. 1976. Available from Environmental
     Protection Service, Water Pollution Control Directorate, Ottawa, Ontario.
14. Chapra, S.C. and Robertson, A., "Great Lakes Eutrophication: The Effect of
     Point Source Control of Total Phosphorus", Science, 196, 1448, 1977.
15. "Fourth Annual Report, Great Lakes Water Quality", International Joint
     Commission, U.S./Canada, 1976.
16. "Supplemental Report on Phosphorus Management Strategies", International
     Joint Commission, U.S./Canada, Ottawa, 1981.
17. "The Aerial Photo-Eutrophication Link", Environmental Science and
     Technology, 11 (8), 742, 1977.
18. Goulden, P.D., "The Effect of Detergent Phosphate Levels on the Cleaning
     Process", Environment Canada, Technical Bulletin No. 70, Canada Centre for
     Inland Waters, Burlington, 1972.
19. "Health Implications of NTA", a Report to the Great Lakes Research Advisory
     Board to the International Joint Commission, May 1977.
20. NTA Fact Sheet, United States Environmental Protection Agency, Washington
     D.C. May 20, 1980.
21. "Union Charges P & Y Detergent is Hazardous", Chemical and Engineering
     News, May 17, (6), 1982.
22. Malaiyandi, M., Williams, D.M. and O'Grady, R., "A National Survey of
     Nitrilotriacetic Acid in Canadian Drinking Water", Environmental Science
     and Technology, 13, (59) 1979.
23. Becking, G.C. and Douglas, G.R., "Nitrilotriacetic Acid (NTA) - The
     Canadian Experience", Paper from the Third International Conference on
     Environmental Mutagens, Tokyo, 1981.
24. "Phosphates Ban", The Globe and Mail, Toronto, May 10, 1983.

RECOMMENDED READING

Most books on environmental science devote some space to
the phosphorus - detergent - eutrophication problem, e.g.
(1,6). Reference (2) gives a summary of the remedial methods
to aid lake recovery.

RADON

With increased emphasis on energy conservation people are insulating their homes.   This can result in deficient venti-lation and subsequently potentially hazardous radon buildup.

Radon, a radioactive gas, is a product of the radioactive decay of radium, which in turn is a product of the decay of uranium (1). The type (isotope) of uranium which decays, exists naturally in trace amounts in most soil and rock. Thus radium and radon also exist naturally (1), mostly in rocky ground. Exposure to higher than normal levels of radon occurs in uranium and other mines and has occurred in the immediate vicinity of some nuclear waste dump sites. As well, houses which are insulated "too well", and thus have a low rate of air exchange, can trap and accumulate naturally-occurring radon. Because radon is a gas, it can be inhaled, and thus can come into direct contact with the sensitive cells which line the air passages of the lungs (1). More importantly, radon itself decays, and the radioactive solid products of this decay can also reach the lungs (2).

RADIOACTIVITY

Radiation is said to occur whenever a substance emits energy (2). This energy can be electromagnetic, as with radio-waves, microwaves, light, X-rays and gamma-rays. The energy can also take the form of particles moving at high velocity, such as when alpha and beta particles are emitted from an atom (2). Whatever form the energy takes, it is called "ionizing radiation" when it can use its energy to disrupt chemical bonds and cause ionization as it penetrates a material, in-cluding biological material (2).

When this ionizing radiation is caused by the unstable nucleus of an atom emitting certain particles, it is called radioactivity (2). The number of protons and neutrons in an atomic nucleus determines its stability. Some combinations give stable nuclei, others unstable. If the nucleus is unstable, it can change spontaneously by emitting an "alpha particle" (2 neutrons and 2 protons) or by emitting a "beta particle" (a negative charge -- electron -- released by a neutron) (2). Gamma radiation, a form of electromagnetic waves, can also be released along with either alpha or beta radiation.

These emissions will result in the transmutation of the unstable nucleus into a new element. The new element itself may or may not be stable. If it is not, it can also transmute, and thus it is possible to have a chain reaction of radioactive decay, called simply a chain decay (2).

Alpha radiation is the most important kind of radiation emitted by radon and its "daughters" (products of radon decay)(1). The alpha particles use up most of their energy over a short distance through the air, but this deposited energy is very intense. If alpha particles strike the skin, virtually no harm is done. But if radon and its daughters are inhaled, then the alpha particles being emitted can irradiate and damage sensitive cells in the lungs (1).

Beta radiation is emitted by 2 of the radon daughters (1). The beta particles can travel much further than the alpha particles can, and thus can penetrate the skin. However, precisely because beta particles travel further, their energy is spread out, and thus their effects are miniscule (10 times smaller) compared to those of alpha particles.

Gamma radiation can also be emitted. It is so penetrating that it can irradiate the whole body, but as with beta particles, the energy is spread out, and thus has much less effect than the alpha particles. When considering the health effects of radon and its daughters, it is the alpha particles that are of most concern.

The danger of radioactive elements to human health varies with the decaying element's properties, including the type of radiation emitted (alpha particles, beta particles, gamma rays have different effects), but also on the "half-life" of the element. A long half-life means very little radioactivity but over a long period of time; a short half-life much radioactivity but over a short period of time.

The different ways radioactivity is measured reflect this variation. A "curie" is a basic measurement of the radioactivity of an element. The "rad" is a measurement of the intensity of energy being absorbed (1 rad=100 erg per gram). A third unit of measurement is called the "rem" (roentgen equivalent man). This is the unit of effective dose expressed in terms of an equivalent dose of X-rays. It takes into account the "RBE" (relative biological effectiveness) of the radiation with respect to biological damage. Alpha, beta, and gamma radiation all have different effects on man. The rem is a measurement of the effect a given source of radiation is having on an exposed human.

RADON

Radon was discovered in 1900, and was first known as "radium emanation" (3). It is the heaviest known gas (7.7 times heavier than air) and at ordinary temperatures is colourless (3). Radon-222 is formed in the chain decay of uranium-238, an isotope of uranium. An element usually has several isotopes. Isotopes of an element all have the same number of protons and electrons, but have a different number of neutrons. Uranium-238 is unstable, and decays very slowly into several other elements before becoming radium-226. The radium then becomes radon-222, which also decays such that one unit of active radium will result in the production of two one millionths of a unit of radon per second (4). This is equivalent to a half-life of 3.8 days, meaning that it takes that long for half a given quantity of radon-222 to decay. Uranium-238 has a half-life of 4.5 billion years (2).

Radon-222 decays into what is called "radium A" (RaA, an isotope of the element polonium). RaA is also radioactive, and with a half-life of 3 minutes decays into "radium B" (RaB). RaB, with a half life of 27 minutes, decays to "radium C" (RaC). RaC (half-life 20 minutes) decays to "radium C prime" (RaC'). RaC' has an extremely short half life of less than one-thousandth of a second. RaA, RaB, RaC and RaC' are collectively called the short-lived "daughters" of radon, or simply "radon daughters" (1). The decay chain stops upon transmutation to a stable isotope of lead.

HEALTH EFFECTS

In 1895, a few years after man began experimenting with radiation, it was first recognized that radiation could have adverse health effects. At the time, a researcher reported that X-rays could injure the skin. In 1902, a skin cancer was attributed to high exposure to X-rays. Early in the 20th century, it was recognized that large doses of any radiation could produce sterility, destroy cells, and reduce the number of white cells in circulating blood. In 1927 it was shown in experiments with fruitflies that ionizing radiation produced genetic mutations (2).

The health effects associated with radon are more the result of the radon daughters, although both radon and its daughters are always, in varying ratios, found and inhaled together (1). The dose of radiation to the lungs from inhaled radon daughters is from 2 to 20 times higher than the dose from radon gas, because radon daughters, being solids, tend to adhere to the lung surface, while radon, a gas at normal conditions, is simply exhaled. Thus the radon daughters tend to remain and decay in the lungs (1). It has been observed that miners who were exposed to high levels of radon and radon daughters had a higher incidence of lung cancer than did other miners (1); this was especially so in miners who smoked cigarettes (1).

There are no genetic effects from inhaled radon, because only the lungs are exposed significantly. However, if one were exposed to very high levels of radon, then there could be enough gamma radiation, which irradiates the whole body, to affect a male's testes or a female's ovaries (1,8).

Studies are being done to determine the effect of long-term low-level exposure to radioactive materials. The International Commission on Radiological Protection (ICRP) has made the assumption that at least for occupational exposure levels, there is no threshhold radiation dose below which the radiation cannot cause certain adverse health effects such as lung cancer (4). Another assumption made by the ICRP is that the effects of radiation on humans varies with the total dose, independent of the rate at which the dose is delivered. Thus it is assumed that low exposure to radiation over a long period of time is equivalent to a higher exposure level over a shorter period (4).

OCCUPATIONAL EXPOSURE

High concentrations of radon and its daughters have been recorded in underground mines, especially uranium and fluorspar mines (4). The exposure level varies with the amount of ventilation. United States uranium mines using only natural draft ventilation in the 1940s had average radon levels of up to 5000 picocurie (1 curie=1000,000,000,000 picocurie) per litre of air (4). Canadian fluorspar mines in Newfoundland with poor ventilation have had average concentrations above 1000 picocurie per litre. The ICRP has developed a limit of 40.5 picocurie of radon and radon daughters per litre of air (5).

In order to concentrate regulation and standards on the dangerous alpha particles emitted by radon daughters, a unit called the "Working Level" (WL) has been introduced (4). The higher the WL, the greater the exposure to these alpha particles. Building on the WL is a unit called the "Working Level Month" (WLM) which is a measure of accumulated exposure (1 Working Level month is exposure to 1 working level for 170 hours). In Canada and the U.S. inhalation limits have been set for occupationally-exposed workers, at 2 WLM for any consecutive 3-month period, and at 4 WLM for any consecutive 12-month period (4). Over a year, in terms of rems (the measurement which reflects the health effects of radiation on humans), this 4 WLM limit is roughly equivalent to 10 times the average exposure of Canadians to radiation (2,4).

NON-OCCUPATIONAL EXPOSURE

The radiation received by Canadians on average from natural sources (terrestrial and cosmic radiation) is about 100 millirem a year (6). A small portion of this radiation is due to nuclear decay occurring in our bodies due to naturally occurring radioactive isotopes such as potassium-40 and carbon-14. This dose varies from one location to another, depending on latitude, altitude, the nature of building material, and the nature of underlying rock (6).

In the U.S. most houses have radon exposure levels of less than 0.004 WL, which is 5 times less than the proposed upper acceptable limit of 0.02 WL (7). But in some experimental houses which were extremely well insulated (called "tight" houses), the exposure levels were found to be approximately 0.14 WL (7). Canada has an extensive data base of radon measurements which includes surveys of natural background levels indicating areas of elevated radioactivity (9,10). In Britain, the National Radiological Protection Board (NRPB) estimates that 400,000 people may experience radioactivity levels in their homes large enough to cause one in 200 of these people to die of lung cancer (14). The drive for energy conservation can thus cause a non-negligible increase in lung cancer (15).

There are also several man-made sources of radiation which to Canadians are exposed, including medical and dental procedures (average of 73 millirem per year), nuclear testing fallout (6 millirem per year), nuclear power (2 millirem per year) and other miscellaneous sources such as colour television (in all, 2 millirem per year) (2). A point source of man-made radiation can be dump sites for radioactive material. The situation at Port Hope, Ontario is an example.

In 1932, Eldorado Gold Mines Limited set up a plant in Port Hope to process ores mined at Port Radium, Northwest Territories (12). Since then, radioactive waste material has been stored in disposal areas around Port Hope. In the early years, disposal practices were relatively lax, and it became evident later that some areas in the town of Port Hope were contaminated.

The Atomic Energy Control Board of Canada, which investigated the situation, has given 4 possible causes for the contamination (12). First, there could have been spillage during shipment by road to disposal areas, or during loading at rail docks. Second, radioactive residues were stored in a variety of temporary storage locations, awaiting recovery of other metals such as cobalt and silver in the residue. It is possible that these temporary locations became contaminated. Third, from time to time, processing plants and laboratories were dismantled, producing building rubble, fill, and reclaimed building material. At a school in Port Hope, an extension to the building was built on contaminated fill, and radon levels were later found to be well above acceptable levels. A fourth possible cause of contamination could have been surface run-off of radioactive residue from certain disposal areas (12). Several houses in Port Hope have been found to have higher than acceptable levels of radon, because of contaminated waste material in and under the house (1).

It was reported that between 1976 and 1981, the federal government spent about $7 million in Port Hope cleaning up waste (13). Part of the clean-up included removing contaminated materials from within and landfill from under about 400 homes and buildings (13). About 130,000 tonne of contaminated material were removed to a waste site at Chalk River, Ontario. Since 1979, that site has no longer been available, and several hundred thousand tonne of waste remain in sites around the city (13). One way Port Hope residents were able to help themselves was to ensure adequate ventilation in their houses (1). Because radon daughters are solids, only radon gas seeps into houses from the ground. Good ventilation can flush out radon before it decays significantly (1).

REFERENCES

1. "Information Bulletin", No. 76-1, Atomic Energy Control Board, May 21, 1976.
2. Basuk, J. and Nichols, A., "An Overview of the Ionizing Radiation Hazard in Canada", Science Council of Canada, 1979.
3. Weast, R., Editor, "Handbook of Chemistry and Physics", Chemical Rubber Co., Cleveland, 1970.
4. "Radioactivity in the Canadian Environment", Associate Committee on Scientific Criteria for Environmental Quality, National Research Council, 1980.
5. "Limits for Inhalation of Radon Daughters by Workers", International Commission on Radiological Protection, ICRP-32, Annals of 6(1), 1981.
6. Newcombe, H., "Public Health Aspects of Radiation", Atomic Energy of Canada Ltd., 1976.
7. "Energy Conservation and Indoor Air Quality", ASHRAE Journal, Mar. 1981.
8. Harley, N.H., Altman, S.M., Pasternack, B.S., "Genotoxic Properties of Radon and Its Daughters", Environmental Science Research, 25, 411, 1982 .
9. McGregor, R.G., Gourgon, L.A., "Radon and Radon Daughters in Homes Utilizing Deep Well Water Supplies, Halifax County, Nova Scotia". J. Environ. Sci. Health A15(1) 25, 1980.
10. McGregor, R.G., Vasudev, P., Letourneau, E.G., McCullough, R.S., Prantl, F.A., Taniguchi, H., "Background Concentrations of Radon and Radon Daughters in Canadian Homes", Health Physics, 39, 285, 1980.
11. McCullough, R.S., Letourneau, E.G., Waight, P.J., "A Four Factor Model for Estimating Human Radiation Exposure to Radon Daughters in the Home". Health Physics, 40, 299, 1981.
12. "Progress Report on Radioactive Waste Investigation in Port Hope, Ontario", Atomic Energy Conrtol Board, Feb. 19, 1976.
13. "Living with Millirems", The Citizen, Ottawa, Oct. 17, 1981.
14. Pearce, F., "Homes that Harbour Radioactivity", New Scientist, July 7, 1983.
15. Shurcliff, W.A., "Radon in the Home", Science 221, 112, 1983.

RECOMMENDED READING

Two easily understood accounts of ionizing radiation are references (1) and (2). Reference (1) is quite brief and was directed at the media. "Indoor Air Pollution: A Public Health Perspective", by J.D. Spengler and K. Sexton, Science, 221, 9, 1983, provides a discussion of the hazards of underventilation of homes in general, including radon.

SULPHUR DIOXIDE

Acidic precipitation is increasing due to the growing introduction of sulphur dioxide into the atmosphere. It has been linked with detrimental effects on fish, vegetation, buildings and people.

Sulphur dioxide, SO_2, is a colourless gas with a pungent and irritating odour at concentrations above 3 ppm (part per million). It is the principal oxide of sulphur which is emitted into the atmosphere, although it is usually accompanied by sulphur trioxide, SO_3, to the extent of 1% to 10% (1). The combustion of any sulphur-containing fuel involves a reaction of sulphur, S, with oxygen, O_2, to produce sulphur dioxide; sulphur dioxide can then react further to produce sulphur trioxide. The latter reaction occurs very slowly unless catalyzed. Possible atmospheric catalysts are hydrocarbon free-radicals or particulate matter (2).

In the mid 1970s, on a world-wide basis, coal consumption accounted for approximately 43% of the sulphur dioxide entering the atmosphere (1). Other industrial processes, transportation, and solid waste disposal contributed a small percentage. Over 50% was generated within the natural environment as a result of the oxidation of hydrogen sulphide (H_2S), which comes primarily from biological decay processes such as those occurring in swamps, tidal flats and estuaries (3). Volcanic activity also generates a small amount of sulphur compounds (2). Shortly after Mt. St. Helens erupted May 18, 1980, it was found that 90% of the aerosol mass was sulphuric acid droplets (4). The eruption of El Chicon in 1982 also introduced large amounts of SO_2 into the atmosphere (21).

In Canada, in the mid 1970s, 5.5 million tonne of sulphur dioxide were emitted annually from man-made sources (5). Forty-four percent of the total was from nonferrous smelters (primarily nickel and copper smelters), nearly 44% was from other industrial sources, 12% was from electrical utilities using sulphur-containing coal, and the small remainder was from transportation and solid waste disposal sources (5,6). The largest emissions of sulphur dioxide in Canada are from the INCO Limited smelter at Copper Cliff, responsible for the emission of approximately 866,000 tonne of the chemical annually in the late 1970s (7).

In the U.S. about 28.5 million tonne of sulphur dioxide were emitted annually from man-made sources in the mid 1970s (5). Electric utilities accounted for 65% of this. In the upper Ohio Valley (eastern Ohio, northern West Virginia, and western Pennsylvania) a number of large power plants burned high sulphur coal, with little control of sulphur emissions (5). Other industrial sources accounted for nearly 25% of the total, while nonferrous smelters emitted another 10%.

Eventually, a considerable amount of the sulphur dioxide emitted into the atmosphere is oxidized to sulphur trioxide which can dissolve in water to form sulphuric acid, H_2SO_4. It may in turn react with other substances (e.g. ammonia) to produce sulphates (1). The aerosol formed by sulphuric acid droplets can be the cause of respiratory problems and a reduction in visibility (8). It has been shown (9,10) that sulphur dioxide can travel distances of more than 1000 km (kilometre) in the atmosphere, but generally it has an average lifetime in the atmosphere of only several days.

Thus sulphur dioxide affects us in 2 ways: as the gas itself, and as a constituent of acidic precipitation better known as "acid rain". The other major constituents of acid rain are nitrogen oxides (see NO_x).

ACID RAIN

Acid rain, or more technically, acidic precipitation, is usually defined as precipitation, including rain, snow, sleet and hail, having an acidity below pH 5.6 (7). Normal rain is slightly acidic, with a pH of 5.6, due to the presence of carbon dioxide in the atmosphere (7). Rain with pH below 5.6 has been observed in locations thousands of kilometres from industrial activity. The extra acidity may be due to sulphuric acid from volcanic eruptions or nitric acid produced when nitrogen oxides (see NO_x) formed in lightning storms dissolve in rain (15).

The pH scale measures acidity. At pH 0, the solution is very acidic (high in hydrogen ions), while at pH 14, it is very alkaline (high in hydroxyl ions). A pH of 7 represents a neutral solution; i.e., the acidic and alkaline components are in equal concentration, and thus neutralize each other. The pH scale is logarithmic, so that there is a tenfold difference in the hydrogen ion concentrations between solutions differing by one pH unit. Vinegar has a pH of a little less than 3, milk has a pH of about 6.6, and baking soda has a pH of a little over 8.

Acid rain is primarily due to the emissions of sulphur oxides, which form sulphuric acid, and of nitrogen oxides, which form nitric acid. The acids are formed in the atmosphere and they travel over distances of up to thousands of kilometres (7). The United Kingdom has often been blamed for the acid rain which falls on the lakes and rivers of Norway and Sweden (11). Acid rain from the U.S. reaches Canada, and vice versa, although a joint government-sponsored Canada-U.S. research group estimated that about 3 to 4 times as much sulphur moves from the U.S. to Canada as in the opposite direction. (5). There is however, according to some officials uncertainty in the identification of specific sources of acid rain (12).

HEALTH AND ENVIRONMENTAL EFFECTS

Most effects of SO_2 on human health are related to irritation of the respiratory system. At concentrations greater than 3 ppm it becomes irritating to sensitive membranes of the throat and lungs (1). The World Health Organization (WHO) suggests the following criteria for environmental standards of sulphur dioxide levels at which adverse effects would begin to appear: 0.04 ppm, respiratory symptoms; 0.11 ppm, worsening of patients with pulmonary diseases; 0.19 ppm, excess mortality and hospital admissions. Asthmatics, the elderly or other susceptible people with chronic respiratory problems may be affected by lower concentrations than these (6).

There have been tragic events attributed to sulphur dioxide (and other contaminants) in the air. A heavy fog containing sulphur dioxide blanketed a valley in Belgium in 1930 and was implicated in the deaths of 60 people. In the much-publicized London "killer" fog of 1952, sulphur dioxide levels reached about 1.5 ppm, averaged over 48 hours, and as a result there was an increase of 1472 deaths among persons over 45; these deaths occurred among persons with pre-existing disease (6). Subsequent episodes have been quite thoroughly studied but scientists have found it impossible to give a

level of sulphur dioxide below which the air may be regarded
as safe (6). The presence of suspended particles in conjunction with SO_2 gas is believed to be of importance.

There are adverse health effects associated with acid
rain as well. The Canadian parliamentary sub-committee on acid
rain has identified 2 such negative effects (7). Acid rain may
cause the leaching of toxic chemicals in rural areas from
watersheds and from water storage and distribution systems,
leading to the contamination of drinking water. Second,
studies in Sweden and North America have found that as the
acidity of lake water increases, so does the level of methylmercury found in fish. There is evidence that dimethylmercury
is transformed under acidic conditions to methylmercury, which
is more soluble in water, and is easily ingested by fish and
other aquatic organisms (7).

Vegetation and materials are affected by sulphur oxides
in the atmosphere. At high concentrations, leaves appear to
have bleach spots on them, although these symptoms are not
conclusive evidence of sulphur dioxide effects (4), and may be
caused by increased ozone from chemical reactions involving
nitrogen dioxide, another precursor of acid rain (7).

There is evidence indicating that acid rain is increasing
the acidity of forest soils and causing an accelerated
drainage loss of useful nutrients (7). West Germany has
recently become very concerned about damage to its forests by
acid rain. Over 8% of the forests there may be damaged (22).

Lakes and streams can become too acidic to support
certain aquatic life (7). This is especially so in lakes and
streams which are not surrounded by alkaline materials, such
as limestone, which can neutralize the acid rain as it runs
off into the body of water. Some lakes and streams are
naturally alkaline (pH> 7), and thus have a capacity to
neutralize the acidic precipitation (7).

Animals can also be affected. "White muscle disease", a
physiological disorder in cattle caused by a deficiency of
selenium in the animals' diet, has been linked to the ingestion of vegetation enriched with sulphur. In Alberta, which
has the second highest level of sulphur emissions in western
Canada (Manitoba has the highest, with 2 large nonferrous

smelters), there is a significant incidence of white muscle disease (7). Acid rain also attacks buildings, metals, nylons, structural materials, such as limestone and marble, and works of art (2,6,13,14,20).

It is possible to estimate only roughly the economic cost of acid rain. In northern Ontario, the local fishing industry, valued at about $600 million annually, forms the basis of the area's tourist industry, worth another $1 billion annually. It has been estimated that the total annual loss there due to acid rain could reach $230 million (7). In Nova Scotia, 9 rivers have become too acidic to support salmon, resulting in an estimated $300 million annual loss to the local economy. Some estimates suggest that the annual damage caused by acid rain to building materials in Canada is at least $285 million In the U. S. estimates indicate that acid rain causes damage amounting to hundreds of millions of dollars annually to the forest industry (7).

A problem in the acid rain controversy is that much of the research on the environmental effects is not as yet definitive. The Edison Electric Institute, an association of American electric companies, has said that there is "little evidence that variations in acidity have had adverse impacts on the environment (15)". The American government's position on the matter so far has been that there is too much scientific uncertainty about the sources of acid rain to set up pollution limits (16,12). The Canadian parliamentary subcommittee on acid rain has recognized that "the data base has to be substantially increased before firm conclusions can be reached about the effect acid rain is having...". But it has agreed with an observation of a member of the Canadian Forestry Service that "it is not...(appropriate that)...a patient should die before being considered ill...(7)".

LEGISLATION AND METHODS OF CONTROLLING SULPHUR DIOXIDE EMISSIONS

The Canadian government deals with air pollution primarily through its Clean Air Act. The Act sets ambient air objectives and places limits on the quantity and concentration of specific pollutants (7). For example, the federal government has set a "tolerable" range for sulphur dioxide of 300 to 800 microgram per cubic metre over a 24-hour period, and has

adopted emission guidelines for new thermal power plants
(7,17). But because the federal government shares jurisdiction
over environmental matters with the provinces, many standards
and guidelines provided in the Clean Air Act require the
approval of and are enforced by the individual provincial
governments. Provincial consent is not required when limits
are set on emissions from stationary sources that are a threat
to human health or that would cause Canada to violate any
international obligation it has undertaken in reference to air
pollution. It has been suggested that the federal government
amend the Clean Air Act to give itself the power to enforce
standards on sources which emit air pollutants which cross
provincial boundaries (7).

Sulphur dioxide, and thus acid rain, can cross international boundaries. In the past few years, the federal
government has been lobbying the American government in an
effort to begin a concerted fight against acid rain. It has
been reported that recently the American Senate Environment
Committee voted 15-0 for such a program, although this program
reportedly falls short of the measures urged by Canada (18).
If passed, 31 states east of the Mississippi River would be
obliged to cut down on annual emissions, and this could add up
to 10% to the power bills of residents in those states (18).
Most of these people live in areas which are not susceptible
to significant damage by acid rain. Acid rain control has many
political ramifications (23).

As the American Senate's proposed legislation indicates,
a considerable proportion of sulphur oxide pollution results
from the combustion of fuels. Thus much attention has been
given to this process. Methods for reducing sulphur dioxide
emission include (19):   energy conservation, resulting in
reduced fuel consumption; a move to fuels with lower sulphur
content; substitution of fossil fuels by other energy sources
such as nuclear, solar, wind or renewable sources; reduction
of the sulphur content of fuel before combustion (e.g. coal
washing, coal gasification, desulphurization of liquid fuels).
Alternatively, it may be possible to reduce the formation of
sulphur dioxide during combustion (fluidized bed combustion)
or reduce the emission of sulphur dioxide after combustion
(stack gas desulphurization) (19).

In nonferrous smelting, sulphur dioxide emissions can be reduced by removing some sulphur from the ore before combustion. It is also possible to recover sulphur dioxide from flue gases, mainly in the form of sulphuric acid, which can be marketed (7). This has already been done by Cominco Ltd. at its huge lead-zinc smelter in Trail, B.C. for over 50 years.

Attempts are also being made to mitigate the effects of acid rain. Liming programs, in which limestone or other alkaline substances are added to lakes, are used to neutralize the acid rain and increase the lakes' pH (7). Such neutralization can occur in the atmosphere. Although considerable SO_2 emission occurs in China, the pH of rain in northern China is often alkaline, i.e. greater than 7. This is because the soil there is generally alkaline and the air contains high concentrations of soil dust, especially from deserts (24).

REFERENCES

1. Stoker, H. S. and Seager, S. L., "Environmental Chemistry: Air and Water Pollution", Second edition, Scott, Foresman and Company, Glenview, Illinois, 1976.
2. Moore, J.W. and Moore, E.A., "Environmental Chemistry", Academic Press, New York, 1976.
3. Miller, G. T., "Living in the Environment: Concepts, Problems and Alternatives", Wadsworth Publishing Company, Inc., Belmont, California, 1975.
4. "Mt. St. Helens Stirs Chemical Interest", Chemical and Engineering News, Aug. 25, 1980.
5. "The Case Against the Rain", Ontario Ministry of the Environment, Oct. 1980.
6. "Sulphur and Its Inorganic Derivatives in the Canadian Environment", Associate Committee on Scientific Criteria For Environmental Quality, National Research Council of Canada, Ottawa, Publication No. NRCC 15015, 1977.
7. "Still Waters: The Chilling Reality of Acid Rain", Subcommittee on Acid Rain of the Standing Committee of Fisheries and Forestry, Supply and Services, 1981.
8. Moriber, G., "Environmental Science", Allyn and Bacon, Inc., Boston, 1974.
9. "Research Institutes Map SO_2 Movement", Chemical and Engineering News, Oct. 24, 1977.
10. Barnes, R. A., "Sulphur Deposit Account", Nature, 268, 92, 1977.
11. "Air Pollution Evidence Stacked Against Sweden", New Scientist, June 15, 1978.
12. "The Menace of Acid Rain", New Scientist, Aug. 12, 1982.
    "It's an Acid Wind that Blows Nobody any Good", New Scientist, July 8, 1982.
13. Rosenquist, I.Th., "Acid Precipitation", Chemical and Engineering News, June 20, 1977.
14. O'Sullivan, D., "Norway: Victim of Other Nations' Pollution", ibid, June 14, 1976.

15. "An Updated Perspective on Acid Rain", Edison Electric Institute, Nov. 1981.
16. "Acid Rain", Library of Parliament, Current Issue Review 79-37E, Nov., 1979, revised Apr. 1982.
17. "The Clean Air Act-Compilation of Regulations and Guidelines", Air Pollution Control Directorate, Environment Canada, Apr. 1981.
18. "Canada Elated on U.S. Vote on Acid Rain", The Globe and Mail, Toronto, July 23, 1982.
19. Persson, G. A., "Control of Sulfur Dioxide Emissions in Europe", Ambio, 5(5/6), 249, 1976.
20. Gauri, K., "The Preservation of Stone", Scientific American, 238, June 1978.
21. Kruger, A.J., "Sighting of El Chicon Sulfur Dioxide Clouds..", Science 220, 1377, 1983.
22. Folster, D., "Europe Faces a New Air War", The Globe and Mail, Toronto, Aug. 2, 1983.
23. Caufield, C., "Acid Rain: Reagan is Told to Act", New Scientist, Sept. 22, 1983.
24. Jernelov, A., "Acid Rain and Sulfur Dioxide Emissions in China", Ambio, 12, 362, 1983.

RECOMMENDED READING

Reference (6) gives a thorough, although technical review of sulphur dioxide in Canada. Reference (7) provides a comprehensive coverage of the acid rain problem.

SWEETENERS

The oldest non-nutritive sweetener, saccharin, has been controversial for almost a century.

Why does man crave sweet foods? British physician John Yudkin suggests that man acquired this craving because sweet food, particularly fruit, contains vital nutrients. Thus, the association between sweetness and nutrition (1). The most common sweetener in use today is sucrose, the white crystalline sugar derived from sugar cane and sugar beets, and composed of equal parts glucose and fructose. While white sugar is sweet, processing has stripped it of all the vitamins and minerals necessary for efficient metabolism; hence the term "empty calories".

Two groups of people need alternate sweeteners. Diabetics cannot handle glucose without the aid of insulin; sweeteners that do not involve the glucose metabolism are important to them. The other group involves people on calorie-reduced diets, whether for medical reasons or personal ones such as weight loss. All the alternative sweeteners are synthetically produced from natural or chemical sources. Some are non-nutritive, making no contribution of calories to the diet. Saccharin and cyclamate are in this category. For nutritive sweeteners, such as aspartame, xylitol, sorbitol and mannitol, the caloric contribution varies; aspartame's is negligible, the rest approximate sucrose.

SACCHARIN

The 2 common forms of saccharin are the calcium and sodium salts. Both are white powders which are 300 times sweeter than sucrose. Their sweetness differs from that of sucrose in that it takes longer to build to a maximum and lingers for a longer time, having a bitter aftertaste.

Controversy regarding saccharin is nearly a century old. It is sufficiently interesting to warrant a brief chronology which also serves to outline the history and methodology of decision-making for food additives (2-7):
1879 -- Saccharin was discovered by Remsen and Fahlberg. It was a sweet, cheap, easy to handle coal tar by-product.

1886 -- The first recorded test on saccharin was published.
European workers were given single doses of saccharin of
up to 5 g (gram) with no ill effects.

1883 -- The Chief of the Bureau of Chemistry of the U.S. felt
that saccharin deceived the public because it had no
nutritive value. His chemical intuition made him suspect
that saccharin was capable of causing kidney disease.
Equally renowned scientists of his time felt that saccharin was quite harmless.

1888 -- In France, tests using diabetics showed that ingesting 5 g a day for 5 months had no immediately harmful
effects.

1890 -- The Commission of the Health Association in France
decreed that saccharin was harmful, after which they
forbade its manufacture or import.

1898 -- The German Government banned saccharin from food and
drink. Similar bans came into effect in Spain, Portugal
and Hungary. Canada and the U.S. permitted the use of
saccharin in food and drink.

1900 -- Food processors began to use saccharin extensively in
Canada and the U.S.

1906 -- The Pure Food and Drugs Act was passed in the U.S.,
leading eventually to the establishment of the Food and
Drug Administration (FDA). The Act dealt with food
additives and adulteration of food. Toxicology and chemical analysis formed the scientific basis of the legislation that was enacted.

1912 -- President Roosevelt appointed a board of scientists to
review the safety of saccharin. The board concluded that
0.3 g per day was safe, whereas more than 1 g per day
caused digestive disturbances. The Referee Board of the
U.S. Dept. of Agriculture promised to prosecute for the
use of saccharin in normal foods, under the Food and
Drugs Act. Saccharin was thus considered a drug for
easing the hardship of diabetics who had to limit their
intake of nutritive sweeteners such as sucrose and fructose.

1951 -- The first significant study of the chronic toxicity
of saccharin was performed. The results showed that high
doses of saccharin (5-10% of diet) caused a distinct
retardation of growth, but that there was no reason to
suspect that saccharin was a carcinogen or harmful in any
other way.

1955 -- The National Academy of Sciences (NAS)/National Research Council (NRC) of the U.S. reviewed the literature pertaining to the safety of saccharin beginning with studies from 1920. The report concluded that up to 1 mg (milligram) per day was tolerable in the diet, and that human consumption was more likely to be in the neighbourhood of 0.3 mg per day.

1957 -- An English study showed that saccharin pellets implanted in the bladders of experimental mice caused bladder cancer.

1969 -- Cyclamates, alternative non-nutritive sweeteners were banned and as a result saccharin was reviewed as a Generally Recognized as Safe (GRAS) compound permitted as a food additive.

1970 -- A pellet study similar to that conducted in England in 1957 was carried out at the University of Wisconsin. It concluded that the pellets could cause bladder cancer in mice.

1970 -- The FDA announced that it was considering restrictions for the use of saccharin with an interim regulation allowing continued use.

1972 -- The Health Protection Branch (HPB) of Health and Welfare Canada conducted a chronic feeding study on one generation of rats using sodium saccharin, lasting 26 months. No bladder cancer was noted, but the males had a reduced lifespan.

1974 -- The FDA denounced the saccharin pellet studies (see 1957) by saying that they had no relation to oral ingestion of saccharin. Chronic feeding studies using 2 generations of rats exposed to saccharin in their diets revealed that it could cause cancer in the urinary bladder of rats. The studies were conducted by the FDA and the Wisconsin Alumni Research Foundation. The Canadian HPB began a 2 generation feeding experiment using procedures that hoped to eliminate possible sources of error.

1977-1979 DEVELOPMENTS

March 9, 1977: The HPB study on rats fed a diet with saccharin initiated in 1974 was concluded and the findings were made public by Health and Welfare Canada. The experiment was designed to test the safety of OTS (ortho-toluene sulphonamide), a common impurity. The results showed that saccharin was carcinogenic, but not OTS (5). The results of the study also indicated that male rats were more prone to cancer than females (5). Scientific authorities in Canada, the U.S., Great Britain and Europe evaluated the findings and the final conclusion was that they "indicated unequivocally that saccharin causes bladder tumours in test animals" (recorded by the FDA in the Federal Register, Apr. 15, 1977) (8). It was on the basis of this HPB test and the 2 American studies preceding it that the proposed saccharin ban in Canada was announced on Mar. 9, 1977 (5). The ban prohibited the use of saccharin in food and drink but allowed its sale, as a non-prescription drug, in pharmacies. The FDA in the U.S., also announced its intention to ban saccharin (8).

March: Senator Edward Kennedy, chairman of the U.S. Senate Health Subcommittee, asked the Office of Technology Assessment (OTA) to review the studies on the safety of saccharin, and specifically to evaluate the importance of the data revealed on Mar. 9, as it related to humans (9).

April 19: Health and Welfare Canada announced that its proposed ban on saccharin would be somewhat delayed because manufacturers of a fructose substitute could not meet the increased demand for the original deadline. The delay was for less than one year. Manufacturers of diet drinks agreed not to take advantage of the extension by promoting saccharin sweetened diet drinks (10).

May 10: Based on the Ames test (see Tris), the HPB reported that a concentrate made from impurities in commercially available saccharin caused genetic mutation in bacteria. Similar results were reported for the "OTS-free" saccharin used in their 1974-1977 chronic feeding experiment. Saccharin itself was not found to be mutagenic (11).

June: There was support from the U.S. Senate and the U.S. Congress to delay by 18 months any action by the FDA to ban saccharin. This would allow valuable data to be collected on the safety of saccharin (12,13). The OTA review requested by Senator Kennedy reported that saccharin was a weak carcinogen in animals and was thus likely to be one in humans as well. The report also suggested that saccharin might increase a person's taste for sweetness and thus cause increased sugar consumption (14).

June-July: A Canadian study involving the National Cancer Institute and 3 Canadian universities showed the first link between human cancer and ingestion of saccharin. Men had a greater chance of getting bladder cancer if they used artificial sweeteners such as cyclamates or saccharin, but most of the men in the study had used only saccharin. The more saccharin used, the greater the incidence of cancer. Females did not appear to have an increased incidence of bladder cancer (15,16).

July: In view of the new human data reported in June and July, the FDA announced that it was going to extend the proposed ban by 2 months, to allow time to consider whether saccharin should be available even as a drug (15).

October: As of Oct. 1, the use of saccharin in diet soft drinks is no longer permitted in Canada (21). The House of Representatives in Washington voted (375 to 23) to delay the FDA's proposed ban for 18 months. The bill called for warning notices on some saccharin-containing food products (17,18,19).

November: Congress mandated the following wording for the warning label: "Use of this product may be hazardous to your health. This product contains saccharin which has been determined to cause cancer in laboratory animals." (20).

December: As of Dec., the use of saccharin in diet foods is no longer permitted in Canada (21). A "modified" Ames test contradicts earlier findings (see May 1977) by showing even highly purified saccharin to be mutagenic (22).

January 18, 1978: The HPB issues an information letter to manufacturers describing legislative changes and new labelling requirements. Prohibition dates are given for the following uses: non-essential drugs, Dec. 31, 1978; toothpaste, mouthwashes and cosmetics, Dec. 31, 1979; and the sale of table top sweeteners outside of pharmacies, Feb. 1, 1978 (23). Two major studies were started; one by the National Academy of Sciences and the other jointly by the National Cancer Institute and the FDA. The studies will undertake a risk-benefit analysis, reassessment of the literature, a review of social and economic impacts of saccharin regulations and epidemiological studies to investigate further the bladder cancer evidence. Reports were made available during 1979 (24).

April: A report was released suggesting that saccharin may be a promoter rather than an initiator of cancer (25).

July: A Johns Hopkins epidemiological study comparing 519 people with bladder cancer to an equal number of controls concludes that neither saccharin nor cyclamate were carcinogens when consumed in moderate quantities (26).

January, 1979: The results of the National Academy of Science Study (see Jan. 1978) is released along with an examination of U.S. food safety policy. The saccharin study concludes that it is a carcinogen, probably a stronger one than believed. However, an immediate and total ban is not recommended on the grounds that the "zero risk" basis of existing food safety regulations ignores the reality that nothing is absolutely safe and excludes consideration of benefits (27).

July: Congress places a 2-year moratorium on the ban of saccharin.

June, 1981: The Reagan administration renews the moratorium for a further 2 years.

THE RISKS AND BENEFITS OF USING SACCHARIN

Without exposure to saccharin, the normal person runs a 1.5% risk of having bladder cancer in a lifetime, i.e., 150 cases in 10,000 people. By drinking one can of diet soft drink a day, the risk is estimated to increase to 1.54%, i.e., 4 extra cases in 10,000 people. Risk is used here strictly in the sense of a probability and does not include any comment on the severity of the event to which it refers. These figures are based on animal experiments; this has given rise to some skepticism concerning their applicability to humans.

The FDA and Health and Welfare Canada promoted some of the controversy surrounding the safety of saccharin by playing down the significance of the HPB findings released Mar. 9, 1977. The news release stressed that "the dose (of saccharin) used in this study exceeded the average human exposure by at least 800 times, based on the consumption of one 12-oz. bottle of diet soft drink per day". It further tried to allay public fears by stating that "no cases of human cancer attributable to saccharin have been identified" (5). Public panic was avoided but an outcry arose over the loss of saccharin, with no non-nutritive replacement in sight (8).

The news release failed to indicate however, that use of large quantities of chemicals, when testing their safety on animals, is a routine, scientifically accepted method. Dr. A. B. Morrison, assistant deputy minister of the HPB, explained later that scientific evidence suggests that man may be more sensitive to certain chemicals than animals. Large doses of chemical allow a margin of safety, because if doses are sufficiently large, a chemical to which animals are much less sensitive than humans would still have a detectable effect when given to animals (28). Using large doses was a means of detecting a significant increase in the occurrence of a rare event such as bladder cancer in rats (8). The use of large amounts of saccharin was justified by the argument that a large dose over the short lifetime of an animal such as a rat may have the same effect as a smaller dose over a longer lifetime as in the case of humans (9). Thus, for people who are predisposed to cancer for genetic or other physiological reasons, drinking just a couple of bottles of diet pop a day may pose a health hazard (9). A non-carcinogenic substance, however, will never cause cancer no matter how large a quantity is used (8).

Population studies of diabetics have been performed in order to determine if the high use of saccharin is linked with bladder cancer. These studies found no increase in bladder cancer in the diabetic population over that of a normal population. Apparently there was no link between the introduction of saccharin around the year 1900 and cancer. Such a link was found with cigarette smoking (29,30) (see Tobacco). Nevertheless a very recent study of humans who used artificial sweeteners extensively indicated that males who used saccharin and cyclamates had a 60% higher chance of having bladder cancer than non-users (16). When the planned ban on saccharin was announced Mar. 9, 1977, this critical link had not been shown in a scientific investigation (5).

One reason for the lack of human data to support or deny the safety of saccharin is that bladder cancer has a latent period of 20 years (time from the cancer causing stimulus to the appearance of cancer), and saccharin was not widely used until World War II when sugar was unavailable (30).

In assessing the risks of allowing use of saccharin, the possible benefits of using saccharin must also be considered. This also necessarily involves a discussion of the hazards of increasing consumption of sugar or other artificial sweeteners. There are no studies to date which show that saccharin is useful in losing or controlling weight. Animal studies using saccharin actually reported a weight gain in animals fed saccharin at doses comparable to what humans might ingest (30).

Saccharin is used not only in an attempt to control obesity and avoid heart disease but is also used with the idea of slimming and becoming more attractive and socially acceptable. It is difficult to measure the extent to which the risk of cancer is acceptable before the benefits no longer justify the use of saccharin (31,32). It has been argued that saccharin is essential for diabetics but researchers in the field acknowledge that the adverse effects of removal of saccharin from the market would be psychological rather than physiological or biochemical (30).

An analogy has been drawn between tobacco and saccharin. The former is a much greater proven health hazard and yet is not banned. Dr. A. B. Morrison argues that while the use of tobacco is an established health hazard of large dimensions, it is also an addiction (see Tobacco). Smugglers, bootleggers and organized crime would step in to supply addicts. Hence to ban tobacco would not achieve the desired purpose, namely to reduce the consumption of tobacco. A ban on saccharin, on the other hand, may reduce consumption (28). About 70% of the saccharin used in Canada is put into soft drinks, much of which are consumed by children. It is unrealistic to expect children to read a warning label (as on tobacco) on soft drinks and comprehend the danger to their health.

ALTERNATIVES TO SACCHARIN

Saccharin provided an alternative sweetener to sugar (sucrose), consumption of which has been associated with many health problems: obesity, dental caries, diabetes, hypoglycemia, excess amounts of cholesterol, pancreatic and breast (44) cancer risk, effects on growth and maturation. Nutritionists, biochemists and toxicologists agree that, if saccharin is banned, the consumption of sucrose will increase to

levels considered to be unhealthy (30). On the basis of medical evidence, the Norwegian government plans to regulate intake of sucrose as part of its new integrated food and
nutrition policy (33).

Other sugars in the human diet include glucose and fructose. Glucose is the natural blood sugar of humans and both
sucrose and fructose are converted to it in the body. It is
rapidly absorbed into the blood (within 15 minutes, compared
to up to 4 hours for some other sugars) and once ingested it
tends to flood the body with sugar. This is what provides
"quick energy" after eating raisins or glucose products. Quick
energy however, is very hard on the pancreas, the organ which
aids the body in burning blood sugar to provide energy.
Glucose has been found to be the only sugar to induce diabetes
in cats (4). Fructose is sweeter than sucrose and can be used
by diabetics who have to limit the amount of sugar they ingest
(25). The soft drink industry is planning to use high-fructose
corn syrup to produce a calorie-reduced soft drink (10,30),
but this trend is causing concern. It has been suggested (30)
that fructose can reduce the body's ability to use glucose.

Of the non-nutritive sweeteners, the first alternative to
saccharin was cyclamate (discovered in 1937) which, although
less sweet than saccharin, was free from aftertaste (34). By
1968, there was concern about the consumption of unrestricted
amounts of artificial sweeteners and in 1969, cyclamates were
banned in the U.S., Great Britain and Canada. The ban followed
the disclosure by Abbott Laboratories, makers of cyclamate,
that large doses of the substance, when fed to rats, were
associated with the formation of malignant bladder tumours
(34). Since that time, cyclamates have been classified as
drugs in Canada. In 1974, Abbott Laboratories applied to have
the ban removed. The data supplied by the manufacturers were
evaluated by the HPB in 1975 and after extensive discussion
and further testing (35), it was decided that the ban on food
and soft drink use should be maintained. It was announced (36)
that Abbott Laboratories has decided to reformulate Sucaryl, a
cyclamate sweetener which has been produced since 1954, but
the ban on cyclamates in soft drinks and diet foods was maintained in an FDA decision in 1982 (37).

Aspartame is manufactured by G. D. Searle and Co., and is
a whitish crystalline powder about 180 times as sweet as

sucrose. It is unique in that it is a non-carbohydrate, nutritive sweetener. Aspartame is synthetically produced from 2
amino acids, compounds which are the building blocks for
proteins. As small amounts are required, it contributes few
calories to the diet. Use is restricted by temperature and
acid conditions during processing and storage which may cause
aspartame's breakdown to another compound, losing the sweetness effect. G. D. Searle of Canada requested that aspartame
be allowed as a sweetener in 1974. As of July 1981, it is
allowed in food and beverages in Canada. In the U.S., G.D.
Searle had permission to produce aspartame beginning in 1974.
The company did not go into production at that time however.
Late in 1975, the FDA suspended its permission to produce
aspartame, pending analysis of animal studies (38). The holdup
in approving the use of aspartame was the lack of scientific
testing concerning its safety and certain "irregularities" in
the animal tests that have been conducted in the past
(9,13,38,39). The decision to approve its use in food in 1981
was still surrounded by controversy concerning test results
(40). It was only in 1983 that the FDA approved use of
aspartame in carbonated soft drinks in the U.S. (37), but
again not without controversy (48).

Xylitol is a naturally-occurring sugar substitute commercially synthesized from birch trees. It has the same sweetness
as sugar, but does not cause cavities. Metabolized indepen-
dently of insulin, diabetics can use it. Xylitol is approved
in Canada for some chewing gums. However, there have been
conflicting reports about its safety (22,41,42).

Sorbitol and mannitol are polyhydric alcohols that have a
sweetness that is 60% and 50% of that of sucrose, respectively, but which make the same calorie contribution. Both are
slowly absorbed by the intestinal tract and converted to
fructose. Because of the slow absorption, they exhibit a
laxative action when consumed in large amounts. In moderate
amounts these sweeteners are useful to diabetics as insulin is
not required for their metabolism. Mannitol, available only in
powder form, has limited use in the food and drug industry.
Sorbitol is also available in liquid form and is used in food,
drugs and industrial products. Food use includes its function
as an additive that increases shelflife by retaining moisture
and improving texture and palatability. Both sweeteners are
synthesized from carbohydrates (43,45).

A chemical (neohesperidin dihydrochalcone, NDHC), derived from the rinds of oranges and grapefruit has been considered for developing new sweeteners. The fruity taste and persisting action make it imperfect for general use (9). Other possible sweeteners (46,47), such as miraculin (extracted form a red berry growing in the jungles of West Africa), serendipty berries and the Katemsa fruit have not seen commercial introduction.

REFERENCES

1. Yudkin, J., "Sweet and Dangerous", Bantam Books, New York, 1973.
2. Hall, R. H., "Food for Nought: The Decline in Nutrition", Vintage Books, New York, 1976.
3. Price, J. M., Biava, G. G., Oswe, B. L., Vogin, E. E., Steinfield, J. and Ley, J. L., "Bladder Tumours in Rats Fed Cyclohexylamine or High Doses of a Mixture of Cyclamate and Saccharin", Science, 167, 1131, 1970.
4. Hunter, B. T., "Consumer Beware", Simon and Schuster, New York, 1971.
5. "Canadian Position on Saccharin", News Release, Health and Welfare Canada, Mar. 9, 1977.
6. "Information on Sweeteners", Field Operations Briefing, May 11, 1977.
7. "GAO Urges Final Decision on Saccharin Safety", Chemical and Engineering News, Sept. 27, 1976.
8. "The Great Saccharin Snafu", Consumer Reports, July 1977.
9. Culliton, B. J., "Fight over Proposed Saccharin Ban Will not Be Settled for Months", Science, 196, 276, 1977.
10. "Short-Term Extension to Permitted Use of Saccharin", News Release, Health and Welfare Canada, Apr. 19, 1977.
11. "Impurities Found in Commercial Saccharin Produce Mutations in Micro-organisms", News Release, Health and Welfare Canada, May 10, 1977.
12. Gwynne, P., "Congressional Intervention Sours Saccharin in Debate", New Scientist, June 16, 1977.
13. "Saccharin Ban Reversal Gains More Support", Chemical and Engineering News, June 20, 1977.
14. "Congress Aiming to Head off Saccharin Ban", ibid, June 13, 1977.
15. "New Saccharin-Cancer Tie Hardens FDA Stance", ibid, July 4, 1977.
16. "First Human Cancer Link to Saccharin Found", ibid, June 27, 1977.
17. "Sweet Success for Opponents of Saccharin Ban", New Scientist, Oct. 27, 1977.
18. "Moratorium on Saccharin Ban Closer", Chemical and Engineering News, Oct. 24, 1977.
19. "FDA Sets Guidelines for Saccharin Labels", ibid, Nov. 21, 1977.
20. "FDA Sets Guidelines for Saccharin Labels", Chemical and Engineering News, Nov. 21, 1977.
21. "Consumers Getting Less for Their Money as Result of Ban on Saccharin", The Globe and Mail, Toronto, Oct. 22, 1977.
22. "Saccharin Fails Ames Test, Xylitol Passes", Chemical and Engineering News, Dec. 12, 1977.
23. "Saccharin in Drugs, Cosmetics and Table-Top Sweeteners", Health Protection Branch, Health and Welfare Canada, Information Letter, No. 518, Jan. 18, 1978.
24. "Federal Agencies Start New Saccharin Studies", Chemical and Engineering News, Jan. 30, 1978.
25. "Saccharin May Be Tumour Promoter", Science/Technology Concentrates, Chemical and Engineering News, Apr. 10, 1978.

26. "Artificial Sweeteners No Danger to People as Used, Report Says", The Globe and Mail, Toronto, July 22, 1978.
27. "Bitter-Sweet Alternatives to U.S. Food Laws", New Scientist, Mar. 8, 1979.
28. Morrison A. B., Letter prepared for the Health and Welfare Minister responding to reactions to News Release of Mar. 9, 1977.
29. "British Studies Raise Doubts on Saccharin Ban", New Scientist, Mar. 17, 1977.
30. Lepkowski, W. C., "Saccharin Ban Goes Beyond Issue of Cancer", Chemical and Engineering News, Apr. 11, 1977.
31. Cohen, B. L., "Relative Risks of Saccharin and Calorie Ingestion", Science, 199, 983, 1978.
32. Ramsay, W., "The Bitter-Sweet Taste of Saccharin", New Scientist, June 16, 1977.
33. "The Saccharin Ban", New Scientist, Mar. 17, 1977.
34. Parker, K. J., "Alternatives to Sugar", Nature, 271, 493, 1978.
35. "When to Ban Nasty Chemicals", New Scientist, Apr. 8, 1976.
36. "New Cyclamate Sweetener on Market", The Globe and Mail, Toronto, May 11, 1978.
37. "Aspartame Okayed for Use in Diet Soft Drinks", Chemical and Engineering News, July 11, 1983.
38. "G. D. Searle's New Sweetener, Aspartame, Has Hit Another Snag", Government Concentrates, Chemical and Engineering News, Dec. 8, 1975.
39. Murray, C, M., "Proposed Saccharin Ban Stirs up Congress", ibid, Mar. 28, 1977.
40. "Aspartame Approved Despite Risks", Science, 213, 986, 1981.
41. "Xylitol Causes Some Cancers in Mice", Chemical and Engineering News, Nov. 21, 1977.
42. Ratzinger, R. P., Ou, S-Y. L. and Bueding, E., "Saccharin and Other Sweeteners: Mutagenic Properties", Science, 198, 944, 1977.
43. "Mannitol U.S.P., F.C.C.", Information Sheet 2037, Pfizer Chemicals Division, New York.
44. "Sugary Foods May Promote Breast Cancer", New Scientist, Mar. 10, 1983.
45. "Sorbitol U.S.P. Solution", Product Information Sheet, Lonza Inc., Fairlawn, New Jersey.
46. "Ten Cancer Cases Reported in Heavy Users of Saccharin", The Globe and Mail, Toronto, Apr. 4, 1977.
47. "Berry From Jungle May Replace Sugar, Saccharin as Sweetener", ibid, Apr. 6, 1977.
48. Jacobs, P., "Scientist Rejects Use of Artificial Sweetener", The Citizen, Ottawa, June 24, 1983.

RECOMMENDED READING

The News Releases, Health and Welfare Canada, from May 9, 1977 onward (references (5), (6), (10), (11), and (22)) are very informative as far as the Federal Government's position on saccharin is concerned. They report some of the results that began the controversy in Canada. Quick reading and factual.

Reference (8) is exciting reading. It tries to outline the roots of the controversy in the U.S. Reference (3) gives a historical background to the saccharin and cyclamate studies, but concentrates on cyclamates. Reference (4) is very heavily against processed food. Sometimes this is annoying, but never boring. It gives an excellent treatment of saccharin alternatives, lashing out strongly against sugar. Reference (34) is an interesting account of alternatives to sugar. Reference (1) looks at the health effects that can or may result from typical sugar consumption.

TOBACCO

The smoking and health controversy continues as the tobacco industry concentrates its efforts on the production of a "safe" low-tar cigarette.

HISTORY

Tobacco was used by the native people of the Americas. Its use spread to Europe when Christopher Columbus was given a gift of tobacco leaves in San Salvador on Oct. 12, 1492, the day now honoured as Columbus Day in the U.S. to celebrate the discovery of America (1). Jacques Cartier in 1535, and Samuel de Champlain in 1615, also found natives "drinking" tobacco when they explored Canada (2). As explorers returned home, so did tobacco. The crews of exploration ships became acquainted with and subsequently addicted to tobacco. These men were so ruled by their addiction that they carried supplies of tobacco and tobacco seeds with them on their voyages around the world. Natives at ports of call were instructed as to the cultivation of tobacco so that seamen, on returning, could replenish their tobacco supplies. Magellan's crew, for example, left seeds in the Philippines. The Dutch introduced the Hottentots (natives of South Africa) to the habit, and the Portuguese brought tobacco to the Polynesians (3). The Portuguese also serviced the tobacco needs of West Coast Africans and eventually the Cape Colony Hottentots. Portuguese tobacco (Nicotiana tobacum) was so preferable to the tobacco that other traders brought, that in Guinea, for example, slave traders only did business with Portuguese business men.

There are 2 different important species of tobacco. Nicotiana tobacum grew only in South America at the time of its discovery by Europeans. It was cultivated exclusively by the Spanish for over 100 years, and is the major species grown now in more than 100 countries. Nicotiana rustica grew in the West Indies and eastern North America when Columbus encountered its use on his explorations. Of the 2 species, N. tobacum was the more popular. It had good flavour and none of the harsh qualities of N. rustica. The demand for good tobacco became very great and thus the Spanish domination of the market was a powerful bargaining tool while the monopoly lasted. The monopoly was broken by the British in 1612 when colonies in

Virginia acquired N. tobacum seeds. The first Virginian
tobacum crop of 1613 was a breakthrough; it was eagerly
accepted in England. By 1619, import of Virginian tobacco
equalled import of Spanish tobacco (1).

The history of tobacco in Canada began with the Petun and
Attawandaron tribes who lived and grew tobacco north of Lake
Erie. Tobacco was part of these Indians' way of life; it was
involved in sacred rituals to cure disease and ward off evil
spirits, and was also a symbol for peace and contentment. In
the middle of the 17th century, these tribes were defeated by
the Huron and Iroquois who were themselves dispersed and later
confined to reservations by white colonists. The farms that
once produced tobacco lay dormant for more than a hundred
years until they were resettled beginning in 1784. During the
1800s, the old Indian plantations were producing once again.
Even to this day, most of the tobacco grown in Ontario,
Canada's largest producer by far, comes from lands originally
cultivated for tobacco by Indians (2).

The popularity of cigarettes developed only in the late
19th century. In 16th century England, men like Sir Francis
Drake and Sir Walter Raleigh set a powerful example by con-
doning smoking, actively taking up the pipe. It became very
popular to smoke, and during the Elizabethan era, smoking took
on national proportions. By 1610 tobacco was worth its weight
in silver because demand was so high. By 1614, the year following the first Virginia tobacco crop of the Spanish variety,
there were an estimated 7000 tobacco shops in London serving
all classes of people. King James I of England tried to control this expansion. In 1603, he ridiculed tobacco in his
anonymously published "A Counterblaste to Tobacco" (4,1). To
lessen the amount imported, he increased the import duty on
tobacco first by 4000%, but later reduced it to 800%. In 1619,
he prohibited the cultivation of tobacco in England and made
tobacco trade a royal monopoly (1).

During the 18th century, pipe smoking gave way to
(tobacco) snuff in popularity in England. The change was
precipitated when the British fleet captured choice Havana
snuff bound for the Spanish market. Several thousand barrels
of this snuff were sold at English seaports at a price low
enough for commoners to afford, the earnings going as prize
money for the sailors and officers (1,3). By 1770, very few of

any class still smoked; most used snuff. Charlotte, the wife of King George III used so much snuff that she was called "Snuffy Charlotte". On the Continent, Napoleon tried smoking but found it so unpleasant that he continued his 7 pounds of snuff a month habit (1).

In America after the Revolutionary War, the men proudly rejected anything British, including tea and snuff. Instead, they began to chew tobacco. By 1897 one-half of all tobacco in the U.S. was prepared for chewing by adding liquorice, molasses and sometimes rum. It was not until 1945 that the last cuspidors were removed from all federal buildings in the United States (1). The death blow to chewing tobacco was probably a public health campaign aimed against it in the early 20th century when the spread of tuberculosis and respiratory diseases were associated with the cuspidor.

The transition from chewing tobacco to cigarettes was mediated by way of the cigar which involved a combination of chewing and smoking. In order to curb the development of the cigarette industry, the cigar industry spread rumours suggesting that cigarettes were laced with opium to make them more desirable, that cigarette paper was bleached with arsenic, and that the product as a whole was inferior to the cigar. However, the change to cigarettes seemed inevitable.

The French were using cigarettes in 1844, and the Crimean War spread the cigarette throughout Europe. During this same period cigarettes were becoming increasingly popular in the U.S. By 1885 over one billion cigarettes were sold in the U.S. The first truly American cigarette, the Camel, appeared in 1912. The first advertisement showing a woman smoking appeared in 1919, the first king size cigarette appeared in 1939, and the first filter cigarette as it is known today in 1951 (1).

TOBACCO AND CANCER

In 1952, the University of Minnesota had reported that there had been a 3000% increase in lung cancer deaths over the pre-1919 rate (3). Significant tumour promoting activity of tar was first reported in 1958, and has been confirmed several times (5). In 1970, an experiment using "smoking" beagles provided a convincing argument to imply that cigarette smoke was a causative factor in lung cancer and other pathological changes in the respiratory system (1). Since that time smoking has been associated with several health disorders. According to the Royal College of Physicians in 1977 (6): "...it may be calculated that the average loss of life of a smoker of 20 cigarettes per day is about 5 years...On average the time by which a habitual smoker's life is shortened is about 5 1/2 minutes for each cigarette smoked...". The major reason why the life expectancy of men is more than 7 years shorter than that of women in the U.S. is reported to be due to greater cigarette use by men (27).

The initial research interest in tobacco smoke had been analytical, but with the development of the health controversy, it became important to identify the toxic substances so that associations with various diseases might be explained. Chemists have now identified at least 1350 chemicals in tobacco and its smoke and with the use of increasingly sophisticated instrumentation, it is probable that many more constituents will be found (7).

Smoke is of 2 types: mainstream and sidestream. These are, respectively, the smoke that is directly inhaled by the smoker, and the smoke that is released into the surrounding air. Because of the different temperatures and oxygen concentrations at the burning end of the cigarette during smoke formation, the chemical composition of the 2 smokes varies. The chemistry also differs according to the puff condition from one puff to another and within any one puff. The significance of this changing chemistry is that the smoker taking a light puff not only receives less smoke, but also a different kind of smoke than that which a long, hard puffer would consume (7).

One of the main constituents of tobacco smoke is tar. Nearly 100 gram can be deposited every year in the lungs of a habitual smoker (4). Tar has been shown to be a complete carcinogen. It can induce cancer experimentally in epithelial as well as connective tissue such as skin and bones. Due to the large body of literature already in existence available for comparative purposes, most such work with tar has been done using mouse epidermis. The development of tumours is a result of the combined effect of the different constituents of the tobacco smoke; it seems that tobacco tar has the tumour promoters, tumour initiators and tumour accelerators involved in carcinogenesis (8).

The Polycyclic Aromatic Hydrocarbons (PAH) such as benzo(a)pyrene (see figure) (BaP) found in the tar are initiators.

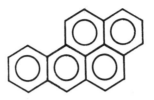

Benzo(a)pyrene

They are present in the products of incomplete combustion of hydrocarbons. Thus, PAH have been also identified in soils near highways (9) and a correlation has been suggested between automobile traffic and observed cancer fatality rate (10). Other studies (11) have shown that cigarette smokers living in urban areas, where air pollution is greatest, are most susceptible to lung cancer. Results of a recent study indicate human breast epithelial cells grown in culture may be transformed, or made cancerous, by exposure to benzo(a)pyrene (26). Nitrosamines (see Nitrites and Nitrates) and arsenic trioxide (see Arsenic) are other possible carcinogens found in tobacco smoke.

In order to reduce the carcinogenicity of tobacco smoke it is not necessary to identify all the carcinogens. Reduction can be achieved on an empirical basis by experimenting with complete fractions of tobacco smoke (e.g., acid, neutral and alkali fractions), each with several unidentified compounds, until a less active fraction is found with respect to carcinogenicity. This could be the result of selective breeding of tobacco or some step in the preparation of cigarettes (8). This procedure would require reliable bioassay techniques and as yet this still poses some problems: activation of carcinogens, species and sex differences in experimental animals, and varying sensitivity to carcinogens among experimental animals (6).

Although the mechanism of tobacco carcinogenesis is not clearly understood, research indicates that effects on nuclear DNA (deoxyribonucleic acid) and on cell respiration are significant (8,12) (see also Tris).

Meanwhile, the Canadian Cancer Society estimates that one out of 10 smokers of one pack a day will die of lung cancer, as opposed to one out of 200 non-smokers. Lung cancer is fatal in 95% of the cases (13).

NICOTINE AND ITS EFFECTS

Initially, the interest in tobacco was in its medical value and it was used in Europe for the treatment of almost anything: it supposedly helped digestion, gout, toothache; purged the stomach; healed wounds; and killed nits and lice. Eventually, however, the development of medical science revealed that tobacco is harmful. In addition to the potential carcinogens already considered, tobacco contains the pharmacologically active ingredient nicotine to the extent of about 1.5% in cigarettes today (2). A typical cigarette contains 15-20 mg (milligram) of nicotine (14). This compound was isolated in 1828 and named after a French ambassador Jean Nicot (1) who was convinced of the medical uses of tobacco.

Nicotine is a naturally occurring liquid alkaloid which is colourless and volatile. On oxidation (burning, aging) it turns brown and smells like burning tobacco (1). Concentrated purified nicotine is highly toxic, acting as quickly as cyanide. In the 19th century in Belgium, Count Bocarme killed his brother-in-law using nicotine (4). Poisoning by nicotine now is usually the result of swallowing or having excessive contact with nicotine-containing insecticide (e.g. Black Leaf 40) or having rectal enemas to combat intestinal parasites (2). Nicotine is one of the more common causes of poisoning in children. In the 3 years from 1969 to 1971 there were nearly 1500 cases in Canada. More than 90% of those were children under the age of 5 (2). Two or three drops of pure nicotine (i.e. about 60 mg) are enough to kill if placed on the tongue (4). The lowest reported fatal dose is about 30 mg.

A cigarette or cigar may have enough nicotine to kill a person. When smoked, however, nicotine is released over a period of about 6 minutes (6) and usually only a fraction enters the blood stream (4). About 25% of the nicotine in a cigarette is inhaled in the mainstream smoke (2). Canadian cigarettes yield from 0.09 to 1.34 mg per cigarette when tested on a standard smoking machine (14). The amount reaching the bloodstream is dependent on several factors: whether the

cigarette is filtered or not, the characteristics of the
filter, the depth and frequency of inhalation, and the length
of the butt (14). Eating a cigarette is not as bad as it would
appear, because although nicotine is easily absorbed from the
skin, the lining of the mouth and the lungs (4), it is not
well absorbed into the acid environment of the stomach (2).
Also, when a sufficient amount of nicotine has been absorbed,
the victim vomits (2). Any nicotine absorbed through the
stomach goes directly to the liver where it is metabolized,
unlike absorption through the lungs which results in nicotine
going first to the brain (4).

Initial symptoms of nicotine poisoning are nausea and
excessive salivation, followed by abdominal pain, vomiting and
severe diarrhea. As the condition advances, the victim becomes
dizzy, has headache, disturbed vision and hearing, and mental
confusion. If left untreated, general collapse, terminal convulsions and death will occur, usually from respiratory
failure (2).

When nicotine is inhaled, the overall sensation produced
is one of increased satisfaction, increased alertness and
tranquility (6). These effects are felt within minutes of
smoking, and subside within 20 to 30 minutes (3). Eighty to
ninety % of an inhaled dose of nicotine intake (about 1 mg per
cigarette) concentrates initially in the central nervous system and is subsequently metabolized, predominantly in the
liver, but also in the lungs and kidneys (2). In about 20
minutes the blood level of nicotine has fallen by about half
of its original value. This is a very rapid breakdown compared
to most other drugs (4). Nicotine and its metabolic end
products are completely eliminated in the urine (2).

Nicotine has a double physiological effect. Low doses
stimulate the nervous system, stimulate the brain wave (EEG)
pattern, increase respiration, heart rate and blood pressure,
and can decrease the appetite (2). A large dose of nicotine
tends to depress activity of the nervous system (2). By
altering the amount of nicotine entering the body the user can
achieve either effect when it is desirable, thus going from a
less preferred to a more preferred arousal level (15). Smokers can indeed alter their puffing habits to deliver different smoke compositions (8).

Additional factors, other than the size of the nicotine dose, have a bearing on the ultimate effect of nicotine: the rate of intake, the personality (introverted or extroverted), the state of mind at the time (depressed or aroused), and the prevailing circumstances (amount of external stimulation). These factors combine to give the smoker what he needs as he smokes. This is very rewarding and becomes a powerful incentive to continue the habit (15).

One rather confusing aspect of the pleasant effects experienced by users of nicotine is that while all physiological signs might point to arousal, an experienced smoker shows and reports signs of being calmed by nicotine. It is referred to as Nesbitt's paradox and does not apply to novice smokers (15). Novice smokers are prone to consume more nicotine than they can comfortably tolerate and may not have a pleasant experience with its use. In addition to clammy skin (small blood vessels in the skin are constricted), diarrhea, nausea and vomiting may follow smoking (2).

The psychological and physiological components of behaviour due to smoking interact in complex ways (4), and there is evidence that smokers become dependent on nicotine (16). They adjust their nicotine intake to their personal needs by modifying their puffing habits or the brand of cigarette they smoke. Animals given nicotine show behaviour characteristic of drug dependence. The Royal College of Physicians (London) concluded in their 1977 report that smokers can become dependent on nicotine (6). The physical dependence of chronic tobacco users manifests itself in clear withdrawal symptoms; restlessness, sleep disturbance, sweating, gastrointestinal changes, fall in heart rate and blood pressure, headache, EEG changes, tremors and weight gain (2).

A historic case of addiction to smoking was that of Sigmund Freud (3). In 1894, he was told by his physician that the irregular beating of his heart was caused by smoking. He tried to cut down his allowance of 20 cigars a day but failed, describing his attempts to quit as "torture beyond human power to bear". He developed cancers on his right palate and jaw and began to suffer "tobacco angina" (strangling sensation of the throat), and even though he admitted that his psychoanalytical studies were suffering due to his smoking, he continued smoking until his death from cancer at age 83 in 1939.

The presence of smoking (i.e. of nicotine) withdrawal symptoms described as "torture" by Freud is one determinant of an addicting drug dependence. A second is that the user develops the toxic effects that a novice would. Third, addiction is usually associated with antisocial behaviour. People are not normally aware of this aspect of addiction until the supply of the drug is somehow limited (3).

Other health effects associated with long-term use of tobacco include: increased mortality rates (2); cardiovascular diseases (2); cerebrovascular disorders (4); cancer of the lungs, lip, tongue, bladder, larynx and oesophagus (2,8,17); non-cancerous oral disease (2); peptic ulcers (17); reduction of Vitamin C; a tendency to reduced fertility; reduction of birth weight of babies; allergies; and wrinkling of the facial skin (4); increased risk of death from heart disease (31).

Passive smoking, i.e. the inhalation of sidestream smoke, is now seen to be a risk for the non-smoker. Recently, a Japanese study of 9,540 non-smoking wives followed up from 1966 to 1979 assessed that wives of heavy smokers had a higher risk of developing lung cancer. The extent of the increase in risk ranged from a factor of 2 to 4.6, the latter figure for non-smoking wives of agricultural workers who smoked more than 20 cigarettes a day (18). Wives of agricultural workers are at a higher risk, it is suggested, because they spend more time with their spouses in comparison to wives of other workers. The Tobacco Institute however questions the validity of this study (30). A study from Greece of lung cancer patients supported the Japanese findings (19). Other studies are in progress to assess the effects of cigarette smoke on non-smokers (25).

GOVERNMENT AND INDUSTRY ACTION

Action to combat the harmful effects of tobacco began in Canada in 1946 when the Federal Department of Pensions and National Health produced a booklet called "Smoking". It was 10 years later before tobacco was really considered a national health problem of high priority. In 1963, the first Canadian Conference on Smoking and Health was held. Federal and Provincial governments, volunteer agencies, professional associations and representatives from the industry were present. One of their recommendations was that the Department of National

Health and Welfare should establish and support a national program of research and education. Thus the Federal Smoking and Health Program was started in 1964. Under this program, tobacco use, related deaths, and the chemistry of smoke were studied. Experimental education programs and withdrawal clinics were established. In 1972, the program was transferred to the Non Medical Use of Drugs Directorate (NONMUD) with an increased budget ($8.5 million) (2). NONMUD is under the Health Protection Branch of Health and Welfare Canada and provides assistance in areas of concern related to the use of mood-altering substances.

Studies of smoking resulted in the introduction in the legislature of Bill C-248. It would have enacted a Cigarette Products Act taking effect on Jan. 1, 1972. The act would have prohibited all advertising and promotion of cigarettes except for identification purposes at the store. Levels of tar, nicotine and other constituents of tobacco would also have been limited and these levels would have had to appear on the product packages. As well, each package would have carried the warning "WARNING: DANGER TO HEALTH INCREASES WITH THE AMOUNT SMOKED, AVOID INHALING" (2).

The Canadian Tobacco Manufacturers Council, representing the industry, responded to this Bill by producing the "Cigarette Advertising Code". This code was to take effect at the same time as the proposed Cigarette Products Act, Jan. 1, 1972. Debate of Bill C-248 was abandoned and with it the Act, but the manufacturers agreed to adhere to their Code instead (2).

The Code was different from the Act in that it did not place a complete ban on advertising of cigarettes, only on radio and television advertising. Warnings similar to those in the Act were to be placed on packages, and although not stated in the Code, the warnings also appear with all advertisements. This may be out of deference to British Columbia where all cigarette advertisements must carry warnings and where the use of outdoor advertising (e.g. billboards) is forbidden. The warning stated in the Code does not caution against inhaling. Under the Advertising Code the industry also agreed to stop using prizes to entice smokers, and agreed to use only "brand preference type" advertising, i.e. not associating romance, prominence or success with the act of smoking. The industry

also limited tar and nicotine content to 22 mg tar and 1.6 mg
nicotine per cigarette (2).

Other legislation concerns the sale of tobacco to minors.
Under the Federal Tobacco Act it is illegal to sell tobacco or
cigarette papers to anyone under 16 years of age. Fines range
from $10 to $100. The Act also prohibits persons less than 16
years owning, smoking, or chewing tobacco in a street or
public place. The maximum fine for the third and subsequent
offence is $4.00. The provinces also have laws governing the
sale of tobacco to minors. Most provinces follow the guidelines of the Federal Tobacco Restraints Act but allow a child
to buy cigarettes for a parent, guardian or employer.
Ontario's Minor's Protection Act, for example, sets the
minimum age at 18 years. These laws are rarely enforced. In
1968 only 3 juveniles in all of Canada appeared before the
court for buying or smoking cigarettes. All 3 cases were
adjourned without a date set for return (2).

Bill C-242, an act concerning smoking in transit has been
debated but as of Nov. 1976 it was still at the committee
stage (20). In 1977, when the Federal Health Minister was
asked if any control of tobacco through the Food and Drugs Act
was being considered he replied "not at this time". He went
on to say that he felt it would require special legislation to
control tobacco and that he would prefer cooperation with
industry rather than legislation (21). Municipal bylaws such
as the one passed in Ottawa in Jan. 1977 can limit the use of
tobacco in public and confined spaces (4). Similar bylaws were
passed or are being considered by Toronto and Mississauga,
Ont., Salmon Arm and Richmond, B.C. and Calgary, Alta. (21).

Laws regarding smoking in public places are for the
protection of the non-smoker. In Sweden, a very ambitious and
pervasive anti-smoking campaign has been set up. It has been
felt that such a program would never work in Canada because it
would be too much of an infringement of personal freedom (4).
But if no action is taken, non-smokers will continue to inhale
sidestream smoke. Special reports in newspapers (28) and
"counter-advertising" by anti-smoking groups (29) have brought
the issue of non-smokers' and smokers' rights to the fore in
recent years.

ECONOMICS

The economic implications of large-scale changes in the production and use of tobacco in Canada are significant. On the production side, tobacco is second only to wheat in agricultural exports in Canada and is more than one-quarter of the total cash crop value (4). Canada rates fifth in the production of flue-cured tobacco with 95% of the tobacco crop coming from Ontario. About $436 million were invested in tobacco farms in 1970; the farms employed 9500 fulltime workers and 40,000 seasonal workers in cultivation and harvesting. In the U.S., the Tobacco industry reports that it accounts directly or indirectly for about 2 million jobs (30).

On the consumption side, in 1977, $3.1 billion was spent on tobacco products (14). The amount collected in tax on tobacco sales exceeds $1.5 billion per year, which is about equivalent to the annual cost of tobacco-related disability. Canada's 6.2 million smokers each spend $483 per year on tobacco. Canada has one of the highest per capita tobacco consumption rates in the world (14). It is reported that Canadians smoked 71 billion cigarettes in 1981 (22), while 630 billion were consumed in the U.S. (30). Per-capita cigarette consumption in the U.S. peaked in 1963, and had in 1981 decreased by over 10% to an average of 10 cigarettes per day per person 18 years and older (30).

The tobacco industry in Canada, with 17,000 shareholders (2), is closely related to the tobacco farmers. While there are no subsidies of tobacco farmers by the federal goverment, the tobacco industry agreed to guarantee an overall crop price for the 1977 crop of flue-cured tobacco of $1.00 per pound. In addition, the 4 major tobacco firms agreed to establish an export subsidy fund of $9.7 million to export 70 million pounds of tobacco. This was done to benefit both industry and the farmer. The farmer is more prosperous and the companies have an increased selection of choice grades of tobacco.

The social costs of the use of tobacco are great. It is estimated that tobacco-related disability costs tax payers over $1.5 billion a year, just less than the amount collected in taxes on tobacco sales (14). In Britain it was estimated that up to 50 million working days may be lost in industry every year as a result of smoking. There too it was found that smokers contributed a great deal to the burden on health services (6). Smoking also causes costly damage and loss of life in forest and urban fires (2).

The economic repercussions of anti-smoking campaigns appear to be minimal. Soon after the release of the widely publicized Surgeon General's report on Smoking and Health in 1964 in the U.S., smoking was back to its pre-report level after sales of cigarettes initially fell 20-25%. Smoking does not seem to rely on continued advertising by manufacturers. In Italy all cigarette advertising has been banned but there has been little change in consumption (3). It has been suggested that, if anti-smoking campaigns continue to operate at the present level, the observed decrease in the number of smokers may continue (3). The amount of carcinogenic activity of tobacco smoke condensate may be successfully modified in conjuction with the development of new bioassay testing techniques (5,23). A unique situation exists in Third World countries where the World Health Organization runs an anti-smoking campaign, but tobacco companies claim that the Third World requires the funds (for development projects) gained from tobacco sales before it can achieve satisfactory health levels (24).

Alternatively, it may be possible to determine methods of administering nicotine without smoke, such as nicotine gums, to find a substitute for nicotine or to fully educate the public about nicotine addiction in an attempt to change attitudes towards the drug (3).

REFERENCES

1. Ray, Oakley, F., "Drugs, Society and Human Behaviour", C. V. Mosby, St. Louis, 1972.
2. Ledain, G. (Chairman), "Final Report of the Commission of Inquiry Into the Non-Medical Use of Drugs", Information Canada, Ottawa, 1973.
3. Brecher, E. M., Ed., "Licit and Illicit Drugs", Little, Brown and Company, Boston, Toronto, 1972, (The Consumer's Union Report).
4. Gilbert, R., "The Nicotine Habit" in "Addictions", Addiction Research Foundation of Ontario, Toronto, Winter, 1976.
5. Bock, F. G., "Methods for Bioassays of Tobacco Smoke" in "The Chemistry of Tobacco and Tobacco Smoke", Irwin Schmeltz, Editor, Academic Press, New York, 1972.

6. Royal College of Physicians of London, "Smoking or Health", Pitman Medical Publishing Co. Ltd., Tunbridge Wells, 1977.
7. Wakeham, H., "Recent Trends in Tobacco and Tobacco Smoke Research" in "The Chemistry of Tobacco and Smoke", Irwin Schmeltz, Editor, Academic Press, New York, 1972.
8. Wynder, E. L. and Hoffmann, D., "Tobacco and Tobacco Smoke", Academic Press, New York, 1967.
9. Blumer, M., Blumer, W. and Reich, T., "Polycyclic Aromatic Hydrocarbons in Soils of a Mountain Valley: Correlation with Highway Traffic and Cancer Incidence", Environmental Science and Technology, 11(12), 1082, 1977.
10. Blumer, M., "Polycyclic Aromatic Compounds in Nature", Scientific American, 234(3), 25, 1976.
11. Butler, J. D., "Air Pollution, Smoking and Lung Cancer", Chemistry in Britain, 11(10), 358, 1975.
12. Dipple, A., "Polynuclear Aromatic Carcinogens" in "Chemical Carcinogens", C. E. Searle, Editor, American Chemical Society, 1976.
13. "Cancer Prevention", Canadian Cancer Society, May 1980.
14. "Facts About Tobacco", Addiction Research Foundation of Ontario, Jan. 1981.
15. Dunn, W. L. Jr., Editor., "Smoking Behaviour: Motives and Incentives", V. H. Winston and Sons, Washington, D.C., 1973.
16. Russell, M. A. H., "Tobacco Smoking and Nicotine Dependence", in "Research Advances in Alcohol and Drug Problems", Volume 2, edited by Gibbins, R. J., Israel, Y., Kalant, H., Popham, R. E., Schmidt, W. and Smart, R. G., John Wiley and Sons, New York, 1976.
17. Hammond, E. C., Garfinkel, L., Seidman, H. and Lew, E. A., "Tar and Nicotine Content of Cigarette Smoke in Relation to Death Rates", Environmental Research, 12, 263, 1976.
18. Takeshi Hirayama, "Non-Smoking Wives of Heavy Smokers Have a Higher Risk of Lung Cancer: a Study from Japan", British Medical Journal, 282, Jan. 17, 1981.
19. Trichopoulas, D., et al., "Lung Cancer and Passive Smoking", International Journal of Cancer, 27, 1, 1981.
20. Bennett, J. S., "Sic Transit Non Fumare", Canadian Medical Association Journal, 115, 836, 1976.
21. "Health-Possibility of Controlling Use of Tobacco", Commons Debates, 6499, June 9, 1977.
22. The Citizen, Ottawa, Apr. 1, 1982.
23. Muller, M., "Benefitting from 'Safe' Cigarettes", New Scientist, May 18, 1978.
24. "Holy Smoke! Batman Meets the Health Freaks!", ibid, Sept. 30, 1982.
25. "Nonsmokers and Cigarette Smoke: A Modified Perception of Risk", Science, 218,197, 1982.
26. "Benzo(a)Pyrene Linked to Human Breast Cancer", Chemical and Engineering News, Nov. 15, 1982.
27. "Smoking Shortens Men's Life Expectancy: Study", The Citizen, Ottawa, Aug. 10, 1983.
28. Benzing, K., "Non-Smokers, Smokers Facing Equal Fumes Risk", "Where to Smoke or Not to Smoke - an Angry Struggle", "Dangerous Chemicals in Smoke", ibid, Aug. 23, 1983.
29. "Anti-Smokers Paint to Make Point", The Globe and Mail, Toronto, July 11, 1983.
30. "Answers to the Most Asked Questions About Cigarettes", Tobacco Institute, Washington, D.C., 1982.
31. "Deaths Due to Heart Disease Caused by Smoking May Rise", The Citizen, Ottawa, Nov. 17, 1983.

RECOMMENDED READING

The Ledain report on the nonmedical use of drugs (2)
contains many surprising facts. There is a good coverage of
the Canadian situation with respect to tobacco. It also covers
health, distribution, legislation, and economic aspects. The
Consumer's Union Report on Drugs (3) contains an account of
the fascinating history behind the spread of tobacco. It
covers the use of tobacco in its different forms. Reference
(1) also contains anecdotes and historical details of great
interest, but from an American viewpoint to the exclusion of
world content. Reference (2) goes into detail about the need
to smoke; psychology is emphasized with physiology taking
second place. Nevertheless anyone with an interest or
background in psychology, or anyone attempting to quit or
appreciate tobacco addiction, might find the book useful and
informative. Reference (6) gives excellent up to date
information on the biological (health) hazards involved with
smoking, but data are almost exclusively British. Material is
presented with the caution of a truly scientific paper.
Reference (4) is a good summary of the problems, controversy,
and history associated with tobacco. Information relevant to
Canada is presented where possible. Reference (16) is a detailed account, with a long bibliography, of the role and
effects of nicotine. The point of view of the Tobacco Industry
can be obtained in reference (30).

2,4-D

2,4-D is Canada's most widely used herbicide. Recently there has been controversy over its use in public areas.

CHEMISTRY AND ITS USES

2,4-D, technically 2,4-dichlorophenoxyacetic acid, is one of the phenoxy herbicides, a group of chemicals that work by imitating auxins, plant growth hormones. They are described as powerful because compared with other types of herbicides, small doses achieve the desired results. The phenoxy group includes: 2,4-D; 2,4,5-T (see Dioxins); Fenoprop (2,4,5-TP), MCPA; Mecoprop; Picloram and Dichlorprop.

Natural auxin was first isolated in 1934 and by 1938, the first organic herbicide, DNOC, was introduced (1). 2,4-D was first synthesised in 1941. Unlike the inorganic herbicides, such as copper sulphate, the phenoxy herbicides were selective, affecting broadleaved plants and doing so at low doses (1). Applied to the leaves, the synthetic growth hormones are absorbed and carried throughout the plant. There they disturb the balance between growth and nutrient handling, the effect being dose-dependent. Applied in low doses, the phenoxy herbicides can act as growth regulators; at moderate doses, weed-killers; and at very high doses, defoliants.

An example of use as a growth regulator was the application of 0.21 kg/ha (kilogram per hectare) of Fenoprop to apple orchards to prevent pre-harvest drop of fruit. This practice is no longer permitted in Canada. For herbicidal use of 2,4-D the following doses are recommended in Ontario (2) and given here on an active ingredient basis: agricultural (wheat, oats and barley) 0.56 kg/ha; parks 1.1 kg/ha; roadside 1.1 kg/ha; and aquatic weeds (Eurasian Millfoil) 4.4 kg/surface hectare for depths to 2.5 m (metre) and 5.5 to 6.6 kg for depths greater than 2.5 m.

Defoliant use is associated with the military, particularly the American use of Agent Orange (see also Dioxins) and Agent White in Vietnam to obliterate jungle foliage which could provide cover for the enemy. Agent Orange, a 50/50 mixture of the alcohol-based n-butyl esters of 2,4-D and

2,4,5-T, was applied at an average rate of 14.6 kg/ha. Agent White, a 20/80 mixture of picloram and amine-based 2,4-D, was applied at a typical rate of 6 kg/ha to eliminate woody foliage not affected by Agent Orange (3). Defoliant use calls for repeated application (3) whereas herbicidal use generally means one application per season (2).

The major uses of 2,4-D in Canada are for grain farming, where it boosts yields 10-15% by eliminating competing weeds; forestry, where it is used to suppress the growth of less desirable hardwoods; and weed control. Since 2,4-D is a hormone herbicide, it must be used with care near certain crops. Tomatoes, grapes and tobacco are examples of sensitive crops.

Phenoxy herbicides are degraded by heat, water, sunlight, microorganisms and other chemicals. The degradation is affected by the rate of application, temperature, moisture conditions and the organic matter content of the soil. The breakdown of 2,4-D takes 2 to 4 weeks (1). One of the breakdown products is 2,4-dichlorophenol. In 1978, B. Akermark reported that sunlight may cause the formation of dioxins from dichlorophenol under alkaline conditions (4)(see also Dioxins).

Contamination with dioxins was originally thought to be limited to 2,4,5-T and 2,4,5-TP, which contain the 2,3,7,8 isomer of dioxin (TCDD), frequently described as "extraordinarily toxic". However, in Oct. 1980 a group of Agriculture Canada scientists presented a paper at a conference in Rome, announcing the discovery of chlorinated dioxins in 2,4-D (5). Sixteen of twenty-six samples of the amine-based product were dioxin-free, the remaining 8 containing di-, tri- and 1,3,6,8/1,3,7,9 tetra-isomers (see figure in Dioxins chapter) of dioxin in a 5 to 587 ppb (part per billion) range. Twenty of twenty-one samples of the ester formulations contained the same dioxins, the concentration ranging from 35 to 8700 ppb. The acute toxicity of all the 75 dioxin isomers is not known, but the di-isomers are believed to be 3000 times less toxic than TCDD (6).

HEALTH EFFECTS

Agriculture Canada's response to the presence of dioxins in 2,4-D was to phase out all use of the highly volatile butyl ester, ban the sale of all technical esters known to contain dioxins (the technical compound is the active ingredient) and to take action to see that all 2,4-D used in 1982 was dioxin-free (7). The latter regulation was amended in Aug. of 1981 to a maximum allowable content of any specific dioxin of 10 ppb (6,8).

2,4-D has a low acute toxicity (9), which was the main criteria for safety in the 1940s. Safety criteria have greatly expanded in the last 20 years to include: chronic (long term) toxicity; teratogenicity, the ability to cause birth defects; carcinogenicity and other aspects. In Apr. 1980, the U.S. Environmental Protection Agency (EPA) and Agriculture Canada informed 2,4-D manufacturers that "they should appreciate the need for toxicological testing to bring their 2,4-D package up to modern standards" (10). Manufacturers may respond to this as there are a number of reports questioning the herbicide's safety. New tests would help resolve the conflicting claims.

Reference (4) provides a survey of the literature on the health effects of 2,4-D. The authors found: reports of health problems related to occupational exposure; evidence that it causes birth defects in laboratory animals; that it is a mutagen in tests with human and mammalian cells; that suggestions of carcinogenicity in laboratory animals are strong but inconclusive; and that the breakdown product 2,4-dichloro-phenol appears to be a tumor promoter. The main paths of exposure are skin contact (dermal) and inhalation. Another summary of the controversy regarding the safety of 2,4-D is given in a series of articles in an Ottawa newspaper (15).

There has been considerable controversy over a decision by the City of Ottawa to resume the use of 2,4-D, following a 2 season hiatus. In late May of 1982, the city's environmental committee voted to resume spraying in parks under several conditions, one being publication of the date and location of spraying in the local newspapers and bilingual warning signs posted at the site (11). As a result, the Concerned Citizens of Ottawa was formed (12). Prior to the first scheduled spraying, the Canadian Union of Public Employees advised city workers to refuse to spray on the grounds that the herbicide may be hazardous (12). It was estimated that non-chemical methods of weed control for Ottawa would cost hundreds of thousands of dollars more each year (15).

This case illustrates the need to compare benefits with cost and risk. The benefits are the elimination of aesthetically-displeasing and allergy-promoting weeds and the assurance that weeds will be kept in check, avoiding expensive re-sodding of weed-infested turf. But the cost of the risk imposed on the spray operators and citizens who may be exposed must be weighed as well. Formal cost-benefit analysis would reduce all the aspects to some similar unit, usually dollars, then determine how these costs and benefits would be distributed. Many of the aspects involved are however difficult, if not impossible, to quantify for such an analysis.

The pesticide registration system in Canada (and the U.S.)(see Captan) makes it difficult to remove a long-registered product unless new evidence indicates an imminent hazard. The momentum of use contributes to this, particularly in the case of 2,4-D; annual use in Canada is over 3.6 million kg. The long-term future of 2,4-D in North America will depend on the new toxicity studies which regulators expect to receive in the next few years. The financial implications of de-registration are considerable; Canadian sales are worth more than $50 million a year (13), world sales are in the billions (14). A ban on the use of 2,4-D for grain production would mean an additional cost of $66 million per year for Canada (16).

REFERENCES

1. Que-Hee, S, S. and Sutherland, R. G., "The Phenoxyalkanoic Herbicides", Vol. 1, Chemistry, Analysis and Environmental Pollution, CRC Press, Inc., Boca Raton, Florida, 1981.
2. "Guide to Chemical Weed Control 1981", Ontario Ministry of Agriculture and Food, Publication 75.
3. Whiteside, T., "The Withering Rain", E. P. Dutton, New York, 1971.
4. Wright, J. S. and Salaves, V., "Health Effects of 2,4-D", Presented to the City of Ottawa on behalf of Pollution Probe (Ottawa), Mar. 26, 1981.
5. Cochran, W. P., Singh, J., Miles, W., Wakeford, B. and Scott, J., "Analysis of Technical and Formulated Products of 2,4-Dichlorophenoxyacetic Acid for the Presence of Chlorinated Dibenzo-p-Dioxins", Paper from the Workshop on the Impact of Chlorinated Dioxins and Related Compounds on the Environment, Rome, 1980.
6. Somers, E. and Douglas, V. M., "Dioxins and Related Compounds as Issues of International Concern", International Symposium on Chlorinated Dioxins and Related Compounds, Arlington, Virginia, 1981.
7. "2,4-D Measures Outlined", Agriculture Canada, News Release F5, Ottawa, Jan. 27, 1981.

8. Trade Memorandum T-1-233, Agriculture Canada, Dec. 1, 1981.
9. "Guide to Chemicals Used in Crop Protection", 7th edition, Agriculture Canada, 1982.
10. Trade Memorandum T-1-236, Agriculture Canada, Apr. 30, 1982.
11. "Ottawa May Again Use Controversial Weedkiller", The Citizen, Ottawa, May 26, 1982.
12. "Union Advises Ottawa Workers to Refuse Order to Spray 2,4-D", ibid, Aug. 21, 1982.
13. Hall, R. H., "A New Approach to Pest Control in Canada", Canadian Environmental Advisory Council, Report No. 10, Ottawa, July, 1981.
14. Warnock, J. W. and Lewis, J., "The Political Ecology of 2,4-D", Alternatives, Fall/Winter, 1982.
15. Spencer, C., "2,4-D Controversy Continues in Science Community", "Herbicide: It's Cheap, It's Effective...It's Poison", The Citizen, Ottawa, May 24, 1983. "Alternatives to 2,4-D Spraying Endorsed", ibid, May 26, 1983.
16. Krystynak, R., "An Economic Assessment of 2,4-D in Canada: The Case of Grain", Canadian Farm Economics, 18, 7, 1983.

RECOMMENDED READING

Reference (1) contains much information on the environmental fate of 2,4-D. A summary of health effects is found in (4). Reference (14) details the use of 2,4-D for Eurasian Millfoil and the problems encountered with provincial regulators. Additional reading: The NRC's "Phenoxy Herbicides -- Their Effect on Environmental Quality", is exhaustive and voluminous, but out of date for TCDD. (NRCC No. 16075)

TRIS

Is the risk of cancer, which may result from the use of insufficiently tested flame retardants, greater than the risk of being burned?

The use of textile flame retardants began over 300 years ago in 1638 with a treatment for canvas used in Parisien theatres (1). The famous French chemist, Joseph Gay-Lussac was commissioned by Louis XVIII to find a suitable method for protection of fabrics. He succeeded in 1820 using mixtures of ammonium chloride and ammonium phosphate or borax which proved to be an effective treatment for hemp and linen textiles (2). This treatment, although still valid, is referred to as non-durable because the chemicals are soluble and are thus removed in washing.

In 1902, W.M.Perkin developed the first semidurable treatment which would withstand gentle washing. His process (the Non-Flam process) for cotton was one in which an insoluble substance, stannic oxide, was precipitated in the fibres of the material. In 1953, the first durable flame retardant for cotton was developed and involved the use of a phosphonium compound (2). Many treatments of cotton are now based on similar compounds (1).

Cotton and synthetic blends (e.g. polyester-cotton) are particularly difficult to render flame retardant because the synthetic part of the material melts and the cotton serves as a support which keeps the synthetic component burning (1). A flame retardant should stop the burning of the material when the flame is removed. There are only a few fireproof fabrics which are completely unaffected by fire (see Asbestos). The key elements in flame retardancy are phosphorus, nitrogen, chlorine, bromine and antimony (1). In most cases, the mode of action is not completely understood. Phosphorus, a constituent of Tris, is thought to promote the formation of char and inhibit the release of combustible carbon-containing gases (3).

With the introduction of synthetic fibres such as polyester, nylon, acetate and triacetate, attention focused on development of effective flame retardant chemicals. Tris (short for tris(2,3-dibromopropyl)-phosphate) was patented in 1951, and marketing began in 1958 as a flame retardant in urethane foam, polystyrene foam and acrylic sheet. It was first used on polyester fabric in 1972 (3). It quickly became the most economical way to meet the newly established (1972) U.S. flammability standard for children's sleepwear. Tris was also convenient to use, as it could be applied in the same bath used to dye the fabric. About 5000 tonne a year were used in fabrics and plastics (1). It has been estimated that the standards reduced the number of deaths and injuries from ignition of children's clothing by as much as 50% (4).

In 1976, Tris became a controversial chemical. Reports of toxicity and its ability to cause eye and skin irritation had already appeared (5) but no information was available regarding the long-term toxicity, carcinogenicity or mutagenicity. Such information could be obtained before the 1970s only through expensive, time-consuming animal studies.

In the 1970s, "quickie tests" for carcinogens were developed (6). The best known of these is the "Ames test", named after its originator , Bruce Ames. It is not completely reliable but is estimated to be 90% efficient in detecting carcinogens and 85% efficient in detecting non-carcinogens. This test is based on the assumption that cancers are related to mutations, or damage to cell DNA. Therefore agents that cause mutations are possibly carcinogenic. The Ames test, or "Salmonella" test, employs a bacterial strain which cannot synthesize a specified amino acid. Therefore the bacteria cannot grow in a culture where the amino acid is lacking. When a given chemical is added the bacteria may begin to grow, indicating that genetic mutation has occurred. The degree of culture growth reflects the strength of the "mutagen". The Ames test takes 3 days and costs hundreds of dollars per chemical. Similar rapid-screening tests use yeast, fruit fly or mammalian cells in place of bacterial cells. A test using mammals takes years and may cost hundreds of thousands of dollars (see Sweeteners).

The Ames test showed Tris to be mutagenic (5). As there is a high correlation between mutagenicity and carcinogenicity (1), the National Cancer Institute (NCI) tested Tris for carcinogenicity and showed that the compound produces kidney cancer in rats (7). A 130-week feeding study on mice and rats reports (8) that Tris is carcinogenic in these animals causing liver, lung, kidney and stomach tumours. Also, experiments with rabbits showed that Tris could be absorbed through the skin (9). There was no proof that Tris would cause cancer in humans, but since children, in particular, would be exposed to the chemical, it was too large a risk to allow its use (7).

Thus, the Consumer Products Safety Commission (U.S.) acting under the Federal Hazardous Substances Act, banned the sale of children's sleepwear treated with Tris, effective Apr. 8, 1977 (3). Subsequently, in July 1977, the Canadian Consumer Affairs Minister, under the Hazardous Products Act, prohibited the importation, advertisement and sale of wearing apparel treated with Tris.

The ban on Tris had important consequences. It alerted the general public to the existence and use of flame re-tardants in general; manufacturers of Tris-treated sleepwear suffered heavy financial losses. There has been controversy in the U.S. over the federal compensation for losses suffered by manufacturers; the Justice Department's Court of Claims sec-tion states that claims of this type have previously been denied (10). Producers of flame-retardant chemicals have be-come much more concerned with the safety of their products and interest has moved toward development of inherently flame-resistant fabrics, several of which are now in use (3). These include (brand names in brackets): modacrylic (Kanecaron and SEF), matrix (Cordelan), vinyon (Valren, Teviron, Clevyl T, Leavil), aramid (Nomex) (3,4) and recently Trevira (11). Ironically, wool, which is inherently flame resistant, does not meet the children's sleepwear standard (1).

Although a U.S. federal report published in 1972 stated that 200,000 burn injuries and 4000 deaths are associated annually with flammable fabrics, these figures have been dis-puted and it has been suggested that the risk from cancer (as a result of the use of insufficiently tested flame retardants) may be much higher than the risk of being burned (1).

REFERENCES

1. Blum, A. and Ames, B. N., "Flame-Retardant Additives as Possible Cancer Hazards", Science, 195, 17, 1977.

2. Connick, W. J., Jr., "Flame Retardant Cotton Textiles: Contributions of the USDA", Chemistry, 51(3), 13, 1978.
3. Sanders, H. J., "Flame Retardants", Chemical and Engineering News, Apr. 24, 1978.
4. "Tris: Confusion over Another Cancer Hazard", Consumer Reports, July, 1977.
5. Prival, M. J., McCoy, E. C., Gutter, B. and Rosenkranz, H. S., "Tris(2,3-dibromopropyl)phosphate: Mutagenicity of a Widely Used Flame Retardant", Science, 195, 76, 1977.
6. Fox, J. L., "Ames Test Success Paves Way for Short-Term Cancer Testing", Chemical and Engineering News, Dec. 12, 1977.
7. "Ban on Flame-Retardant Tris Appears Imminent", ibid, Apr. 11, 1977.
8. "NCI Says Tris Is an Animal Carcinogen", Science/Technology Concentrates, Chemical and Engineering News, May 8, 1978.
9. Abelson, P. H., "The Tris Controversy", Science, 197, 4299, 1977.
10. "Justice Opposes Compensation for Tris Losses", Chemical and Engineering News, June 26, 1978.
11. "Hoechst Develops Flame-Resistant Fiber", ibid, Oct. 31, 1977.

VINYL CHLORIDE

The allowable exposure levels for vinyl chloride were lowered to protect the health of workers. Industries found that they could comply with stricter standards without excessive expense.

MANUFACTURE AND USES

One of the most common plastics used today is polyvinyl chloride (PVC). It is used for plastic film, siding, pipe and fittings, flooring, wall covering, automotive upholstery and numerous other consumer products. PVC is a polymer made up of monomer segments of vinyl chloride joined together. While PVC is a high molecular weight solid material, vinyl chloride monomer (VCM), C_2H_3Cl, has a molecular weight of 62.5 g (gram) per mole (as compared to 28.9 g for air) and is a gas at normal temperature and pressure.

The VCM gas is colourless and has a pleasant ethereal odour (1). Because of its higher molecular weight the heavier VCM molecules have a tendency to sink when dispersed in air. VCM can be liquefied at room temperature if it is under a pressure of about 3 atmosphere (300 kiloPascal); this is usually how it is stored and transported. This property also suggests its use as an aerosol propellent. It was used as such in the U.S. until 1975, when it was banned. It was seldom used in Canada as an aerosol and as of 1974 such a use was prohibited (2).

VCM is almost totally insoluble in water but will dissolve in alcohol, ether, carbon tetrachloride and fats. This means that vinyl chloride monomer present in container material could migrate from the container to the liquid contents. VCM has been found in some wines in PVC containers, but there is as yet no evidence that this had deleterious effects.

When PVC was developed in Germany in the late 1930s, it was the first wholly synthetic plastic. Production started in the U.S. in 1937 and in Canada in 1943. Since the Second World War, production of PVC has increased at an average rate of about 6% per year. In the past few years, the increase in Canadian production has been remarkable, from 125,000 tonne in

1978 to 222,000 tonne in 1981. Mexico is also increasing its
PVC capacity, expecting it to go from 135,000 tonne in 1981 to
310,000 tonne in 1983. The capacity for PVC production in the
U.S. in 1981 was about 3.55 million tonne, but only about 77%
of this capacity was utilized (3). Essentially all the VCM
produced is used for PVC manufacture, but not necessarily in
the same location. VCM is transported both within Canada and
from and to the U.S.

VCM is usually regarded as an occupational rather than an
environmental hazard (4). Because of the physical properties
of VCM (low boiling point, insolubility in water) it tends to
migrate to the air, not concentrating to any great extent in
water or soil. Once in the air it is destroyed by the action
of the sun's rays with a half life of only 2 days (1). It was
estimated that emissions to the air from North America were
about 126,000 tonne. In 1973, the ambient air concentration,
assuming a steady state (see Fluorocarbons), was calculated to
be around 1.4×10^{-6} ppm (part per million) by volume.
Measurements outside a plant have given concentrations of VCM
of 0.1 ppm two-thirds of a mile away; none was detected one
mile away (1).

The sources of VCM's escape into the workplace atmosphere
are in the monomer-production process, the polymer-production
process and secondary processes in which the raw PVC resin is
made into other products (2). Exposure to VCM as an unreacted
constituent of PVC resin has been shown to be an unimportant
source of contamination so that the first 2 of the above are
the chief sources of emissions; this includes loading and
unloading of trucks and tank-cars. The greatest exposure risk
occurs for those workers who clean the polymerization vats
(1).

HISTORY OF HEALTH EFFECTS

In Dec. 1973, B.F. Goodrich Co. revealed that since 1971,
3 workers at its PVC polymerization plant in Louisville,
Kentucky, had died of angiosarcoma, a rare and fatal form of
liver cancer. As of Mar. 1976, 45 workers had died of VCM-
related hepatic angiosarcomas (1) and the majority of these
had worked in the polymerization process and had cleaned the
vats used in that process.

In Italy, in 1971, Cesare Maltoni began studies on the toxicity of vinyl chloride. In Aug. 1972, he reported his findings to an International Symposium on Cancer Detection and Prevention held in Bologna (5): rats exposed to vinyl chloride developed angiosarcoma. In Jan. 1973, a team of scientists representing the U.S. chemical industry (6) visited Maltoni and at a subsequent meeting of the Manufacturing Chemists Association reported that at all exposure levels above 50 ppm, liver cancer was induced. Maltoni's findings were made public on Feb. 15, 1974 (5) and by May 1974, a cause and effect relationship between vinyl chloride and human angiosarcoma was generally accepted (6).

It appears that there is a dose-response relationship between VCM exposure and human angiosarcoma. This relationship serves as the basis for current regulations concerning atmospheric concentrations of VCM permitted in factories. As is usual for carcinogenic chemicals, there is a latency period of about 10 years between exposure and detection of cancer. It may thus be expected that further cases will be reported in the future. During the past 14 years, the deaths due to hepatic angiosarcoma have increased from year to year, perhaps due to expansion of the PVC industry, or perhaps to greater awareness (and thus reporting) of the VCM hazard. Between 5000 and 6000 people in the U.S. are estimated to be still at risk because of previous exposure. Unfortunately, diagnosis of the disease is difficult and necessitates an aware physician, sophisticated hospital techniques, detailed medical and work history, and an autopsy. Liver scans on workers can be done regularly but they are too crude to detect hepatic fibrosis, which appears to be a precursor of angiosarcoma (1).

Studies with rats have indicated that VCM is metabolized in the body and that it is the products of this metabolism (metabolites) which cause the cancer. There are other indications that the level of glutathione, which normally counters the metabolites, is lowered by VCM itself, thus allowing the metabolites to attack macromolecules (such as DNA, RNA) in the cells. This is a well-known route by which chemicals cause cancer in animals although it is not known whether this holds for humans.

Although it was the occurrence of angiosarcoma which brought vinyl chloride to the world's attention, there are other toxicological effects also associated with this chemical. Acute exposure to vinyl chloride is generally followed by a complete narcosis, which in turn can be followed by death. Two such deaths have been noted. Chronic or repeated exposure can result in a number of effects, including Raynaud's syndrome and acroosteolysis. The latter, occurrence of which was published in the mid-1960s, was the first well-documented toxic effect due to vinyl chloride. It is an unusual disorder, characterized by dissolution of the terminal bones of the fingers, which can be accompanied by clubbing, shortening and swelling of these bones and the nail beds. There are also skin changes and nervous effects such as tingling and sensitivity to cold (Reynaud's syndrome) associated with the disease which is primarily related to the hand-cleaning of polymerization vessels. Procedures for prevention and detection of the above disorders have been introduced and include: use of gloves, annual medical examination and X-ray of the hands (1).

REGULATIONS FOR CONTROL OF VCM EXPOSURE

Initially when VCM and PVC were introduced there were no controls or limits on VCM levels in the workplace, because the chemicals were not considered to be dangerous. It might be argued that the potential danger of vinyl chloride should have been recognized as it is one of the chlorinated hydrocarbons, a group of chemicals known to be liver toxins. In 1949, when liver disorders were discovered among Russian VCM workers, the plasticizer rather than VCM was thought responsible. Nevertheless a maximum concentration of 12 ppm was established in the U.S.S.R. although it is not known whether this standard was enforced. It has been acknowledged that in the past workers could have been exposed to VCM concentrations as high as 3000 ppm during their working hours. According to industry, however, exposure levels for 1970-1973 had a weighted average of 28 ppm (1).

Until 1962 the recommended limit of long-term exposure of U.S. workers to VCM was 500 ppm as a time-weighted average over an 8-hour day. In 1972 this was reduced to a time-weighted average of 200 ppm. After the Goodrich announcement the situation rapidly changed. In June 1974, an emergency standard of 25 ppm time-weighted average with a 50 ppm maximum was set in the U.S. In Apr. 1975, an Occupational Safety and Health Administration (OSHA) peak limit of 25 ppm over 15 minutes and a time-weighted average of 10 ppm over 8 hours was put into effect; the peak limit was lowered to 5 ppm in Apr. 1976. Above this level, respirators are required for all personnel. The limit for air and water emissions from new and existing plants has been set by the Environmental Protection Agency (EPA) at 10 ppm (1).

In Canada response occurred after the 1973 announcement by the B.F.Goodrich Company. Canadian companies became aware of the problem through their (American) parent companies; Canadian regulators through their counterparts to the south. Federal reaction was slow as the provinces generally have jurisdiction over the workplace. In 1975, the sale, advertisement and importation of aerosol products using VCM as propellent was banned, both in Canada and in the U.S. Infant goods containing detectable levels of the monomer were also banned. In 1975, the Bureau of Chemical Safety of Health and Welfare Canada banned the use of packaging in which VCM could be found. Food in which VCM is detected due to residual monomer in PVC wrapping is rejected.

Environment Canada introduced emissions standards for VCM and PVC plants on July 1, 1979. Under these regulations, part of the Clean Air Act, the maximum VCM emitted per day shall not exceed 10 ppm or 2 kilogram total (7). The Ontario Ministry of the Environment has established a guideline for VCM emissions measured at the point of impingement: 0.1 ppm over 24 hours with a peak limit of 0.2 ppm over 30 minutes. (Note: this is an unpublished (i.e., internal) guideline that is less strict than the federal regulation due to the method of measurement.)

In Ontario, the occupational exposure guideline followed is that of the American Conference of Government Industrial Hygenists: 5 ppm over an 8 hour time-weighted average with 15-minute peak values (at least an hour apart) of 10 ppm. Notice of intent to regulate vinyl chloride under the Occupational Health and Safety Act was published in June 1980 and proposed regulations appeared in the Ontario Gazette in Aug. 1980, calling for a time-weighted average of 2 ppm over a 40-hour week. At this time, the regulations have not been passed. Alberta, British Columbia and Quebec have regulated vinyl chloride under the Occupational Health and Safety Act, the Workman's Compensation Act and the Environmental Quality Act respectively. The limits are: Alberta, 2 ppm time-weighted average with a peak of 10 ppm; B.C., a maximum 8 hour limit of 1 ppm; and Quebec, a maximum level of 0.5 ppm (8).

The reduction in allowable VCM levels has not been without difficulties. Some industries using VCM doubted that the new, more stringent guidelines could be met, and that the subsequent closures of VCM and PVC plants would cause serious economic disruptions. The EPA standards in the U.S. have, on the other hand, been challenged in the courts by the Environmental Defense Fund as being too lenient. At the same time, the Society of the Plastics Industry has stated its intention to resist any further lowering of the standards set by the EPA (9). There have been some suits filed for violations of VCM emission limits (10). The labour movement of Canada has expressed its concern regarding exposures to VCM in the workplace, and takes exception to the implications that enforcement of strict standards would mean loss of jobs for many workers (11).

There has also been a positive response from industry. New air samplers allow small levels of VCM to be measured. Personal badges and in-plant monitors have been installed to detect exposure levels. As well, personnel are now required to have an annual physical examination. Improvement in loading and cleaning techniques and greater awareness by the workers have all contributed to lower exposure levels (1,12). It has been estimated (1) that technological and process changes have resulted in a 95% reduction since 1973 in levels of VCM emitted into the environment.

The vinyl chloride experience can be considered an example of successful industry-government cooperation and emphasizes some important facts. Vinyl chloride is one of the many chemicals found to be harmful after being considered safe for many years. This underlines the need for emphasis on anticipation, work-related research on industrial chemicals, adequate medical and diagnostic services, better communication between medical, scientific, government, industry and labour personnel and standards of exposure which can be monitored and enforced (1).

REFERENCES

1. Science Council of Canada, "An Overview of the Vinyl Chloride Hazard in Canada", Chemistry in Canada, 29(7), 23, 1977.
2. "Vinyl Chloride as an Airborne Hazardous Contaminant 1", Ontario Ministry of the Environment, Toronto, Report No. ARB-TDA-01-7 4, 1974.
3. Chemical and Engineering News, June 14, 1982; Jan. 12, 1981; Aug. 31, 1981.
4. Doern, G. B., "Regulatory Processes and Jurisdictional Issues in the Regulation of Hazardous Products in Canada", Science Council of Canada, Ottawa, Background Study, No. 41, 1977.
5. "Vinyl Chloride Hazard", Chemistry, 47(10), 27, 1974.
6. Moore, J. W., "The Vinyl Chloride Story", Chemistry, 48(6), 12, 1975.
7. "Canadian Environmental Law", Clean Air Act -Vinyl Chloride Emission Regulations, Butterworth & Co. Ltd., Toronto.
8. "Canadian Occupational Health and Safety Law", Corpus Information Services Ltd., Don Mills.
9. "EPA Will Tighten up Further on Vinyl Chloride Emissions", Chemical and Engineering News, June 6, 1977.
10. Chemical and Engineering News, Jan. 12, 1981.
11. Stellman, J. M., "Health Hazards in the Work Place", Canadian Labour, Dec. 1975.
12. Bertram, C. G., "Minimizing Emissions From Vinyl Chloride Plants", Environmental Science and Technology, 11(9), 864, 1977.

RECOMMENDED READING

References (1) and (2) are both comprehensive discussions of the problem. References (4) and (12) indicate jurisdictional procedures and problems of overlap and gaps due to the different agencies involved.

APPENDIX

Comparison table of acute toxicity of chemicals

The "lethal dose 50" (LD_{50}) for some of the chemicals mentioned in this book are listed below for comparison. The LD_{50} is the dose of the chemical, which is expected to cause the death of 50% of an animal population. It is expressed here as mg/kg (milligram per kilogram body weight). For the sake of simplifying the comparison, only oral exposure data are listed for rats (whenever available). Data are shown for 3 species for dioxin to indicate the great variability of LD_{50} with species (reference (4) in Dioxins).

Substance	Animal	LD_{50}(mg/kg, oral)
Alcohol	rat	14000.
Arsenic trioxide	rat	20.
Arsenic trioxide	man	1.4
Benzene	rat	3800.
Cadmium	rat	225.
Caffeine	rat	192.
Captan	rat	10000.
Chloroform	rat	800.
Carbon tetrachloride	rat	2800.
DDT	rat	113.
Dioxin (2,3,7,8-TCDD)	guinea pig	.001
Dioxin	mouse	.11
Dioxin	hamster	5.
Formaldehyde	rat	800.
Fenitrothion	rat	250.
Nicotine	rat	50.
PCP	rat	50.
Sucrose	rat	29700.
Tris	rat	1010.
2,4-D	rat	370.
2,4,5-T	rat	300.

Routes of exposure other than oral are the crucially important ones for several chemicals, e.g. inhalation in the case of asbestos, benzene, formaldehyde, tobacco products, vinyl chloride; skin contact for benzo(a)pyrene, PCBs. It is also often not the acute lethal toxicity of a chemical which is the aspect of concern. Chronic exposure leading to medical problems such as cancer, sterility, birth defects, or environmental effects can be the major concern.

A thorough listing of all the various toxic effects can be obtained from the reference used for the LD_{50} (oral) data: Lewis, J.R. Sr. and Tatken, R.L., "Registry of Toxic Effects of Chemical Substances" 1980 ed., U.S. Department of Health and Human Services, National Institute for Occupational Safety and Health, Feb. 1982.

INDEX

Numbers in **bold face type** indicate pages on which terms are more thoroughly explained. The index contains references to only those organizations and illnesses which are mentioned on several pages.